HANSARD'S CATALOGUE AND BREVIATE OF PARLIAMENTARY PAPERS 1696-1834

HANSARD'S
Catalogue and Breviate of
Parliamentary Papers
1696—1834

Reprinted in Facsimile
With an Introduction by

P. FORD
Professor of Economics

AND

G. FORD

University of Southampton

BASIL BLACKWELL
OXFORD
M CM LIII

PRINTED IN GREAT BRITAIN BY
HENDERSON AND SPALDING LONDON W 1

INTRODUCTION

THIS *Catalogue and Breviate of Parliamentary Papers, 1696-1834,* is reprinted as a companion volume to the *Select List of Parliamentary Papers, 1833-1899,* by P. and G. Ford. The two volumes together give access to the main streams of Parliamentary inquiry for over two centuries. When the Select List was being prepared, it appeared to the authors that it was unnecessary to repeat work which the Hansards had done so well, and that, quite apart from the historical and bibliographical interest of the work, its value as a practical guide to the papers more than justified its separate publication.

A few words must be said on the relationship of the two books. Hansard's volume deals with the papers of the unreformed, the Select List with those of the reformed Parliament. It was therefore still possible for Hansard to survey the whole field of Parliamentary Papers, and to include many 'Accounts and other Papers' as well as 'Reports'. The contents of the Select List, on the other hand, is clearly marked by the increase in the activity of the reformed Parliament, its committees and commissions, and the consequent growth in the volume and range of papers which flowed from them; this presented sharp problems of selection which could be resolved only by the exercise of clear principles of exclusion. While Hansard's subject classification was appropriate to the problems of the period he covered, as expressed in the papers, that of the Select List, though having much in common with his, required a change of emphasis to make room for the different interests of the 'new democracy'. Again, since Hansard's work was based on the House of Commons' papers, it does not contain any references to those papers of the House of Lords which were not 'communicated' to the House of Commons and were therefore available only in the Lords' set of papers. We have added a short list of the most significant of these as an Appendix. It is, as its name implies, much more than a catalogue; the 'Breviate' of the contents makes it an admirable guide to the papers of the period. We feel that now it is once more available, it will again establish its practical value without needing any further commendation than is implied by the decision to reprint it.

What led to the production of this remarkable book? What part was played by the Hansards? The name of Hansard has been so closely associated with the famous Reports of Parliamentary Debates, produced by Thomas Curson Hansard, that the contribution of other members of the family to our instruments for studying Parliamentary Papers, in a form which might easily have become known as 'Hansard's Indexes', has been almost completely overlooked. These were the work of the father, Luke, and his two other sons, James and Luke Graves. That the initiative should come from the Hansards is due to the fact that in addition to performing their official duties, as Printers to the House, of printing and holding stocks of papers, they became the centre of information on the papers and their contents.

The Catalogue and Breviate here reprinted was the last of three subject indexes produced and printed by the Hansards. The first was a subject index to the Parliamentary Papers for 1713–1800, which were collected into fifteen volumes and known as the *First Series*. This index shows the arrangement of the papers within each separate volume, gives an analytical table of topics within each subject, and has an alphabetical index. In the preface to the

Catalogue of the Library of the House of Commons (1830 (80) iv), John Rickman, in appreciative references, states that (Luke) Hansard furnished an analysis of the subjects under the nineteen subject headings, and that the Breviate or precis of the reports was 'an instance of persevering labour and intelligence not often surpassed'. The preface to the index, which was signed 'Luke Hansard and Sons', contains an interesting statement of his aims in producing it:

> In forming this General Index it has been endeavoured to bring the subjects of the volume before the reader in a perspicuous order, leaving the details of particulars to be dwelt upon at option, rather than rendering the study of such particulars necessary to a previous comprehension of the whole.
>
> Contemplating this object, it appeared not likely to be obtained by a general or promiscuous alphabetical arrangement, for by that method all relative connection of the subjects, and chronological dependence, would be lost, and a mass of undigested matters would forbiddingly present itself to the mind. It is hoped these inconveniences are avoided by the plan adopted.

*   *   *   *   *   *   *

> In order that the mind might be more readily led to the knowledge of the contents of each Report, or subject of each Index, in most cases a short digest has been made, and introduced immediately after the main head. The DATES, likewise, have been carefully inserted, as many facts derived much of the importance from their chronological arrangement; which if omitted, the enquirer would often be needlessly sent in search of what would be inapplicable to his views, from the irrelevancy of the period.
>
> With the hope of unfolding, succinctly, yet perspicuously, the important contents of the Reports of the House of Commons it has been attempted to compile an Analytical Table of their subjects. Nineteen heads have been selected, comprising all the matters which, in these Reports, have come under the investigation of the Committees of the House.

It may be noted that he was fully aware of the importance of making his index comprehensive, since he added a list of reports which were not part of the collection in the bound volumes but were printed only in the Journals, and gave a brief abstract of each of these reports.

The second subject index bore the new title of 'Classification of Parliamentary Papers and a Breviate of their Contents, 1801–1826', and was ordered to be printed in February, 1830. The formal recommendation that this should be done was made by the Select Committee on Committee Rooms and Printed Papers, in its 3rd Report (1825 (516) v), which considered Hansard's plan for 'digesting the contents of Reports' set out in Appendix 2, VII. Luke Hansard died in 1828, before the Breviate was published, and it was issued under the signature of his sons, James and Luke Graves Hansard. If we ask whose work this Breviate was, the answer is given by Luke Graves in evidence before the Select Committee on the State of the Library of the House (1831–2 (600) v). In reply to Q. 83 he says that it was compiled 'by myself, under the direction of my Father'. In the preface to the volume, the two sons say that 'Mr. Luke Hansard, senr., was prevented by death from seeing the accomplishment of this task, which he always looked forward to with pleasing expectation that it would show, in a connected form, the works in which he had been engaged during a great part of the period in which he had discharged the duty of Printer to the House. The materials, however, were all prepared, and the Arrangement approved of by him; and his Sons have been anxious that its completion should not suffer by devolving on them, and have endeavoured that it should be done in his spirit, and represent the distinctness of his mind.'

At this point we must interrupt the story of the evolution of the Breviate to take up another of Luke's activities, carried on concurrently with the production of the first Breviate. This was the compilation of the first General (Alphabetical) Index, 1801–1826, to the bound volumes. The Committee of 1825, which recommended the printing of the first Breviate, also stated that a General Index to the sessional papers had been prepared by Mr. Hansard, that it should be completed to the accession of His Majesty and printed for the use of the House. The Hansards were continually asked for papers on particular topics and in consequence, as Luke Graves said in evidence before the Committee, 'We have for some length of time combined them [the Sessional Indexes] for the general use of our establishment'; and he saw no difficulty in consolidating them up to date. The form in which he proposed to do it is set out in Appendix 2, VI. To the Committee of 1831–2, which recommended its extension, in answer to Q. 94 he repeated his reasons for compiling it: 'When any subject is under discussion requiring information on any particular point, then applications are made for a Selection of Papers, either individually or collectively, on those subjects. Without the means which the Index affords, we should find extreme difficulty in making the selection required, but with that we find the Papers with great facility and are enabled to furnish them with accuracy and expedition.' The Alphabetical Indexes successively compiled during the century remain excellent working instruments, despite the difficulties of dealing with a great range of papers without 'author' or 'title'. Those difficulties were first encountered and mastered by Luke and Luke Graves Hansard. The bearing of this project on the story of the Breviate is twofold. The first Breviate and the first General Alphabetical Index, both covering the same period, were regarded by the Hansards as a single piece of work, for they suggested that the two should be bound together to form 'one volume of Helps to Consultors of the Papers'. Secondly, there seems little doubt that the further experience gained in this work contributed to the great improvements in the third index; that is, to the second and final Breviate.

The *Catalogue and Breviate of Parliamentary Papers, 1696-1834*, of which this volume is a reprint, shows a great development both in range and form. It now includes the period covered by the first subject index, and is extended up to 1834; and there are great improvements in the lay-out of the summaries of the separate reports. The formal recommendation that it should be prepared came from the Select Committee on the Library and State of the Printed Papers (1831–2 (600) v), which stated in paras. 37 to 39 of its report, that the General Index and Classification of Papers this firm had prepared were eminently useful, that the work was out of print and often applied for in vain. But the suggestion that it should be done came from Luke Graves Hansard, who in evidence stated in answer to Q. 84, that if the Alphabetical Index were to be continued, it would be desirable to extend the 'Classification of Papers' also. 'The Breviate,' he said in answer to Q. 100, had been 'designed as a substitute for the want of indexes to the particular reports.'

The classification and cataloguing of Parliamentary Papers of a modern state is not an easy task; nor is the problem limited to British Papers, as Poore, Ames and Crandall show in their introductions to the catalogues of American papers. When we consider the discussions of librarians on the difficulties in performing this function for their own collections of papers, even with the advantage of a century of experience and the development of modern library techniques, we may well admire the quality first of Luke and then of Luke Graves and James who, facing the problem of classifying Parliamentary Papers for the first time, produced a guide so good as to be still workable after a century has passed. The secret of their success lies in their fresh and modern approach. They set out, as Luke wrote in the preface to the first subject index, 'to give a perspicuous view of every important document, bearing upon any given point, which has proceeded from the Committees of the House of Commons', and 'not to omit anything which might become the object of research'; or, as Luke Graves wrote later in the preface to the first Breviate, 'to provide an ample means of rendering fully available the Reports, Accounts and other Papers printed by the House, for the purpose of any information which public discussion or private research may require'. It will be seen that the preface to the reprinted Breviate is written in the same spirit. By the preparation of this Breviate and of the first general alphabetical index, Luke and Luke Graves made a permanent contribution to our apparatus for reaching the data in the papers for which scholars cannot be too grateful. We think it will be agreed that they exhibited the 'persevering labour and intelligence' and qualities of 'distinctness of mind' for which Luke was commended by his contemporaries.

P. AND G. FORD

ACKNOWLEDGMENTS

Our thanks are due to H.M. Stationery Office for their courtesy in agreeing to the reprint of the Breviate. We wish to thank Mr. J. Hansard for his interest in the reprint of this Breviate and for his assistance in enabling it to be reproduced in a manner worthy of the work of those members of the Hansard family who originally prepared it.

SELECT LIST OF HOUSE OF LORDS' PAPERS
NOT IN THIS BREVIATE

HANSARD's Breviate was based on House of Commons' papers; it includes Lords' papers which were 'communicated' to the Commons, but not those which were not so communicated. We have included the relevant Lords' papers in the *Select List*, *1833–1899*, and have made a similar selection for this reprint. Through the courtesy of Mr. Dobson, Assistant Librarian of the House of Lords, we are also able to include some Lords' papers which are not indexed. A few odd Commons' papers omitted by Hansard have also been inserted. The list below sets out these papers in the subject order of the *Select List*.

1788	(HL.–)	Not indexed	State of His Majesty's health. Examination of H.M.'s Physicians. Lords Cttes. Rep.
1811	(H.L.3)	xliii	Precedents when personal exercise of royal authority is prevented by sickness, infancy, etc. Lords Cttees. Rep.
1806	(HL.94)	vi	Privilege of Peers to decline attending the House of Commons. Lords Cttees. Rep.
1817	(HL.42)	lxxxiv	Precedents of Peers advanced to higher dignity entering their proxies according to their former titles. Cttees. for Privilege. Rep.
1824	(HL.86)	clxviii	Reversal of attainders, and restoration and restitution in blood. Precedents of Bills. Lords Cttees. apptd. to search the Journals. Rep.
	(HL.102)	,,	—— Addenda.
1825	(HL.43)	cxcii	Trial of Peers for offences committed in Scotland.
1826	(HL.6)	ccxxxvii	Arrest of Peers not having seats in the House of Lords. Lords Cttees. for Privileges. Rep.
1831–2	(HL.123)	cccvii	Election of representative Peers for Scotland. Sel. Cttee. HL. Rep.
1819	(HL.129)	cxi	Barnstaple election. Mins. of ev. taken before House of Lords on 2nd reading of Bill.
1801	(HL.–)	[i]	Standing orders. Private Bills, Ireland. Lords Cttee. Rep.
1806	(HL.42)	v	Manner of proceeding to Judgment on Impeachments. Lords Cttees. apptd. in 1795. Rep.
1826–7	(HL.114)	ccxix	Fees and charges payable on Private Bills. Sel. Cttee. HL. Rep., mins. of ev., etc.
1824	(HL.132)	clxviii	Office of Clerk of the Parliaments. Lords Cttees. Rep.
1825	(HL.206)	cxcii	Parliament office. Committee rooms and conveniences for placing and keeping the records, etc. Lords Cttees. Rep.
1826–7	(HL.58)	ccxix	Parliament office. Safe keeping of the records. Lords Cttees. Reps.
1826–7	(HL.82)	ccxix	Office of Clerk of the Parliaments. Sel. Cttee. Rep.
1828	(HL.181)	ccxxxvii	—— Sel. Cttee. Reps.
1829	(HL.105)	ccxliv	——
1831	(HL.126)	ccxci	Ventilation of the House and further accommodation for Peers. Sel. Cttee. HL. Rep.
1823	(HL.106)	clvii	Government of the City of Limerick Bill. Lords Cttees. Mins. of ev.

1800	(HL.–)	Not indexed	Inclosure Bills. Sel. Cttee. Mins. of ev.
1810	(HL.15)	xxxvi	State of the distilleries and corn trade. Lords Cttees. Rep.
1810	(HL.19)	xxxvi	Prohibition of the distillation of corn or grain in Great Britain. Mins. of ev.
1810	(HL.67)	xxxvi	Prohibition of distillation from grain. Sel. Cttee. HL. Rep., mins. of ev.
1818	(HL.41)	xcv	Bedford Level drainage. River Ouse Navigation Bill. Lords Cttee. Mins. of ev.
1788	(HL.–)	Not indexed	Exportation of Wool Bill. Mins. of ev.
1790	(HL.–)	,,	Tobacco and Wool (Duties). Mins. of ev.
1800	(HL.–)	,,	Woollen manufactory. Mins. of ev.
1830	(9)	viii	Coal trade of the United Kingdom. Sel. Cttee. HL. Rep., mins. of ev., etc.
1830	(HL.12)	cclxxv	—— Rep.
1803	(HL.–)	[vii]	Repair of the road from Worcester through Droitwich, etc., Bill. Lords Cttees. Mins. of ev.
1797	(HL.–)	Not indexed	Navigation of the Trent to the Mersey to make a navigable canal. Mins. of ev.
1801–2	(HL.–)	[iii]	Glenkenns Canal Bill. Lords Cttees. Mins. of ev.
1830	(251)	x	Birmingham and London Junction Canal petitions. Cttee. Rep.
	(260)	,,	—— Mins. of ev.
1807	(1)	ii	Reform and Improvement of the Post Office, etc. Agreement made with J. Palmer, 1797. Reprint. Further Reprint: 1812–3 (222) iv.
	(31)	,,	—— Petition of J. Palmer. Sel. Cttee. Rep.
1808	(241)	vi	—— —— Mins. of ev.
	(HL.111)	xviii	—— Lords Cttees. Rep. Reprint: 1812 (HL. 137) liii.
	(294)	iii	—— Percentage due to J. Palmer. Sel. Cttee. Rep.
1812–3	(HL.123)	lxiii	—— Sel. Cttee. HL. Rep., mins. of ev.
1812–3	(222)	iv	—— Rep., etc.
1812–3	(260)	iv	—— Sel. Cttee. Mins. of ev.
1807	(HL.36)	xiv	Fourdrinier. Invention for making paper by means of machinery. Lords Cttees. Mins. of ev. on the Bill.
1829	(HL.82)	cclxii	Langton. Profits and emoluments (seasoning of timber). Lords Cttees. Mins. of ev.
1818	(HL.25)	xcv	Regulation of chimney sweepers and their apprentices. Lords Cttee. Mins. of ev.
1818	(HL.61)	xci	Chimney sweepers and their apprentices Bill. Lords Cttees. Rep.
1817	(400)	vi	Chimney sweepers. Practicability of using machinery instead of boys. Rep., mins. of ev.
1819	(9)	xvii	—— Surveyor General, Bd. of Works. Rep.
1825	(154)	xx	—— Accounts relating to apprentices.
1830	(281)	xxix	—— Letter by Home Secretary in favour of the Society for superseding climbing boys, etc.

1834	(HL.107)	xxiii Pt. I	Regulation of chimney sweepers and their apprentices. Bill. Sel. Cttee. HL. Mins. of ev.
	(HL.118)	„	—— Mins. of ev., etc.
1818	(HL.90)	xcvi	Preservation of the health and morals of apprentices and others employed in cotton mills and factories Bill. Lords Cttees. Mins. of ev.
1819	(HL.24)	cx	State and condition of the children employed in cotton factories, etc. Lords Cttees. Mins. of ev.
1823	(HL.86)	clvi.	Wages of persons employed in the manufacture of silk, and of silk mixed with other materials. Lords Cttees. Mins. of ev.
1805	(HL.59)	xv	St. Pancras Poor Bill. Sel. Cttee. HL. Mins. of ev.
1803–4	(109)	v	Support of the poor, and care of lunatics and idiots. Rep.
1828	(HL.85)	ccxxxvii	Care of lunatics, etc. Sel. Cttee. HL. Mins. of ev. on Bills.
1811	(HL.70)	xliv	Hearing and decision of Appeals and Writs of Error. Sel. Cttee. HL. Rep.
1823	(HL.65)	cliii	Hearing of Appeals, Writs of Error, etc. Sel. Cttee. HL. 1st Rep. Reprint: 1824 (HL.5) clxiii.
	(HL.74)	„	—— 2nd Rep.
1824	(HL.99)	clxiii	—— Rep.
1825	(HL.157)	cxcii	Officers of Courts of Justice (Compensation). Lords Cttees. Rep., mins. of ev.
1810	(HL.83)	xxxv	Penalty of death for breaches of the Revenue Laws. Sel. Cttee. HL. Rep.
1809	(HL.61)	xxvii	Imprisonment for Civil Debt. Lords Cttees. Reps.
	(HL.16)	„	—— Mins. of ev.
1813–4	(HL.119)	lxxii	Debtors confined in Gloucester Gaol. Cttee. of the whole House. Mins. of ev.
1820	(HL.46)	cxvii	Insolvent debtors. Lords Cttees. Rep., mins. of ev.
1819	(HL.31)	xcix	State of the gaols in the United Kingdom. Sel. Cttee. HL. Rep., mins of ev.
1823	(HL.33)	cliii	Marriage Laws. Sel. Cttee. HL. Rep.
1801	(HL.–)	[i]	Seditious and treasonable practices, societies and meetings. Lords Cttees. 2nd, 3rd Reps.
	(HL.–)	„	—— Persons apprehended or detained. List, etc.
1812	(HL.158)	liii	The disturbances in Nottinghamshire and adjacent counties. Secret Cttee. HL. Rep.
1817	(HL.5)	lxxxiv	Meetings and combinations endangering public tranquillity. Secret Cttee. Reprint: 1818 (HL.7) xci.
1817	(HL.65)	lxxxiv	Traitorous conspiracy for the overthrow of the Government. Secret Cttee. HL. Rep.
1818	(HL.8)	xci	—— Rep.

NOTES

1. For papers issued from 1801 onwards, the main references in this Breviate are to the sessional bound sets of papers. An additional reference in square brackets, e.g. [23], indicates that the paper was also in that volume of the collection of 363 volumes which were the basis of the first Breviate. Hansard calls the 154 report volumes the Second Series, to distinguish it from the First Series of 15 volumes for which he made his first subject index (Report, App. 10, p. 38; 1831–2 (600) V).

2. For a description of the various indexes to the reports of Committees, see *British Parliamentary Catalogues and Indexes*, Bulletin of the Institute of Historical Research, Vol. XI, 1933.

CATALOGUE

OF

PARLIAMENTARY REPORTS,

AND A

BREVIATE OF THEIR CONTENTS:

ARRANGED UNDER

HEADS ACCORDING TO THE SUBJECTS.

1696—1834.

Ordered, by The House of Commons, *to be Printed,*
15 *August* 1834.

PREFACE.

THE first attempt at an Arranged CATALOGUE of Parliamentary Reports was made by direction of the Library Committee in 1825. The continuation now presented to The House, was undertaken by direction of the Library Committee in 1832. The first Catalogue was restricted to such Reports as commenced in 1801 and terminated with 1826. In forming the present, it was thought desirable to comprise all the Reports on public subjects that had been made to The House, from the earliest period, whether inserted only on the Journals, or contained in the printed collections of Reports. This comprises a period from 1696 to 1834. Thus the inquirer will have before his eye a view of the whole of any subject that has been treated on, by this description of official document. Considered separately, perhaps some of these early Reports may be deemed of too little importance, or too long out of date, to need mention in the Catalogue; but when their connexion with subsequent Reports on similar subjects is observed, their relative importance may make them interesting : thus the Report in 1698 on the state of East India Affairs, from which the present Company took its rise, may be thought fit to precede the long series of Reports relating to that most important portion of the British Empire which have since been printed; and the Reports in 1778 and 1779 on the State of Prisons, in which the philanthropist Howard suggested improvements in Prison Discipline; and on Penal Colonies, in which Sir Joseph Banks proposed the settlement, under the name of Botany Bay, in the new discovered country, which is now considered the Australian Continent,—must be deemed worthy of notice : nor will the Reports on Approaches to the Houses of Parliament in 1793 be thought unfit to precede the entries of those on the Rebuilding of the Houses now engaging the attention of the Legislature and the Public. As some of these Reports have not been printed separately, but exist only on the Journals, their subjects would be lost to many inquirers unless brought to their notice by the mode here adopted.

The difficulties felt in ·classing subjects under heads characterising their nature, can be appreciated by those who have made similar attempts. Many Reports have titles which do not directly indicate their subjects, and many contain a great diversity of subjects, which render it difficult to determine the class under which they should be placed : thus Plague and Contagion are treated on in Reports specifically bearing those titles, and are placed under Scientific Subjects, with the sub-head Medical; they are likewise treated on in one of the series of Reports on Foreign Trade. Steam-boats and Steam Navigation bear titles distinctive of those subjects, but no inquirer would expect to find a discussion on the construction of Steam-boats and on the

machinery

machinery for propelling them, in a Report on Holyhead Roads. These, however, could only be placed under their ostensible titles; but a remedy is found by Cross References, and which is more effectually applied in the INDEX, in which all matters of the like nature are concentrated into one view.

The Abstracts of the subject-matter of the Reports, which are placed after the entry of the titles, may refresh the memory of those inquirers who already possess general knowledge of their contents; while they will impart information to those unacquainted with them; and many matters of interest, not indicated by the title, but collaterally arising in the course of investigation or mode of illustration, are brought before the mind by these notices of the leading subjects.

In surveying the extent and variety of the subjects upon which information is collected in these Reports, it will be allowed that every means should be adopted to render such information useful; and it is hoped the present endeavour will assist in advancing this object.

The draft of this Catalogue was laid before The House at the close of the Session 1834, and was then ordered to be printed; but many circumstances intervened to retard its early completion. The delay, however, has not been disadvantageous, as it has afforded an opportunity of bringing the compilation down to 1834, and therefore comprises the notice of many important Reports, which would otherwise have been omitted.

The mode of References adopted points out the different classes of Reports: Thus the Reports which are to be found only on the Journals, or in the early collection prior to 1801; are marked by a bracket [at the beginning of the title, and reference is made to the volume and page of the Journal where they will be found. Those which are comprised in the collection of Fifteen Volumes, terminating with 1800, are referred to as the *First Series of Reports.* The Modern Reports from 1801 are referred to by the Session, the number of the paper as ordered to be printed, and the volume of the collection as annually arranged, and preserved in the Library. The ordinal numbers which precede each entry under the respective heads, are of use for distinct means of identification and reference.

June 1836.   *James & Luke G. Hansard & Sons.*

HEADS OF ARRANGEMENT.

EXTRACT FROM REPORT OF THE LIBRARY COMMITTEE,

1832.

" The General Index and Classification of the Sessional Papers from 1801 to 1826, have been found eminently useful.   The Work is now out of print, and it is often applied for in vain ; a continuation of it has been prepared by direction of Mr. Speaker."—Report on the Library of the House of Commons, 16 July 1832, (600.) p. 11.

CATALOGUE OF REPORTS,

WITH A

BREVIATE OF THEIR CONTENTS:

1696——1834.

N. B. The inquirer is reminded, that, with few exceptions, Accounts and Papers, illustrative of the subjects of the Reports in the following Catalogue, will be found under their proper heads in the series of volumes containing the Collection of ACCOUNTS AND PAPERS. It has not appeared necessary to add particular references, as the inspection of the *General Index to the Sessional Printed Papers* will point out whatever has been printed on the subject of inquiry.

The Ordinal Number at the beginning of each entry is useful for identification and reference. Those marked with a bracket [are in most instances printed only in the Journals, or in the *First Series of Reports, in 15 Vols. of large folio,* from 1701 to 1800, and are difficult to be procured in their original editions. The dates or session of the Reports are in all cases inserted; and the number (501.) which the paper bears in each session is marked between parentheses, to all such as have been printed from 1801. Where the figures between brackets [23] occur at the end of the other references, it is indicated that such articles are contained in the *Second Series of Arrangement in Volumes* deposited in the Library of The House.

I.

Ecclesiastical Subjects.—Revenues.—Churches.

Roman-catholics :

Religion and Pontifical Authority :

1.—Report from the Select Committee on Regulations in foreign states of their Roman-catholic subjects in Ecclesiastical Matters.

Sess. 1816, (501.) vol. 7–A–1. [23.]

These Papers are very systematically arranged. The press was revised with great care under the direction of Sir J. C. Hippisley.

2.—Supplemental Papers in continuation of the same subject.

Sess. 1817, (174.) vol. 15, p. 329. [23.]

see *Education in Ireland*, under Head II., and *State of Ireland*, under Head V.

Land Tax :

3.—Report from the Select Committee on the Land Tax, as affecting Roman-catholics.

Sess. 1828, (550.) vol. 4, p. 231.

SUBJECTS.—Origin of the assessments on land.—Ancient valuations.—Valuation of 4 Will. 3, and which continue to the present time.—Double charge thereby on lands belonging to Roman-catholics.—Intended relief from such charge in 1794.—Inoperative from the Acts conditioning that Roman-catholics should not pay *double* the *present* annual value of rents ; and when relieved by the commissioners, they are unable to apportion the abated sum on other lands in the district, by reason of operation of the law of redemption.

Sabbath-day :

4.—Report from the Select Committee on the laws and practices relating to the Observance of the Lord's-day.

Sess. 1831–32, (697.) vol. 7, p. 253.

SUBJECTS.—Statutes relating to the observance of the Lord's-day.—Its violation by Sunday trading and marketing.—Evils of having pay-tables at public-houses.—Eating-houses and coffee-shops.—Bakers' journeymen.—Fishmongers' and poulterers' shops at the west-end of the town.—Stage-coach travelling on Sunday.—Number of coaches licensed.—Alteration of Smithfield market-day. — Steam-packets to Gravesend and Richmond.—Sabbath there.—Profanation of the Sabbath on the Newmarket road.—Public meetings on Sunday.—Amendment of the law recommended to be supported by the example of the higher classes.—Insufficient accommodation in churches.— Observance of the Sabbath increasing among the higher classes.—Inconvenience to persons in their way to church from closing public-houses just before the commencement of Divine service.—Informations by the police against Sunday traders.— Sunday trading and profanation of the Sabbath at Westminster.—Ineffectual attempt to stop Sunday trading in Lambeth.—Mr. Owen's Sunday meetings at the Westminster Theatre and other places.—Sunday newspapers have a pernicious influence on the public.—Stamps issued for Sunday newspapers published in 1831.—Dr. Farr's opinions upon the rest of the Sabbath.—Characters of carriers and boatmen.—State of the city and Smithfield market on Sunday.—Evils of the Book of Sports.—Sabbath breaking the first cause of crime.—Non-observance of the Sabbath in Scotland increasing.—Laws of Scotland with regard to profanation of the Sabbath.—Commission by the General Assembly in Scotland to inquire into the abuses of the Sabbath.—Reasons for the relaxation in the observance of the Sabbath in Scotland.—Modification of the law of patronage.—History of religion and observance of the Sabbath in Scotland.—Summary of statutes for the observance of the Lord's-day.—Summary of Scottish Acts.—Extracts from proceedings of the Church Courts in Scotland, showing how the laws against Sabbath breaking were administered.

Tithes, England :

5.—Report and Resolutions of the Select Committee respecting.

Sess. 1816, (486.) vol. 4, p. 511.

Tithe Causes :

6.—Papers respecting Tithe Causes.

Sess. 1817, (173.) vol. 16, p. 59.

Tithes, England—continued.

Tithes Composition:

7.—Return of the several parishes in England and Wales in which Com-
mutations for Tithes have been authorized under Act of Parliament.

Sess. 1831–32, (38.) vol. 30, p. 73.

Ecclesiastical Courts :

8.—Returns of all Courts which exercise Ecclesiastical Jurisdiction, and of all
Courts which exercise Peculiar and Exempt Jurisdiction, in England and
Wales.   Sess. 1828, (232.) vol. 20, p. 229.

SUBJECTS.—Style of the courts exercising·jurisdiction.—Names of the judges.—In what
character they preside, and by whom appointed.—Names of registrars, and their deputies,
and by whom appointed.

9.—Reports of the Commissioners on the Practice and Jurisdiction of the
Ecclesiastical Courts of England and Wales.   Sess. 1831–32, (199.) vol. 24, p. 1.

10.—Report from the Commissioners on Ecclesiastical Revenues in England
and Wales.   Sess. 1834, (523.) vol. 23, p. 5.

Probates of Wills :

11.—Return of all Courts in England and Wales empowered to grant Probates
of Wills and Letters of Administration; also, Return of the Number of
Causes instituted in the several Courts which exercise Ecclesiastical Jurisdiction in the Provinces of Canterbury and York : 1824 to 1827.

Sess. 1828, (372.) vol 20, p. 751.

SUBJECTS.—Style of the courts and other authorities.—Their powers.—Extent of their
jurisdiction.—Period during which they exercise their powers.—When and by whom inhi-
bited.—Places where wills are deposited, and in whose custody.—Number and nature of
causes, and fees paid.

Records, Fees, &c.

12.—Returns respecting Jurisdiction, Records, Emoluments and Fees, of
Ecclesiastical Courts in England and Wales.   Sess. 1830, (205.) vol. 19, p. 51.

————————

Ministers of Scotland, 1751 :

13.—[Report from the Select Committee on the Petition of the Commissioners
for the General Assembly of the Church of Scotland, &c.

First Series, vol. ii. p. 317.

SUBJECTS.—Provision made by law for the maintenance of the clergy.—Commissioners of
teinds constituted for adjusting the value of benefices, and apportioning stipends.—Stipendiary allowances to the clergy.—Minimum fixed by law.—Augmentation of stipends desired
by the clergy.—Routine of suits for obtaining augmentation of insufficient stipends, and
for the recovery of those withheld.—The law favourable to the clergy.

Church Patronage, Scotland, 1834 :

14.—Report from the Select Committee on the state of the Law of Church
Patronage in Scotland, and on the accordance of that system with the constitution and principles of the Church of Scotland.   Sess. 1834, (512.) vol. 5, p. 1.

SUBJECTS.—*Act of Anne :* The only one affording a precedent for the assumption by
Government of the rights of the Church.—Objections made to the Act at the time of its
passing, and subsequently.—Benefits derived by the Act.—Evil effects thereof.—Modifications made and to be made therein.————*Acts of Assembly :* Are more binding upon the
Church Courts than the Books of Discipline.————*Act of* 1592 : Considered the Magna
Charta of the Church.————*Act of* 1649 : Abolished the right of patronage in the Crown
and laymen.————*Act of* 1690 : Its revival would not be attended with good effects.————
Act of 1719 : Gave great satisfaction to the Church.————*Act of* 1732 : Not sufficiently
extended in its operations.————*Bishops' Revenues :* Taken possession of by the Crown
without, and are still held without, an Act of Parliament.————*Calls :* Nature thereof.—
Method of obtaining them, and period when it is required.————*Church Courts :* Any
additional power given them will cause great dissent.————*Church of Scotland :* Statutes
establishing it, and definition of the term " Kirk " therein.—Has always protested against
the people having the power of appointing and ordaining ministers.—In all matters, eccle-
siastical and spiritual, she is independent of the civil power.————*Clergy of Scotland :*
Their character higher at present than at any former period of modern times.————*Crown
Patronage :* Forms a most useful link between the Church and State.————*Books of
Discipline :* Variation between them.—Authorities for them, and proceedings under them.
————*Episcopacy :* Never introduced into Scotland in all its extents.————*General
Assembly :* Has the power of legislating on all ecclesiastical matters.————*Landed Pro-
prietors :* Possess comparatively little of Church patronage in Scotland————*Lay
Patronage :*

Church Patronage, Scotland—continued.

Patronage : Period of its introduction, and abuses to which it is subject.———*Ministers :* Duty and style of preaching.—Effect of patronage on them.—Appointment thereof by the congregation and communicants; by presbyteries; by secession churches.——— *Parliament :* Difficulties in the way of Parliament legislating for the abolition of patronage. ———*Patronage :* In whom vested.—-Evils thereof.—Advantages of the present over proposed system.—Improvements of late years in the manner of its exercise.—Amendments necessary to be made in the law thereof.—Opinions in favour and against its abolition. ———*Popular Election :* Evils and advantages thereof.———*Presbyteries :* Should not have more power of election than at present.———*Reformation :* Greater part of the churches at the time thereof were attached to bishoprics and monasteries.———*Reform Bill :* Benefits thereof as regards patronage.———*Seceders :* Causes of the departure of the seceders from the Church, and measures taken by the Assembly to heal the breaches thereof.———*Seceding Ministers :* But few instances of heats or divisions in the election thereof.———*Thirds of Benefices :* Period at which they were made effectual for the support of the clergy.———*Ulster Synod :* Of whom composed, and mode of conducting elections therein.———*Violent Settlements :* The effect thereof very injurious to Scotland. ———*Voluntary Churches :* The voluntary principle would be overthrown by the abolition of patronage.

Church Establishment, Ireland :

15.—Papers relating to the state of the Established Church of Ireland.
Sess. 1820, (93.) vol. 9, p. 1. [27.]

SUBJECT.—*Ecclesiastical Revenues.*—Tabular Returns of the state of benefices in Ireland. ———see Reports on *Education in Ireland*, under Head II.

Tithes :

16.—Reports (first and second) from the Select Committee on Tithes in Ireland.
Sess. 1831-32, (177. 508.) vol. 21, pp. 1. 245.

SUBJECTS.—Resistance to the payment and collection of tithes.—Violence committed in opposing the valuing and distraining for them.—Arrears of tithes.—Evils of the present system of collection.—Legal and equitable proceedings.—Difficulty of collecting without military force.—State of the clergy.—Opinions of the manner in which they should be supported.— Presbyterian and Roman-catholic.—Clergy residence.—Conduct of the Protestant clergy in enforcing tithes.—State of their incomes.—Origin of tithes.—Distribution of tithes.—Lay impropriations.—Opinions generally prevailing in respect to them.--Evils in the existing system, and necessity of alteration.—Articles titheable.—Rate and method of valuing.—Necessity of a settlement of the question.—Plan for transferring the payment of tithes to landlords.—Operation of the Act for the composition of tithes.—Advantages and disadvantages to the clergy in France.—Opposition to it.—Plans for making it effectual.— Plans for effecting a commutation of land for tithes.

17.—Reports from the Lords' Committee on the same subject.
Sess. 1831-32, (271. 663.) vol. 22, pp. 1. 181.

Lay Tithes :

18.—Return of the number of parishes the Tithes of which are the property of Laymen.   Sess. 1831-32, (326.) vol. 30, p. 249.

Benefices, Ireland :

19.—Second Report from the Commissioners for inquiring into the Union of Parochial Benefices in Ireland.   Sess. 1834, (406.) vol. 23, p. 1.

Ecclesiastical Inquiry, Ireland :

20.—Report of His Majesty's Commissioners; dated 18 April 1831.
Sess. 1831, (93.) vol. 9, p. 73.

SUBJECTS.—State of parochial benefices.—Whether separate or united parishes.—Authority for unions.—State and annual value.—Contiguity of parishes.—Possibility or fitness of dissolving the unions.—Payment of legal salaries to curates.—Explanation of the kinds and nature, and origin and causes, of parochial unions.—State of impropriations and appropriations.—Authority under which the present unions were formed.—Extent of impropriations.—Unprovided state of many spiritual cures.—Leading to extensive unions in order to provide for the minister.—Legal claims on impropriators to maintain curates.—Recommendations for creating legal powers for the dissolution of the unions in certain cases, and for carrying other measures relating thereto into effect.

21.—First Report of the Commissioners on Ecclesiastical Revenue and Patronage ;—dated 1 March 1833.   Sess. 1833, (762.) vol. 21.

22.—Second Report ;—dated 15 April 1834.   Sess. 1834, (589.) vol. 27, p. 7.

CHURCHES.

New Churches in England :

Of Queen Anne, 1711 :

23.—⌈Report of the Select Committee on a petition for rebuilding Greenwich Church; on the state of the rebuilding of St. Paul's; and on the want of Churches in London.   Journals, vol. 16, p. 580.

> SUBJECT.—This report is closed with a resolution that Fifty New Churches are necessary in the cities and suburbs of London and Westminster.

Of King George III. 1821—1834 :

24.—Report of Commissioners, under Acts 58 & 59 Geo. 3, and 3 Geo. 4, for building New Churches.   Sess. 1821, (29.) vol. 10, p. 1. [**124.**]

> SUBJECTS.—*Appropriation of the Parliamentary Grant.*—Statement of the proceedings of the Commissioners.—Regulations and conditions of affording assistance.—Additional churches to be built.—Churches, &c. building.—Applications for additional churches.

25.—Second Report of the Commissioners.for building and promoting the building of Additional Churches in populous Parishes.   Sess. 1822, (605.) vol. 11, p. 1. [**124.**]

> SUBJECTS.—*Appropriation of the Parliamentary Grant.*—Tenor of former Report summarily stated.—Progress since made.—New churches built.—The whole of the fund appropriated.—List of new churches built, and building.—Style of building.—Amount of sum contracted for each.—Progress of the work.—List of plans approved, but not commenced.—Plans under consideration.—List of applications.—Applications deferred.

26.—Third Annual Report of the Commissioners.   Sess. 1823, (573.) vol. 7, p. 1. [**124.**]

> SUBJECTS.—*Appropriation of the Parliamentary Grant.*—Account of the progress made in building new churches.—Places where plans are approved of, or under consideration.—Applications postponed on account of insufficiency of funds.

27,—Fourth Annual Report of the Commissioners.   Sess. 1824, (430.) vol. 9, p. 1. [**124.**]

> SUBJECT.—Appropriation of the Parliamentary Grant.

28.—Account of Churches built and building.   Sess. 1824, (175.) vol. 18, p. 55. [**124.**]

29.—Account of Charges and Expenses of the Commissioners.   Sess. 1824, (409.) vol. 18, p. 63. [**124.**]

30.—Returns of the Expenditure of Grants for building.   Sess. 1824, (465.) vol. 18, p. 65. [**124.**]

31.—Fifth Annual Report of the Commissioners.   Sess. 1825, (511.) vol. 15, p. 91. [**124.**]

> SUBJECTS.—Progress of providing new churches.—Twenty-six built.—Accommodation furnished for 36,650 persons.—Twenty other churches and chapels built.—Thirty in progress of building.—Steps taken by the Commissioners for assigning ecclesiastical districts.—Advance of money to Lambeth and other parishes.—Application for assistance, and determination of the Commissioners to advance half the funds.—Communications with places desiring additional churches and chapels.—Provision of burial grounds.—Surrender of land and buildings for the purpose of building or converting into chapels.—Church of St. Bridget, in Chester, building under the direction of the Commissioners, but not out of the public fund.—Exchequer bills issued.

32.—Account of Charges and Expenses paid by the Commissioners.   Sess. 1825, (497.) vol. 21, p. 31. [**124.**]

33.—Sixth Annual Report of the Commissioners.   Sess. 1826, (422.) vol. 11, p. 1. [**124.**]

> SUBJECT.—Further proceedings of the Commissioners.

34.—Seventh Annual Report of the Commissioners.   Sess. 1826-27, (533.) vol. 7, p. 1.

> SUBJECTS.—Progress of the Commission.—Provision made for erecting One hundred and ninety-nine additional churches and chapels.

35.—Eighth Annual Report of the Commissioners.   Sess. 1828, (566.) vol. 9, p. 1.

> SUBJECTS.—Proceedings of the Commissioners.—Number of churches and chapels built.—In progress.—Plans under consideration.—Additional burial-grounds provided.

36.—Ninth Annual Report of the Commissioners.   Sess. 1829, (326.) vol. 5, p. 1.

New Churches in England—continued.
Of King George III.—*continued.*

37.—Tenth Annual Report of the Commissioners.　　Sess. 1830, (677.) vol. 15, p. 1.

SUBJECTS.—Progress of the Commission.—Number of churches and chapels built and building.

38.—Eleventh Annual Report of the Commissioners.　　Sess. 1831, (336.) vol. 9, p. 1.

SUBJECTS.—Proceedings of the Commissioners.—Churches and chapels completed and building.—Plans, and applications for others.

39.—Twelfth Annual Report of the Commissioners.
Sess. 1831–32, (687.) vol. 23, p. 309.

SUBJE TS.—Further proceedings of Commissioners.—Continuation of the statement of church-accommodation afforded; of churches built, and in progress; of grants in aid of parishes for building churches and enlarging burial-grounds.

40.—Thirteenth Annual Report of the Commissioners.
Sess. 1834, (400.) vol. 40, p. 33.

41.—Fourteenth Annual Report of the Commissioners.
Sess. 1834, (585.) vol. 40, p. 43.

Churches in the Highlands of Scotland :

42.—First Report of the Commissioners for building Churches in the Highlands and Islands of Scotland; under Act 4 Geo. 4, c. 79.
Sess. 1825, (514.) vol. 15, p. 117. [124.]

SUBJECTS.—*Object of the Commissioners, and proceedings to accomplish it.*—Scale of expense to be incurred in any one instance.—Conducted under the same persons who were Commissioners under the Roads and Bridges Act.—Commencement of the Commissioners' proceedings.—Defect in the Act requiring two heritors—remedied; and provision made for upholding the church and manse.—Regulations of ministers' stipends.—List of places to which churches have been assigned.—List of applications for repairs.—Union of Highland parishes.—Plans of churches and manses.—Necessity of the prompt proceedings of the Commissioners in their commencing buildings.—State of accounts.—Probable time of completing the object of the Act.

43.—Second Report of the Commissioners.　　Sess. 1826, (358.) vol. 11. p. 23. [124.]

SUBJECT.—Further proceedings of the Commissioners.

44.—Third Report of the Commissioners.　　Sess. 1826–27, (508.) vol. 7, p. 99.

SUBJECTS.—Progress of the works under the direction of the Commissioners.—Substantiality of the buildings necessary to avoid the frequent recurrence of repairs.

45.—Fourth Report of the Commissioners.　　Sess. 1828, (508.) vol. 9, p. 261.

SUBJECTS.—Proceedings of Commissioners.—Churches built or proposed to be built.—Nomination of ministers.

46.—Fifth Report of the Commissioners.　　Sess. 1829, (341.) vol. 5, p. 199.

SUBJECTS.—Progress of the Commissioners—object nearly completed.—Number of applications unsuccessful for want of funds.

47.—Sixth Report of the Commissioners.　　Sess. 1831, (330.) vol. 9, p. 19.

SUBJECTS.—Proceedings of Commissioners.—Churches and manses completed.—Summary view of the benefit produced by the Parliamentary grant.—Amount expended.——A map of the situation of the churches, and a plan of the buildings, are inserted.

II.

Education and Charities.

EDUCATION.

Education of the Lower Orders, 1816—1818 :

1.—Reports from the Select Committee on the Education of the Lower Orders in the Metropolis.   Sess. 1816, (498. 427. 469. 495. 497.) vol. 4. [100.]

> SUBJECTS.—I. *General State of the Education of the Lower Orders.*—Deficiency of means of education.—Prevailing desire of education.—Children in the metropolis ; their morals, education and industry :—conduct of their parents.—State of religion, as influenced by education.—Dissenters' exertions for promoting education.—Irish poor.—Education in Scotland.———II. *Institutions and Charitable Donations for promoting Education.*—Charities and societies of various kinds connected with education.—Parochial, Sunday and Daily schools ; and schools attached to corporations.———III. *Misapplication of Funds.*—Investigation into the management of the funds of several endowments ; particularly of St. Bees, Pocklington, Lewisham, Spital, Mere, and Croydon charities.———IV. *System of General Education.*—National establishment.—Parochial schools.—Associations of individuals.—Application of the Holy Scriptures and national forms of prayer.———V. *Universities and great Schools.*—Trinity and St. John's colleges, Cambridge, and Eton college ; their statutes.—Westminster, Winchester, St. Paul's, and Christ's Hospital schools ; their foundations.—Scholarships attached to particular places.

2.—Report from the Select Committee on the Education of the Lower Orders in the Metropolis.   Sess 1817, (479.) vol. 3, p. 81. [100.]

> Same subjects.

3.—Report from the Select Committee on the Education of the Lower Orders.
                    Sess. 1818, (136.) vol. 4, p. 1. [100.]

> SUBJECT.—Recommending proceedings.

4.—Second Report from the same Committee.   Sess. 1818, (356.) vol. 4, p. 3. [100.]

> SUBJECT.—Parochial and other schools.

5.—Third Report from the same Committee.   Sess. 1818, (426.) vol. 4, p. 55. [100.]

> SUBJECTS.—British and Foreign School Society.—Eton college.—Schools of St. Bees, Winchester, Highgate, Pocklington, Brentwood, Mere, Spital, Yeovil, Huntingdon.—Education of the poor in Ireland.—Institution for instruction of the poor at Hofwyl, near Berne, in Switzerland.—Croydon and Wellingborough charities.

6.—Fourth Report from the same Committee.   Sess. 1818, (427.) vol. 4, p. 223. [100.]

> SUBJECT.—Statutes of Eton college.

7.—Fifth Report from the same Committee : with an Index to the Five Reports.
                    Sess. 1818, vol. 4, p. 367. [100.]

> SUBJECTS.—Statutes of Trinity and St. John's colleges, Cambridge.———Index.

8.—Digest of Parochial Returns made to the Committee of 1818.
                    Sess. 1819, (224.) vol. 9 ; Sess. 1820, vol. 12. [101. & 102.]

> Exhibiting a state of the schools and means of instruction in every parish throughout the kingdom.

State of Education, 1834 :

9.—Report from the Select Committee of Inquiry into the present state of the Education of the People in England and Wales, and into the application and effects of the Grant made by Parliament for the erection of Schools.
                    Sess. 1834, (572.) vol. 9, p. 1.

> SUBJECTS.—Average ages at which children are admitted and usually leave public schools.—Impracticability of devising a different mode of education for agricultural and manufacturing districts.—Greater extent of education given in England than America.—Schoolmaster to every regiment.—Constitution of the Board of Education in Ireland.—Compilation of books for the use of schools of first rate importance.—Good effects from the Society for the Diffusion of Useful Knowledge reducing the price of books.—Advantages from the establishment of the British and Foreign School Society and the National Society.—Course of instruction at different public schools.—Compulsory education not justifiable.

Education of the Lower Orders—continued.

State of Education, 1834—*continued.*

justifiable.—No system of national education would extirpate crime.—An extended system of education very desirable.—Payment for education preferable to gratuitous instruction.—Employment in factories prevents attendance at day schools.—Advantages of Dr. Bell's plan.—Value of Infant and Sunday schools.—Inspection of schools very important.—Institution of Normal schools recommended.—Good effects from Parliamentary grants for education.—Prosperity of schools in Prussia.—Difficulty in forming a system of general instruction in religion suitable to the habits of the different sects.—Education and qualification of schoolmasters ; their pay and residence.—Effect of voluntary contributions on the stability of schools.

Education in Scotland :

10.—Returns showing the state of Parochial Education in Scotland ; made pursuant to an address of the House of Commons on 30th March 1825.

Sess. 1826, (95.) vol. 18, p. 1. [103.]

SUBJECTS.—Name of the parish, and account of the school.—Salary and emoluments of the schoolmaster.—School fees.—Number of scholars attending.—Branches of education the master is qualified to teach, and those actually taught.—Any other schools in the parish, whether established by Dissenters or others.—Distances from which scholars attend.—Whether any so far as to prevent attendance.—Proportion of population in towns or villages to the population of the parish.

The information contained in these Returns is similar to that contained in those made to the Education Committee, as to England, in 1818.—They are not arranged in the form of columns.

Universities, Scotland :

11.—Report made to His Majesty by a Royal Commission of Inquiry into the state of the Universities of Scotland.　　Sess. 1831, (310.) vol. 12, p. 111.

SUBJECTS.—General report.—Powers of visitations.—Code of laws.—Constitutions of the colleges.—Property.—Professorships.—Courses of study : In Arts : duties of professors ; confession of faith ; discipline ; prizes ; degrees.—In Theology : professorships ; classes ; degrees.—In Law : examination ; degrees.—In Medicine : preliminary education ; course for medical degree ; examinations ; certificates.—Miscellaneous : fees ; endowments of professorships ; bursaries ; tutors ; buildings ; libraries ; &c. &c.═══The report on each University is arranged under the following heads : I. History of the University ; II. Property and revenue ; III. Present state of the University ; IV. Suggestions.

Education in Ireland, **1809—1812 :**

12.—Fourteen Reports of the Commissioners, dated 1809—1812, on Education in Ireland : with an Index.　　Sess. 1813-14, (47.) vol. 5. [119.]

SUBJECTS.—An inquiry into the state of the public foundation, charter, and charity schools in Ireland.

13.—Report from the Select Committee on the Education of the Poor.

Sess. 1814-15, (399.) vol. 6, p. 1749.

SUBJECT.—Application for Parliamentary aid to a society for educating the poor, without religious distinction.

Education Inquiry, 1825—1828 :

14.—First Report of the Commissioners of Inquiry on Education in Ireland.

Sess. 1825, (400.) vol. 12, p. 1. [120.]

SUBJECTS.—*General State of Education.*—*Schools and Societies.*—*Plan for establishing Public Schools.*═══*General State of Education :*—Roman-catholic views of education.—State of the education of the lower orders of that persuasion.—Statutory regulations of Henry the Eighth and Elizabeth, for enforcing the learning of the English language.═══*Societies for promoting Education :*—Protestant Charter Schools :—their state described by Mr. Howard in 1784.—Improved state in 1808.—Unfavourable tendency of schools where children are abstracted from their relations, and attachments to home.—*Plan of instruction.*—Its deficiency.—*Inaptitude of the children* when sent out into the world for servants.—Children living with their parents in cabins, instructed at day schools, better suited for the duties of life.—*Number of children educated,* and the cost.═══*Society for discountenancing Vice :*—Establishment, and object.—*Parochial Schools.*—*Kildare-street Society :*—Object of the establishment to comprehend all persuasions.—Outline of plan.—Progress of the plan.—Comparative number of children of different persuasions educating.—Plan of training teachers.—Opposition of the Catholic priests.—*Lord Lieutenant's School Fund.*—*Sunday School Society.*—*London Hibernian Society.*—*Baptist Society.*—*Irish Society for promoting Education in the Native Language.*═══Schools of Roman-catholics.═══*General Observations :*—Inefficiency of the present mode of instruction.—The instruction carried on by Bible-reading.—Opposed by the Roman-catholics.═══*Proposed Plan for establishing Schools of General Instruction :*—Preference of a system that would embrace all persuasions, having religious instruction for the base.—Consideration of a plan for the religious instruction of Catholics.—Institution to be managed by a Board.

Education in Ireland—continued.

15.—Second Report of the Commissioners of Inquiry on Education in Ireland.
Sess. 1826–27, (12.) vol. 12. [121.]

SUBJECTS.—*Returns.*—Abstract of Returns from the Protestant and Roman-catholic clergy, of the state of education.—General results.—Proportions of children of different religious persuasions.—Children in schools of the several societies for education.—Proportion of schools in which the scriptures are read and not read.—Comparison of the progress of education in 1811 and 1824.

16.—Third Report of the Commissioners of Inquiry.
Sess. 1826–27, (13.) vol. 13, p. 1. [122.]

SUBJECTS.—*Foundling Hospital.*—Origin.—An imperfect substitute for parental care.—Proportion of mortality.—Children do not turn out so well when brought up in seclusion from all intercourse with the world.—Ill effects on the morals of girls, by being kept ignorant of the temptation to vice.—Expense of maintenance and clothing of children.—Weakness of their sense of right and wrong.—Some children, six or seven years old, while at nurse, receive the sacrament from a Romish priest.—Manner of marking the children for identifying them.—Treatment, morals and state of health of the children in the Hospital.—Opinions of the bad effects of boarding and educating children separate from their parents and homes.—Education while at nurse, particularly as to religious persuasions.—Advantages of day-school education.—Receipts and expenditure of the Hospital.—State of the infirmary.

17.—Fourth Report from the Commissioners of Inquiry.
Sess. 1826–27, (89.) vol. 13, p. 157. [122.]

SUBJECTS.—*Belfast Academical Institution.*—*Education of Superior Classes.*—*Presbyterian Clergy.*—*Tendency to inculcate Arianism, or unorthodox Doctrines.*—Origin of the institution.—Intended for classical and mercantile education.—Depressed state of the funds.—Fears of the prevalence of Arianism.—Inquiry into the subject.

18.—Fifth Report from the Commissioners of Inquiry.
Sess. 1826–27, (441.) vol. 13, p. 359. [122.]

SUBJECTS.—*Diocesan Schools.*—Origin.—Neglected state in 1809.—Regulations by 53 Geo. 3, c. 107, and 3 Geo. 4, c. 79.—Plan of arrangements by Board of Education.—Existing state.—Proposed improvement in the arrangement.—Difficulty of establishing permanent school-houses.—Proposed plan for providing houses, and apportioning aid by presentments of grand juries.—Provisions for substituting other masters when the school fails by their neglect.—Masters not to have cure of souls.—Rate of payments by scholars to be regulated.—Inspector to be appointed.

19.—Sixth Report from the Commissioners of Inquiry.
Sess. 1826–27, (442.) vol. 13, p. 385. [122.]

SUBJECTS.—*Hibernian Society for the Care of Soldiers' Children.*—*Marine Society for Sailors' Children.*—*Female Orphan House.*———*Incorporation of the Society for Soldiers' Children.*—Object.—Rules.—Officers and salaries.—Manner of appointing teachers.—The boys taught trades.—Favourable appearance of the children ascribed to gymnastic exercises, and the regularity of military habits—Preference given by the boys to the army, and dislike of being apprenticed to trades.—Difficulty of disposing of the girls.—Approbation of the good management of the institution.———Incorporation of the *Marine Society.*—Objects and rules.—Children of seamen only admitted.—Applicants for admission greatly exceed the vacancies.—Officers and salaries.—Duties of chaplains not properly performed.—Arrangements for putting the office on a better footing—Mode of instruction.—Funds not sufficient to pay the expense of a vessel given by Government for nautical instruction.—Revenues.—The boys have generally turned out well.———*Female Orphan House.*—Incorporation and object.—Officers and rules of the establishment.—Success of the establishment.—Laudable conduct of Mrs. Latouche.—Funds.—Employment as domestic servants.———General approbation of the three institutions.—Diseases affecting the children.—Ophthalmia, itch and sore head, frequent.—Discipline and management of the school.—Moral and religious instruction.—Few instances of the children becoming Roman-catholics.—Statements of funds.

20.—Seventh Report from the Commissioners of Inquiry.
Sess. 1826, (443.) vol. 13, p. 501. [122.]

SUBJECTS.—*Royal Cork Institution.*—Origin.—Object.—Diffusion of knowledge and improvement of arts and agriculture.—Lectures and professors.—Lectures well attended, and their effects beneficial in exciting a desire for knowledge.—Botanic garden connected with the Institution—of doubtful use.—Library contains a good collection of books.—A collection of natural history wanted.—United with the Society of Fine Arts.—Collection of casts, and philosophical apparatus.—Funds.

21.—Eighth Report from the Commissioners of Inquiry.
Sess. 1826–27, (509.) vol. 13, p. 537. [122.]

SUBJECTS.—*Roman-catholic College at Maynooth.*—Foundation.—System of education.—Doctrines and principles of Roman-catholics in relation to Church and State.—As connected with civil duties.—Doctrines taught as to oaths.—Jurisdiction, authority and infallibility of the Pope.—Class books in use by the professors.—Opinions taught as to the authority of the established church.—Conduct of Dr. MacHale in publishing a book on the policy of discontinuing the established church in Ireland.—Connexion of the College with

Education in Ireland—continued.

with the Societies of Jesus and Sodality of the Sacred Heart of Jesus.—Origin of these societies.—Establishment of the College.—Chiefly supported by Parliamentary grants.—Bequest of Lord Dunboyne.—Admission and maintenance of students.—Description of persons introduced into the priesthood.—Routine of education.—Discipline.—Extent of the capability of the College to educate the priests for Ireland.—Prohibition of books and newspapers.—Study of the Scriptures.—Doctrines taught as to the infallibility of the Pope, and obedience to his bulls; and the interference of the catholic doctrines with civil affairs.—Marriage.—Excommunication.—Deposition of sovereigns.—Absolving subjects from their oaths of allegiance.—Of keeping faith with heretics.—State of discipline.—Election of professors.—Restriction of books allowed to be read.—Political feelings of the students towards the established church and civil government.—Principles of moral philosophy inculcated.—Natural philosophy and mathematics.—Prohibition of books by the Congregation of the Index not enforced in Ireland.—Cardinal Protector of Ireland at Rome.—Nature of his office.—Obedience of bishops to the Pope.—Laws of the Roman-catholic church as to marriages between protestant and catholic, or heretic and catholic.—All baptized persons considered subject to the Roman-catholic church, although baptized by protestants.—Their situation in regard to the censures of the catholic church.—Right of resuming church property from heretics.—Right claimed by the Popes to interfere in the transfer of ecclesiastical property.—Such property in the hands of heretics must be restored—but the Pope will grant possession if the heretics become reconciled to the church.—Discussions at Maynooth on the validity of the church of England.—Opinions of the catholics that crime has increased in England concurrently with the establishment of Bible societies.—Established church considered only as a political creation, deriving no authority from true religion.—Catholic bishops the legitimate heirs of the apostles.—The title of the protestant bishops derived from the law, and could be annihilated by Parliament that created it.—The title of the catholic bishops eternal.—Protestant clergy not heirs of the doctrine of Christ, nor legitimate successors of the apostles.—Deified titles given to the Pope—and his alleged divinity.—Lists of trustees and officers.—Courses of study, and books used.—Accounts of receipts and expenditure.

CHARITIES.

Charitable Donations, 1788 :

26.—Report from the Select Committee appointed to inspect and consider the Returns relative to Charitable Donations for the Benefit of Poor Persons, made pursuant to Act 26 Geo. 3, c. 58.

Sess. 1810, vol. 2, p. 255; and vol. IX. of the First Series.

SUBJECTS.—The imperfect returns, mentioned in the Report 23 May 1787 (see POOR, under Head XXI.), made nearly complete by answers to circular letters, sent by the chairman of that Committee.—Supplementary returns inserted in *red ink*, to show what information was acquired by the original returns, and what since.—Great amount of the annual value of charities in the produce of land and money.—A confident belief expressed that this amount will be increased whenever proper means can be found of extending these inquiries.—The Appendix contains an Abstract of the Totals of Counties.

27.—Abstract of the Returns described in the above Report.

Sess. 1816, (511.) large folio, vol. XVI. A–B. and [I. & II.

THESE were printed, by order of The House, in 1816, and form two volumes large folio.— The additional information obtained from the Supplementary Returns are distinguished by being printed in *red ink*, in imitation of the original MS., as mentioned in the Report, and in the preceding article.—☞ The arrangement is alphabetical, and therefore forms an Index to itself.

See likewise POOR, under Head XXI.

28.—Return of Rents and Profits of Messuages, Lands, Tenements and Hereditaments, belonging to any Hospital, School, or Almshouse, or vested in Trustees for Charitable Uses.   Sess. 1820, (28.) vol. 6, p. 1. [123.]

29.—Amount of Stock or Dividends belonging to any Corporation or Society of Persons, or of any Trust established for Charitable Purposes.

Sess 1820, (29.) vol. 6, p. 161. [123.]

Charities and Education, 1819—1835 :

30.—Two Reports of the Commissioners appointed to inquire into Charities for the Education of the Poor.—1819 : March 4; July 5.

Sess. 1819, (83. 547.) vol. 10-A. 10-B. [104 & 105.]

These Reports arise from the commissions issued under the authority of Acts 58 Geo. 3, c. 91, and 59 Geo. 3, c. 81, and 5 Geo. 4, c. 58, passed in consequence of the Committee's Reports in 1816 to 1818. (*see* Nos. 1 to 7.) They contain an examination into the state of the grammar and other schools for gratuitous education, and into the appropriation of bequests for charitable purposes.
Berks — Hertford — Kent—London — Middlesex — Oxford — Southwark — Surrey — Sussex—Westminster.

31.—Third Report of the Commissioners.—1820 : May 1.

Sess. 1820, (5.) vol. 4. [106.]

Cumberland—Devon—Lancaster—London—Salop—Somerset—Surrey—Sussex—York.

32.—Fourth Report of the Commissioners.—1820 : September 18.

Sess. 1820, (312.) vol. 5. [107.]

Devon—Hereford—London—London Chartered Companies—Middlesex—Nottingham— Oxford—Salop—Somerset—Stafford—Worcester—York—General Charities.

33.—Fifth Report of the Commissioners.—1821 : March 6.

Sess. 1821, (159.) vol. 12. [108.]

Bedford—Cumberland—Devon—Rutland—Salop—Somerset—Stafford—Worcester— York.

34.—Sixth Report of the Commissioners.—1822 : February 13.

Sess. 1822, (12.) vol. 9. [109.]

Bedford—Devon—London—Middlesex—Southwark—Bristol—Somerset—York— General Charities.

35.—Seventh Report of the Commissioners.—1822 : March 28.

Sess. 1822, (129.) vol. 10. [110.]

Devon — London — London Chartered Companies — Bristol — Stafford — Lichfield— Westmorland.

36.—Eighth Report of the Commissioners.—1823 : February 14.

Sess. 1823, (13.) vol. 8. [111.]

Bedford—Devon—London; Chartered Companies — Middlesex — Oxford — Rutland— Somerset—Bath, City—Bristol—Stafford—Surrey—York.

Charities and Education, 1819—1835—continued.

37.—Ninth Report of the Commissioners.—1823 : April 18.

Sess. 1823, (258.) vol. 9. [112.]

Devon—Middlesex—Salop—Bristol—Somerset—Stafford—Westmorland—York.

38.—Tenth Report of the Commissioners.—1824 : March 8.

Sess. 1824, (103.) vol. 13. [113.]

Bedford—Devon—London—Westminster —Middlesex — Oxford—Bristol—Somerset—Surrey—York—Skinners' Company.

39.—Eleventh Report of the Commissioners.—1824 : June 17.

Sess. 1824, (433.) vol. 14. [114].

Devon—Exeter—Lancaster—Somerset—Stafford—Surrey—York.

40.—Twelfth Report of the Commissioners.—1825 : May 26.

Sess. 1825, (348.) vol. 10. [115.]

Bedford—Gloucester—Hereford—London ; Chartered Companies—Middlesex—Oxford—Bristol, City—Somerset—Southampton—Stafford—Surrey—York—General Charities.

41.—Thirteenth Report of the Commissioners.—1825 : May 26.

Sess. 1825, (349.) vol. 11. [116.]

Northampton—Somerset—Southampton—Stafford—Surrey—York—General Charities.

42.—Fourteenth Report of the Commissioners.—1826 : May 18.

Sess. 1826, (382.) vol. 12. [117.]

Gloucester—London—Middlesex—Northampton—Somerset—Southampton—Southwark—Surrey.

43.—A General Index to the First Fourteen Reports of the Commissioners appointed to inquire concerning Charities in England and Wales.

Sess. 1826–27, (281.) vol. 8. [118.]

44.—Fifteenth Report of the Commissioners.—1826 : May 18.

Lancaster—Somerset—Southampton—Warwick—York.   Sess. 1826, (383.) vol. 13.

45.—Sixteenth Report of the Commissioners.—1826 : December 4.

Sess. 1826–27, (22.) vol. 9.

Gloucester—Lancaster—Middlesex—Southampton—Surrey—York.

46.—Seventeenth Report of the Commissioners.—1827 : June 1.

Derby—Gloucester—London—Warwick—York.   Sess. 1826–27, (426.) vol. 10.

47.—Eighteenth Report of the Commissioners.—1828 : February 21.

Derby—Gloucester—Middlesex—Warwick—York.   Sess. 1826, (62.) vol. 20.

48.—Nineteenth Report of the Commissioners.—1828 : May 30.

Sess. 1828, (144.) vol. 11.

Derby—Gloucester—Lancaster—Nottingham—Suffolk—Worcester—York.

49.—A Return of Proceedings in Chancery, at the instance of the Commissioners.

Sess. 1828, (292.) vol. 21. p. 7.

SUBJECTS.—For rectifying abuses, and recovering dormant rights : I. Proceedings by information.———II. Proceedings by petition.—Names of defendants or respondents; object of each proceeding; result of each cause terminated ; costs, by and to whom paid; present state of the causes in progress.———III. Cases certified by the attorney-general, and settled without proceedings.—Names of cases ; results ; costs ; and by and to whom paid.

50.—A List of Counties reported upon, and not reported upon.

Sess. 1828, (389.) vol. 21, p. 31.

SUBJECTS.—Number and page of report.—Parish, &c.—Donor or title of charity.—Income; and whether real or personal estate.—Observations on the objects of the charity.

51.—A Return of the Expense incurred by the Commissioners.

Sess. 1824, (277.) vol. 21, p. 5.

52.—Twentieth Report of the Commissioners.—1829 : February 18.

Sess. 1829, (19.) vol. 7.

Bristol—Gloucester—Lancaster—London—Middlesex—Nottingham—Suffolk—Warwick.

53.—Twenty-first Report of the Commissioners.—1829 : June 19.

Sess. 1829, (349.) vol. 8.

Derby—Durham—Gloucester—York—Rutland — Nottingham —Lancaster—Stafford—Suffolk.

Charities and Education, 1819—1835—continued

54.—Returns of Informations filed in the Courts of Equity at the instance of the Commissioners, from March 1828 to March 1829.   Sess. 1829, (270.) vol. 20.

55.—Return of Charities and Charitable Donations in England and Wales, registered in the Office of Clerks of the Peace.   Sess. 1829, (274.) vol. 20.

56.—Twenty-second Report of the Commissioners.—1830 : March 11.
London—Middlesex—Gloucester—Suffolk—Worcester.   Sess. 1830, (139.) vol. 12.

57.—Twenty-third Report of the Commissioners.—1830 : January 30.
Sess. 1830, (462.) vol. 12.
Durham—Northampton — Newcastle-upon-Tyne— Northumberland—London—York—Berwick-upon-Tweed—Somerset—Suffolk—Worcester.

58.—Account of Law Proceedings at the instance of the Commissioners.
Sess. 1830, (658.) vol. 29, p. 40.

59.—Twenty-fourth Report of the Commissioners.—1831 : September 6.
Sess. 1831, (231.) vol. 11.
Durham—London—Salop—Suffolk—Worcester—Huntingdon—Northampton—Shrewsbury—Surrey—Ashton's Charities.

60.—Analytical Digest of the Twenty-four Reports of the Commissioners.
Sess. 1831–32, (63.) vol. 29, p. 1.

SUBJECTS.—The information contained in this Digest is arranged under the heads of counties, and of every city and town in each county; and shows quantity of land, the number of houses, with the nature of the tenure, and the rent paid ; the amount of money in the funds, upon mortgage and personal and other security, and the annual produce thereof; unimprovable rents and other charges; the amount of deductions made for land tax; and also the amount of sums applied to parochial purposes.—The number of endowed schools, and a statement of the total income, and the number of free scholars.—Also, an account of the number of scholarships and exhibitions.—The number of the Report, and the page where the information may be found, are stated.

61.—Twenty-fifth Report of the Commissioners.—1833 : March 11.
Sess. 1833, (60.) vol. 18.
Bedford—Bucks—Essex—Hertford—Middlesex—Nottingham—Worcester—York.

62.—Twenty-sixth Report of the Commissioners.—1833 : August 16.
Sess. 1833, (681.] vol. 19.
Bucks—Essex—Kent—Middlesex—Norfolk—Northampton—Suffolk—Wilts, and City of Salisbury—Worcester—Anglesea.

63.—Twenty-seventh Report of the Commissioners.—1834 : April 21.
Sess. 1834, (225.) vol. 21.

64.—Twenty-eighth Report of the Commissioners.—1834 : August 13.
Sess. 1834, (606.) vol. 22.

III.

Judicial.

Fees in Law Courts, 1832 :

1.—[Report from the Select Committee respecting Fees in Courts of Law, 1732.
Journals, vol. 21, p. 892.
Subjects.—Origin of Fees.—Ancient regulations and commissions of inquiry.—Present fees.—Opinions on them.

Expiring Laws, 1796—1802 :

2.—[Report from the Select Committee, in 1796, upon Temporary Laws Expired and Expiring; and, in 1802, upon Laws Expired and Expiring of the United Kingdom.
First Series, vol. xiv. pp. 34. 73.
Subjects.—Investigation into the nature, extent and duration of the temporary laws of the realm; also into the propriety of further temporary or permanent renewal of specific statutes.
For the Annual Reports, from 1803 to 1834, *see* General Index to Sessional Papers.

Promulgation of Statutes, 1796—1801 :

3.—[Report from the Select Committee, in 1796, as relating to Great Britain; and, in 1801, as relating to the United Kingdom. First Series, vol. xiv. pp. 119. 138.
Subjects.—On the most effectual means of promulgating the statutes of the realm; with observations in reference to a preceding inquiry into the state of the temporary laws.
See likewise under Head IV. No. 96.

Administration of Justice, England :
Chancery Court, 1810—1833 :

4.—Report from the Select Committee on the Lords' Proceedings on the state of Causes in the Court of Chancery. Sess. 1810–11, (194.) vol. 3, p. 923. [1.]

5.—First Report from the Select Committee on the causes that retard the Decision of Suits in the High Court of Chancery.
Sess. 1810–11, (244.) vol. 3, p. 925. [1.]

6.—Second Report from the same Committee. Sess. 1812, (273.) vol. 2, p. 343. [1.]
Subject.—Procrastination of proceedings in Chancery.

7.—Report made to His Majesty by the Commissioners appointed to inquire into the Practice of Chancery. Sess. 1826, (143.) vol. 15, p. 1. [2. 3.]
Subject.—On the present Practice, and proposed Regulations, in the Court of Chancery.

8.—Report of the Lords Commissioners appointed to make a survey of the different Courts in England, Wales and Berwick-upon-Tweed ;—as to the Court of Chancery:—dated 8 November 1740. Sess. 1814–15, (98.) vol. 11, p. 9. [4.]

9.—List of Fees payable to the several Officers of the High Court of Chancery, conformable to the Report of 8th November 1740.
Sess. 1814–15, (183.) vol. 11, p. 111. [4.]
Chancery Offices:

10.—Report from the Select Committee on Chancery Offices.
Sess. 1833, (685.) vol. 14, p. 1.

Saleable Offices :

11. Report from the Commissioners on Saleable Offices in Courts of Law.
Sess. 1810, (358.) vol. 9, p. 125. [6.]
Subject.—On the Practice respecting them in Courts of Law.

Administration of Justice, England—continued.
Courts of Justice :

Duties, Salaries, &c., 1816–1824 :

12.—Report of the Commissioners for examining into the Duties, Salaries and Emoluments of Officers of Courts of Justice in England ;—dated 9 April 1816.

SUBJECT.—As to the Court of Chancery.   Sess. 1816, (428.) vol. 8, p. 91. [4.]

13.—Second Report of the Commissioners ;—dated 20 December 1817.

SUBJECT.—Court of Chancery.   Sess. 1818, (156.) vol. 7, p. 225. [4.]

14.—Report of the Commissioners ;—dated 5 January 1818.

SUBJECT.—Court of King's Bench.   Sess. 1818, (292.) vol. 7, p. 243. [4.]

15.—Report of the Commissioners ;—dated 3 July 1819.

SUBJECT.—Court of Common Pleas.   Sess. 1819, (3.) vol. 2, p. 175. [5.]

16.—Report of the Commissioners ;—dated 9 February 1822.

Sess. 1822, (125.) vol. 11, p. 99. [5.]
SUBJECT.—Court of Exchequer and Exchequer Chamber.

17.—Report of the Commissioners ;—dated 16 May 1823.

Sess. 1823, (462.) vol. 7, p. 27. [5.]
SUBJECTS.—*Courts of the Archbishop of Canterbury :* viz. Court of Arches, Court of Prerogatives, and Court of Peculiars.

18.—Report of the Commissioners ;—dated 4 July 1823

Sess. 1824, (43.) vol. 9, p. 25. [5.]
SUBJECTS.—Court of Consistory of the Bishop of London, and the Court of the Commissary of the same Bishop, within the city of London and suburbs thereof, and the deaneries of Middlesex and Barking.

19.—Report of the Commissioners ;—dated 7 February 1824.

Sess. 1824, (240.) vol. 9, p. 75. [5.]
SUBJECTS.—High Court of Admiralty, Court of Delegates, and Court of Appeals for Prizes.

In Wales :

20.—Report from the Select Committee on the Administration of Justice in Wales.   Sess. 1817, (461.) vol. 5, p. 307. [1.]

SUBJECT.—On the state of the courts in Wales.

In Wales :

21.—Report from the Select Committee on the Administration of Justice in Wales.   Sess. 1820, (273.) vol. 2, p. 45. [1.]

SUBJECTS.—*Constitution and Practice of the Welsh Courts :*—Inefficiency of the court of Chancery.—Expense of actions.—Appointment of judges.—Expense of searching records.—Frivolous actions promoted by the cheapness.—Attornies numerous.—Practice of the court in trying actions.—Actions of debt.—Number of judges.—Character of Welsh juries.—Origin of equity jurisdiction in Wales traced.—Security of suitors' money.—Inconvenience to suitors from but few counsel attending.—Equity practice.—Welsh judges practising as barristers.—Opportunities of creating delay.—Costs of actions in Great Sessions.—Inconvenience from attornies practising in various branches of law.—Frivolous actions.—Want of experience to qualify practisers in the equity business.—Inefficiency of the equity jurisdiction.

In Wales :

22.—Report from the Select Committee on the Administration of Justice in Wales.   Sess. 1821, (662.) vol. 4, p. 233. [1.]

SUBJECTS.—*Origin, Jurisdiction and Practice of the Court of Great Session :*—On the same subject as the Reports of 1817 and 1820.—Origin and jurisdiction of the court of Great Session.—Reports of 1817 and 1820 referred to.—Objection to the want of permanency in the character of the judges ; acting as advocates when not in the discharge of the office of judge in Wales.—Inconvenience in the manner of practice.—No power of compelling the attendance of witnesses from adjoining counties.—Difficulty of recovering fines.—Opportunity of evading the force of decrees by withdrawing into adjoining counties. —Comparative expense of proceedings.—Number of attornies.

Northern Circuit :

23.—Report from the Select Committee on the Administration of Justice upon the Northern Circuit.   Sess. 1818, (240.) vol. 7, p. 83. [1.]

Recognizances :

24.—Report from the Select Committee on Forfeitures of Recognizances.

Sess. 1821, (636.) vol. 4, p. 329. [1.]

Courts of Justice—continued.
Recognizances:

25.—Report from the Select Committee on Recognizances.

Sess. 1822, (135.) vol. 4, p. 63. [1.]

Subjects.—*Neglect in recovering Fines, &c.*—Several facts are stated as to the amount of fines and recognizances, and the small part recovered; being, in 1816, 169 *l.* out of 34,165 *l.*—Defects of the present mode of recovering.—A bill proposed to be framed for remedying the defects.

Courts of Justice Patronage:

26.—Return of all Places and Offices in the gift or at the disposal of the Lord High Chancellor of England, and others; and the names of the persons by whom those places and offices are now filled.

Sess. 1825, (430.) vol. 19, p. 293. [1.]

Admiralty Courts:

27.—Report from the Select Committee on the Prerogative Court, Admiralty Courts, and Dean of Arches and Consistory Courts, and to whom the Reports of the Ecclesiastical and Common Law Commissions, and Irish Admiralty Courts, were referred.

Sess. 1833, (670.) vol. 7, p. 379.

Subjects.—Future constitution of these tribunals.—Report of Ecclesiastical and Real Property Commissioners referred to.—Proposed consolidation of courts.—Courts for probate of wills.—Proposed extension of Admiralty Court.—Number of judges.—Increase of the business of the Prerogative Court.—Fees, salaries and sinecures.—Effect of the proposed consolidation of all ecclesiastical tribunals, and the number of courts thereby abolished.—Arrangements to be made for the preservation and access to testamentary documents.

Real Property:

28.—First Report of the Commissioners of Inquiry into the Law of England respecting Real Property.   Sess. 1829, (263.) vol. 10, p. 1.

29.—Second Report of the Commissioners.   Sess. 1830, (575.) vol. 11, p. 1.

30.—Third Report of the Commissioners.   Sess. 1831–32, (484.) vol. 23, p. 321.

31.—Fourth Report of the Commissioners.   Sess. 1833, (226.) vol. 22, p. 1.

General Register:

32.—Report from the Committee on the expediency of a General Register of all Deeds and Instruments affecting Real Property in England and Wales.

Sess. 1831–32, (609.) vol. 18, p. 365.

Subjects.—Expediency of the plan.—Its great importance as affecting law of real property.—Ancient mode of conveyance.—Modern system.—Want of protection to secret acts of the seller—would be effected by a General Register of Deeds—but difficulty in establishing it.—Secret transfers of very rare occurrence.—Evil from this uncertainty.—Distinction of legal and equitable estates.—Difficulties of investigating titles.—Advantage of a General Register in remedying evils, and in giving better security to mortgages.—In what respect registration would affect loans on deposit of deeds.—Answer to objections from exposure of private affairs.—Plan of registration recommended.

Lancaster Common Pleas:

33.—Report of the Commissioners on the Practice of that Court.

Sess. 1831–32, (621.) vol. 35, p. 201.

Common Law:

34.—First Report of the Commissioners of Inquiry into the Practice and Proceedings of the Superior Courts of Common Law.   Sess. 1829, (46.) vol. 9, p. 1.

35.—Second Report of the Commissioners of Inquiry on the same subject.

Sess. 1830, (123.) vol. 11, p. 547.

36.—Third Report of the Commissioners of Inquiry on the same subject.

Sess. 1831, (92.) vol. 10, p. 375.

37.—Fourth Report of the Commissioners of Inquiry.   (second part of the appendix.)   Sess. 1831–32, (239.) vol. 25, p. 1.

38.—Fifth Report of the Commissioners of Inquiry on the same subject.

Sess. 1833, (247.) vol. 22, p. 195.

Subject.—Provisional Courts in England for the Recovery of Small Debts.

39.—Sixth Report of the Commissioners of Inquiry on the same subject.

Sess. 1834, (263.) vo . 27, p. 449.

Criminal Law :

40.—Report from the Select Committee on the Criminal Laws, (as relates to Capital Felonies).   Sess. 1819, (585.) vol. 8, p. 1. [**21.**]

> SUBJECTS.—Returns of commitments and convictions.—Decrease in crime of murder.—Propriety of repealing some laws inflicting capital punishment.—Larcenies.—Effects of capital punishments.—Disinclination to prosecute.—Punishment of forgery.

41.—Report from the Select Committee on the Criminal Laws of England.
Sess. 1824, (205. 444.) vol. 4, pp. 39. 349. [**21.**]

> SUBJECTS.—*Consolidation of Laws.*—Proposed mode, by A. Hammond, Esq., collecting together different enactments relating to the same subject, and bringing them under their proper heads.—Suggestions for simplifying the laws, and for arranging them as a general code.

Debtor and Creditor :

Bankrupt Laws :

42.—[Report from the Select Committee on Laws respecting Bankrupts, 1759.
Journals, vol. 28, p. 602

> SUBJECT.—The chief object to which the inquiries of this Report are directed is the power possessed by the creditor of withholding the bankrupt's certificate, and the hardship often resulting from its exercise.

43.—Report from the Select Committee on the Bankrupt Laws.
Sess. 1817, (486.) vol. 5, p. 1. [**22.**]

> SUBJECTS.—The Report declines offering any opinion ; but the Committee hope the renewal of their appointment will enable them to enter fully into the subject.—There is a great quantity of evidence.

44.—Reports from the Select Committee on the Bankrupt Laws.
Sess. 1818, (127. 276. 277.) vols. 5 & 6. [**22.**]

> SUBJECTS.—A general inquiry into the operation of the bankrupt laws ; the practice of suing out commissions, and evils prevailing ; with suggestions of remedies.

Bankrupts' Estates :

45.—Report from the Select Committee on the Bill for investing in Government Security a portion of the Cash lying unemployed in the Bank of England belonging to Bankrupts' Estates, and applying the Interest in discharge of the Expense of the Court of Bankruptcy, and for the Relief of the Suitors in the said Court.   Sess. 1834, (362.) vol. 18, p. 187.

> SUBJECTS.—Amount of cash and security standing in the name of the Accountant-general on April 1834.—Amount of the balance of cash and interest on dividend account. —Amount thereof that may remain as a permanent investment.—Consideration of the most beneficial mode of applying the interest arising therefrom.—Disposition of unclaimed dividends.—Compensation recommended to the chief clerk of the secretary of bankrupts.—Advantages resulting from the constituting the new court of Bankruptcy, and from the appointment of Official Assignees.—An Accountant-general distinct for Bankruptcy recommended.—Proposed reductions in the establishment of the court.

Extents in Aid :

46.—Report from the Select Committee on the Mode of issuing Extents in Aid, &c.   Sess. 1817, (505.) vol. 5, p. 137. [**22.**]

> SUBJECT.—On the hardships occasioned by the present mode of issuing extents.

Imprisonment for Debt :

47.—[Report from the Select Committee on the Practice and Effect of, 1792.
Journals, vol. 47, p. 640.

> SUBJECTS.—Law and practice of arrest and imprisonment, showing how a debtor may defraud his creditor, and the creditor oppress the debtor.—Affidavits of debt.—Bail.—Times and manner of arrests.—Defects of the law in not allowing alleviation in the strict enforcement of arrest, in case of sickness, &c.—The defendant not protected against malicious arrests.—Cannot deposit a sum to abide the event.——Mode of custody in lock-up-houses.—Statute regulations.—Declaration of cause of action.—Possible length of time of imprisonment before trial of the cause.—*Supersedeas.*—Process of obtaining it —The defendant, if unable to pay the expense attending it, must remain in prison.—Taxed costs insufficient to compensate the defendant.—Difficulty of maintaining an action for malicious arrest.—— Proceedings in court on arrest.—Justifying bail.— Special bail.— In case of insufficient bail, assignment of bail bond.—Responsibility of the Sheriff.—Surrendering.—— Imprisonment in execution.—Duration may be indefinite.—Rules of the King's Bench, &c. —Origin and regulations.——Imprisonment by courts of conscience.—Relief under *Lords' Act*, 23 Geo. 2, c. 28.—No remedy against indefinite imprisonment.— None devised against a dishonest debtor's dissipating his property by extravagant living ——Evidence taken.—Number of bailable writs issued.—Great proportion under 20*l.*—Expense of action.—Discharges by the *Thatched-house Society*, of those prevented from having their liberty from inability to pay fees.—Persons preferring to remain in prison.—Total number in prison —Number of deaths.—Instances of very long imprisonments for small sums.—Greatest proportion of prisoners married and have families.—Description of prisons and prisoners for small debts.— Great disproportion of debts and costs.——Lodging of prisoners in the
> King's

Debtor and Creditor—continued.

Imprisonment for Debt—continued.

King's Bench and the Fleet.—Letting of rooms.—Instances of extreme sufferings from want.—Gaolers have profit from liquor sold.—Want of medical attendance, and of regulations for removing the dead.——Extravagance and dissipation in a gaol.—Remarkable instance of a debtor remaining in gaol though able to pay; his debt being 10,000*l.* and his worth 100,000*l.*

Insolvent Debtors:

48.—Report from the Select Committee on the Insolvent Debtors' Acts, 53 and 54 Geo. 3.   Sess. 1816, (472.) vol. 4, p. 345. [22.]

SUBJECTS.—On the effect of those Acts.—Abuse.—Necessity of alteration.——*The Report is expressed in a short paragraph, stating the importance of the subject, and recommends the renewal of the Committee ; the rest is Minutes of Evidence.*

49.—Report from the Select Committee on Acts respecting Insolvent Debtors.
     Sess. 1819, (287.) vol. 2, p. 321. [22.]

SUBJECTS.—Principle of the Acts approved of.—Alterations necessary to compel an equitable division of property.—Defects in the constitution of the court.—Establishment of fees.—Other increase of expenses.—Undue appointment of agents, not being attornies.—Remedies suggested.—Conduct of debtors generally.—Law of debtor and creditor in Scotland.

Small Debts:

50.—Report from the Select Committee on the Recovery of Small Debts in England and Wales.   Sess. 1823, (386.) vol. 4, p. 183. [22.]

SUBJECTS.—*Utility of Small Debt Courts.*— Origin of courts baron, county courts, &c.—Disproportion of expenses of suits for recovery of sums under 15 *l.*—Utility of courts of requests.—Manner of conducting business in the county courts of Middlesex and Lancaster,—of Hackney and Stepney.—Proposition to render the county courts more efficient, by extending their jurisdiction.

County Courts:

51.—Minutes of Evidence taken before the Select Committee on the Bill for preventing Delays, &c. in the Proceedings of County Courts, and for the more easy and speedy Recovery of Small Debts in England and Wales.
     Sess. 1825, (276.) vol. 5, p. 515. [22.]

Game Laws:

52.—Report from the Select Committee on the Game Laws.
     Sess. 1816, (504.) vol. 4, p. 507. [23.]

SUBJECTS.—Nature of the right in game.—How affected by statute.—Inexpediency of the laws.—Resolution for their repeal.

53.—Report from the Select Committee on the Laws relating to Game.
     Sess. 1823, (260.) vol. 4, p. 260. [23.]

SUBJECTS.—*Expediency of altering the Game Laws, and legalizing the Sale of Game.*—Inefficiency of the laws relating to the sale of game.—Clandestinely carried on.—Description of persons who supply game.—Market over-supplied,—and great waste.—The laws so generally unobserved, as to show that their breach is not considered a moral offence.—Supply in the hands of poachers.—Recommendation to repeal the laws, and to allow game to be purchased by persons qualified by property to kill game.—The practice of poaching likely to be suppressed in time by the alterations proposed.

54.—Report from the Lords' Committee on the Laws relating to Game.
     Sess. 1828, (235.) vol. 8, p. 333.

SUBJECTS.—On the operation of the game laws.—Their demoralizing effects.—Violence and murders arising from the practice of poaching.—Description, habits and character of persons engaged in poaching.—Evidence of poulterers and dealers in game of the manner in which game is procured and sold.—To what extent by poachers and proprietors of preserves.—Mode of consignment to salesmen.—From parts sent.—Foreign game from France and Sweden.—Quantity sold, and prices.—Manner of clandestinely taking pheasants and other game.—Manner and difficulty of artificially rearing pheasants for stocking preserves.—Probable effect of legalizing the sale of game.—Feeling of dissatisfaction of occupiers not qualified, from being deprived of the right of killing game.—Probable effect of giving this right.—On the expediency and probable effect of legalizing the sale of game.

Habeas Corpus:

55.—Report from the Select Committee on Writs of Habeas Corpus ad Subjiciendum.   Sess. 1814-15, (418.) vol. 3, p. 73. [23.]

SUBJECT.—On the inconvenience resulting from judges not being able to issue such writs during vacation.

Inns of Court:

56.—First Report from the Select Committee of Inquiry into all the circumstances attending the regulation of the claim by Daniel Whittle Harvey, esquire, to be called to the Bar.   Sess. 1834, (503.) vol. 18, p 313.

> SUBJECT.—A special report on a matter of privilege arising in course of the Committee's inquiries.—*See* PRIVILEGE, under Head IV.

57.—Second Report from the Select Committee of Inquiry into all the circumstances attending the regulation of the claim by Daniel Whittle Harvey, esquire, to be called to the Bar.   Sess. 1834, (555.) vol. 18, p. 317.

58.—Documents relating to the same subject.   Sess. 1834, (349.) vol. 48.

High Sheriff:

59.—Report from the Select Committee on the Expense of the Office of High Sheriff, with a view to regulate and reduce the same.
                                        Sess. 1830, (520.) vol. 10, p. 235.

> SUBJECTS.—The heads of expense.—Appointment to office.—Execution of office; providing judges' lodgings; processions to meet and attend judges; providing dinners.—Discharge from office; passing accounts.———Recommendation for appointing permanent under-sheriffs.———Duties of the high sheriff; expense incurred by him.—How nominated.—Duties, expense and profits of under-sheriffs.

Attornies and Solicitors:

60.—Report from Select Committee on Admission of Attornies and Solicitors.
                                        Sess. 1821, (137.) vol. 4, p. 325.

> SUBJECTS.—*Qualification for Admission.*—On the expediency of allowing the admission of members of the universities as attornies and solicitors, who shall have taken a degree after a service of three years.

Administration of Justice, Scotland, 1816—1826:
Jury Court:

61.—First, Second and Third Reports of the Lord President of the Court of Session, the Lord Justice Clerk, and the Lord Chief Commissioner of the Jury Court; per Act of 55 Geo. 3, c. 42.
                        Sess. 1816, (174.) vol. 8, pp. 261. 295. 301. [6.]

62.—Supplementary Report respecting the Jury Court.
                                        Sess. 1817, (148.) vol. 9, p. 131. [6.]

63.—Second Report on the same subject.   Sess. 1817, (165.) vol. 9, p. 135. [6.]

64.—Third Report on the same subject.   Sess. 1817, (177.) vol. 9, p. 143. [6.]

65.—Report of the Lord Chief Commissioner and the other Commissioners, on the same subject.   Sess. 1818, (141.) vol. 10, p. 61. [6.]

66.—Three Reports on the same subject.   Sess. 1818, (288.) vol. 10, p. 75. [6.]

67.—Three Reports on the same subject.   Sess. 1819, (150.) vol. 11, p. 273. [6.]

68.—Papers; References made to the Judges, or Law Officers of the Crown, of the Reports of the Commissioners of the Courts of Justice, Scotland.
                                        Sess. 1819-20, (12.) vol, 4, p. 273. [6.]

Juries, Scotland:

69.—Report of the Commissioners for inquiring into the Forms of Proceeding in Trial of Civil Causes by Jury in Scotland.   Sess. 1826-27, (340.) vol. 7, p. 173.

Courts of Law:

70.—Report of the Commissioners for inquiring into the Forms of Process in the Courts of Law in Scotland, and the course of Appeals from the Court of Session to the House of Lords.   Sess. 1824, (241.) vol. 10, p. 1. [6.]

> SUBJECTS.—*Present Forms of Proceedings in Courts of Law; and Improvements proposed.—Appeals.*——1. The forms of process and pleading in the Court of Session.—2. The forms in the Jury Court.—3. Appeals to the House of Lords.—4. Forms of proceedings before the Commission of Teinds.—5. Forms in Inferior Courts of Law.—Prize jurisdiction.——The present practice is described, and the proposed improvements stated.

*Administration of Justice, Scotland—*continued.

Court of Session :

71.—Warrant authorizing Compensations under 1 & 2 Geo. 4, c. 38, to Macers of Court of Session, and Macer of Teind Court.

Sess. 1824, (65.) vol. 10, p. 369. [6.]

72.—Account of the Fee Fund.   Sess. 1824, (396.) vol. 10, p. 373. [6.]

73.—Acts of Sederunt of the Court of Session.   Sess. 1826, (38.) vol. 23, p. 185. [6.]

Commissary Courts :

74.—Act of Sederunt, anent Tables of Fees.   Sess. 1824, (78.) vol. 10, p. 379. [6.]

Court of Admiralty :

75.—Warrant for Compensation to William Campbell, Esq. principal Clerk for loss of Fees.   Sess. 1824, (83.) vol. 10, p. 378. [6.]

Courts of Justice :

76.—Papers; being the Warrant appointing Commissioners of Inquiry; and their Report, concerning Appeals to the House of Lords.

Sess. 1809, (257.) vol. 4, p. 385. [7.]

77.—Three Reports of the Commissioners appointed to inquire into the Administration of Justice in Scotland.

Sess. 1810, (6. 109. 238.) vol. 9, pp. 53. 93. 115. [7.]

Subjects.—On Matters of a Civil Nature.

78.—First Report of Commissioners on Courts of Justice, Scotland.

Sess. 1816, (419.) vol. 8, p. 311. [7.]

Subject.—Court of Session.

79.—Second Report of the Commissioners.   Sess. 1817, (3.) vol. 9, p. 161. [7.]

Subject.—Court of Session continued.

80.—Third Report of the Commissioners.   Sess. 1818, (16.) vol. 10, p. 91. [7.]

Subject.—Sheriff and Commissary Courts.

81.—Fourth Report of the Commissioners.   Sess. 1818, (157.) vol. 10, p. 239. [7.]

Subjects.—Inferior Commissariat Courts, and Courts of Admiralty.

82.—Fifth Report of the Commissioners.   Sess. 1819, (4.) vol. 11, p. 69. [7.]

Subject.—Court of Justiciary.

83.—Sixth Report of the Commissioners.   Sess. 1819, (546.) vol. 11, p. 173. [7.]

Subject.—Court of Exchequer.

84.—Report of Sir W. Rae, Bart. Lord Advocate, on the recommendation in the Sixth Report of the Commissioners.   Sess. 1820, (36.) vol. 7, p. 261. [6.]

Subject.—Regarding the discontinuance of one of the Barons.

85.—Seventh Report of the Commissioners on Courts of Justice, Scotland.

Sess. 1820, (6.) vol. 7, p. 65. [8.]

Subject.—Court of Exchequer continued.

86.—Eighth Report of the Commissioners.   Sess. 1820, (7.) vol. 7, p. 231. [8.]

Subject.—Office of Chancery.

87.—Ninth Report of the Commissioners.   Sess. 1821, (729.) vol. 10, p. 485. [8.]

Subject.—Justice of Peace Courts.

88.—Tenth Report of the Commissioners.   Sess. 1822, (412.) vol. 8, p. 33. [8.]

Subject.—Office and Court of the Lord Lyon.

89.—Eleventh Report of the Commissioners.   Sess. 1822, (558.) vol. 8, p. 117. [8.]

Subject.—Burgh Courts.

90.—Twelfth and Supplementary Report of the Commissioners.

Sess. 1822, (595.) vol. 8, p. 293[1]. [8.]

Subject.—Charges of Agents or Law Practitioners before the Inferior Courts.

Exchequer Court, 1832 :

91.—Report from the Select Committee on the Bill for the dispatch of business in the Exchequer Court, Scotland.   Sess. 1831-32, (307.) vol. 5, p. 113.

Scotch Entails, 1828—1833 :

92.—Report from the Select Committee on the Bill for altering the law concerning Entails in Scotland.   Sess. 1828, (198.) vol. 7, p. 151.

> SUBJECTS.—State of the laws relating thereto, and evil consequences attending them.— Extensive power of making entails, and regulating the administration of property for future generations.—Power for assuming names and arms.—Restrictions on alienations.—Number of deeds of entails registered.—Proportion and value of land in Scotland under entails.— Detrimental effects on the interests of the country.—Power of leasing.—Retardation of improvements by the restrictions of entail.—Difficulties of making marriage settlements.— Power of raising money for improvements; but insecurity of such advances.—Power of burthening estates for the provision of widows and children.—Claims of entailer's creditors. —Effect on the price of land in Scotland.—Advantageous operation of the English law of entail compared with Scotland.

93.—Second Report from the Select Committee on the Bill for altering the law concerning Entails in Scotland.   Sess. 1828, (404.) vol. 7, p. 315.

> SUBJECTS.—The same subject continued.—Tendency and effect of the law of entail in Scotland.—Disadvantageous condition of possessor of entailed property.—Complicated nature of the rights of claimants.—Difficulty of providing for widows and children.—Impediments to obtaining relief from pecuniary embarrasments.—Necessity of immediate alteration.—Suitableness of the Bill under consideration for that purpose.—Prospective change of the law proposed, and the assimilating it to the law of England.—Gradual merging of existing entails into the new system.—Relief of heirs in possession.

94.—Third Report from the Select Committee.   Sess. 1829, (102.) vol. 3, p. 413.

> SUBJECTS.—Recommendation to bring in a Bill to regulate future Talzies in Scotland, and to grant certain powers to heirs of talzie ; and to relieve such heirs from statutory burdens affecting talzied estates, and from debts incurred in the improvement of the same.

95.—Report from the Select Committee on the law concerning Entails.
                                                        Sess. 1833, (109.) vol. 16, p. 35.

> SUBJECT.—Resolutions founded on the inquiries of the preceding Reports, and recommending bringing in a Bill to carry the proposed alteration of the law into effect.

Judges' Salaries, 1834 :

96.—Report from the Select Committee appointed to consider how far the Salaries of the Judges of the Supreme Court in Scotland are commensurate to the importance of their station.   Sess. 1834, (438.) vol. 11, p. 1.

> SUBJECTS.—Present salaries of the Judges of the Supreme Courts in Scotland not adequate to maintain their respectability and independence.—Proposed increase therein.—Salary paid to one of the Judges of the Court of Session under 2 Will. 4, to be abolished.—The whole duties connected with the Courts of Session, Justiciary and Exchequer, to be distributed among the Judges.—Allowance to be continued to Judges going the circuit.—The right of appointing Clerks of Justiciary to be vested in the Crown.—No Judge of the Supreme Courts to officiate as a member of any other Court in Scotland, whether civil or ecclesiastical.— Retiring pensions of Judges.—Judges retiring from ill-health, in case of restoration to resume his former situation, if required, under forfeiture of his retiring pension.

Law Commission, Scotland, 1834 :

97.—First Report of the Commissioners on Fees and Establishment of Clerks in the Court of Session ; the Preparation of Records ; the Constitution and Jurisdiction of the Sheriff Courts ; the Law of Imprisonment for Debt ; the Expense of Criminal Proceedings ; and of Heritable Rights.
                                                        Sess. 1834, (295.) vol. 11, p. 197.

Administration of Justice, Ireland :
    Courts of Justice, 1817—1832 :

98.—First Report of Commissioners appointed to inquire into the Duties, Salaries, &c., of the Officers and Ministers of Justice in Ireland.

> SUBJECT.—Court of Chancery.   Sess. 1817, (9.) vol. 10, p. 1. [9.]

99.—Second Report of the Commissioners.   Sess. 1817, (10.) vol. 11, p. 1. [9.]
> SUBJECT.—Court of Exchequer.

100.—Charges against J. Pollock, Esq. founded upon the Second Report of the Commissioners of Inquiry.   Sess. 1821, (700.) vol. 20, p. 47. [12.]

Administration of Justice, Ireland—continued.

Courts of Justice—continued.

101.—Third Report of the Commissioners on Duties, Salaries, &c. of Officers and Ministers of Justice.   Sess. 1817, (487.) vol. 11, p. 173. [9.]
    SUBJECT.—Court of Error.

102.—Fourth Report of the Commissioners.   Sess. 1818, (140.) vol. 10, p. 557. [9.]
    SUBJECT.—Offices in the disposal of the Crown.

103.—Copy of a Communication, dated 29 November 1820, by the Barons of the Exchequer in Ireland, upon the subject of the Fourth Report of the Commissioners, as far as it relates to the Court of Exchequer.
                                  Sess. 1821, (401.) vol. 11, p. 25. [9.]

104.—Fifth Report of the Commissioners.   Sess. 1819, (5.) vol. 12, p. 5. [10.]
    SUBJECT.—Court of Common Pleas.

105.—Copy of a Communication by the Judges of the Court of Common Pleas, upon the subject of the Fifth Report of Commissioners.
                                  Sess. 1820, (118.) vol. 8, p. 197. [10.]

106.—Sixth Report of the Commissioners.   Sess. 1819, (6.) vol. 12, p. 287. [10.]
    SUBJECT.—Court of King's Bench.

107.—Copy of a Communication by the Lord Chief Justice, &c. upon the subject of the Sixth Report of the Commissioners.   Sess. 1820, (113.) vol. 8, p. 191. [10.]

108.—Seventh Report of the Commissioners.   Sess. 1819–20, (33.) vol. 3, p. 51. [10.]
    SUBJECT.—Clerks of Nisi Prius, or Judges' Registers.

109.—Observations of the Judges on the Seventh Report of the Commissioners.   Sess. 1820, (160.) vol. 8, p. 217. [10.]

110.—Eighth Report of the Commissioners on Duties, Salaries, &c. of Officers and Ministers of Justice.   Sess. 1820, (94.) vol. 8, p. 1. [11.]
    SUBJECT.—Office of Registry of Memorials of Deeds, Conveyances, Wills and Devises concerning Lands, &c. in Ireland.

111.—Ninth Report of the Commissioners.   Sess. 1821, (411.) vol. 11, p. 29. [11.]
    SUBJECT.—Court of Exchequer.

112.—Copy of a Letter from the Lord Chief Baron of the Exchequer in Ireland, 5th June 1821, addressed to W. Gregory, Esq. under secretary to the Lord Lieutenant of Ireland, upon the subject of the Ninth Report on Courts of Justice.   Sess. 1821, (635.) vol. 8, p. 439. [11.]

113.—Letters addressed by the Irish Government to the Judges of the Courts of Equity and Law, in transmitting for their consideration the several Reports of the Commissioners of Inquiry.   Sess. 1821, (742.) vol. 20, p. 25. [12.]

114.—Report from the Select Committee on the Ninth Report of the Commissioners of Inquiry.   Sess. 1821, (736.) vol. 8, p. 465. [1.]
    SUBJECTS.—On the Ninth Report of Commissioners, as to the Court of Exchequer.— Charges against the Lord Chief Baron of Ireland.

115.—Letter from the Commissioners appointed to inquire into Judicial Fees in Ireland.   Sess. 1822, (516.) vol. 14, p. 503. [12.]
    SUBJECT.—Stating that, having closed the investigation, they think it expedient to accompany their Report, not only with the Evidence, but likewise the Documents relating to the subject.

116.—Tenth Report of the Commissioners on Duties, Salaries, &c. of Officers and Ministers of Justice.   Sess. 1822, (31.) vol. 14, p. 1. [11.]
    SUBJECT.—Equity Side of the Court of Exchequer.

117.—Eleventh Report of the Commissioners.   Sess. 1822, (332.) vol. 14, p. 363. [11.]
    SUBJECT.—Court of Exchequer.

118.—Letter addressed by the Lord Chief Baron of the Court of Exchequer, to W. Gregory, Esq. on the subject of the Eleventh Report of the Commissioners of Inquiry.   Sess. 1822, (429.) vol. 14, p. 449. [11.]

119.—Report from the Select Committee on the Eleventh Report of the Commissioners of Inquiry.   Sess. 1823, (352.) vol. 6, p. 1. [1.]
    SUBJECTS.—Respecting the Charges against the Lord Chief Baron of Ireland.

Administration of Justice, Ireland—continued.

    Courts of Justice—continued.

120.—Twelfth Report of the Commissioners on Duties, Salaries, &c. of Officers and Ministers of Justice.   Sess. 1824, (467.) vol. 12, p. 1. [11.]
        SUBJECT.—Revenue Side of the Court of Exchequer.

121.—Thirteenth Report of the Commissioners.   Sess. 1825, (313.) vol. 15, p. 169. [12.]
        SUBJECTS.—*Sheriffs' Office.—Difficulties in the way of the Commissioners' Proceedings.*—Endeavours to obtain information—unsuccessful, from neglect and refusal to answer inquiries.—But partial returns to circular letters to governors of counties.—Powers of the Commissioners insufficient.—Attempts to enforce their authority, by criminal proceedings for contempt, ineffectual.—Principal opposition given by the Sheriff of Dublin.—Additional powers requested.

122.—Fourteenth Report of the Commissioners.   Sess. 1826, (68.) vol. 17, p. 1. [12.]
        SUBJECT.—Judge or Commissary of the Courts of Prerogatives and Faculties.

12.3—Fifteenth Report of the Commissioners.   Sess. 1826, (310.) vol. 17, p. 29. [12.]
        SUBJECTS.—*Office of Sheriff.*—Counties at large.—Bail.— Jury process. — Final process. — Fees and emoluments. — Regulations. — County of the city of Dublin. — Mesne process. — Grand juries. — Nisi Prius and petit juries. — Lunatic, Wide Street, and Valuation juries.—Counties of cities and towns.

124.—Sixteenth Report of the Commissioners.   Sess. 1826–27, (341.) vol. 11, p. 163.
        SUBJECT.—The Crown Office.

125.—Seventeenth Report of the Commissioners.   Sess. 1828, (144.) vol. 12, p. 161.
        SUBJECT.—Courts of Quarter Session and Assistant Barristers Court.

126.—Eighteenth Report of the Commissioners.   Sess. 1829, (5.) vol. 13, p. 195.
        SUBJECT.—High Court of Admiralty.

127.—Report from the Select Committee on the Eighteenth Report of the Commissioners of Judicial Inquiry in Ireland, relating to the conduct of Sir Jonah Barrington in discharge of his judicial functions.
                                  Sess. 1829, (293.) vol. 4, p. 1.

128.—Deposition of Sir Jonah Barrington relating to charges against him in the Eighteenth Report of the Commissioners of Judicial Inquiry.
                              Sess. 1829, (85.) vol. 22, p. 357.

129.—Resolutions of the whole House on the conduct of Sir Jonah Barrington, Judge of the High Court of Admiralty in Ireland.   Sess. 1830, (382.) vol. 4, p. 749.

130.—Nineteenth Report of the Commissioners on Duties, Salaries, &c. of Officers and Ministers of Justice.   Sess. 1830, (311.) vol. 20, p. 199.
        SUBJECT.—Courts of Prerogative and Faculties.

131.—Supplement to the Nineteenth Report.   Sess. 1830, (518.) vol. 15, p. 413.

132.—Twentieth Report of the Commissioners.   Sess. 1830–31, (365.) vol. 6, p. 217.
        SUBJECT.—Office for Registry of Deeds, &c.

133.—Twenty-first Report of the Commissioners.   Sess. 1831, (146.) vol. 10, p. 739.
        SUBJECT.—Metropolitical and Consistorial Courts.

134.—Answers to a Letter of the 26 January 1831, from the Chief Secretary of Ireland, to the several Courts of Justice, as to the suggestions of the Commissioners of Judicial Inquiry.   Sess. 1831–32, (192.) vol. 25, p. 67.

    Registry of Deeds, Ireland :

135.—Report from the Committee on the Bill to regulate the Office for Registering Deeds, Conveyances and Wills in Ireland.
                              Sess. 1831–32, (592.) vol. 18, p. 751.
        SUBJECTS.—Duties of the registrar of deeds.—Mode of registration.—Establishment of the office.—Manner in which the duties are performed.—Defective state of Indexes.—Difficulty of enforcing performance of duties.—Provisions of the Bill for regulating the office.—Great responsibility of the officer, and salary proper for him.——Inquiry concerning two Treasury Minutes of the same date, but not agreeing in purport.

IV.

Parliamentary.

King's Illness; 1788, 1789:

1.—⌈Reports from the Select Committee appointed to examine His Majesty's Physicians, touching the state of His Majesty's Health.   Journals, vol. 44, pp. 6. 47.

2.--⌈Report from the Select Committee appointed to examine Precedents respecting Cases of the personal exercise of the Royal Authority being prevented or interrupted by Infancy, Sickness, &c.   Journals, vol. 44, p. 11.

Extracts from Rolls of Parliament;—from Records in the Tower;—and from other Records.

Impeachments:

Warren Hastings, 1794:

3.—⌈Report from the Select Committee on the Lords' Proceedings on the Trial of Warren Hastings, Esq.   Journals, vol. 49, p. 504.

SUBJECTS.—What has contributed to the duration of the impeachment of Mr. Hastings, —and division of business among the days occupied.———The subjects of the Report are divided into the following heads:—Relation of the judges, &c. to the Court of Parliament. —Jurisdiction of the Lords.—Law of Parliament.—Rule in pleading.—Conduct of the Commons in pleading.—Publicity of the judges' opinions.—Publicity, general.—Mode of putting the question.—Debates on evidence.—Circumstantial evidence.—Order and time of producing evidence.—Practice below.———The Appendix contains arguments of Lord Ferrers' case,—and questions put to judges, as to points of evidence in Mr. Hastings' trial, with their answers thereto.

Lord Melville, 1805:

3*.—Proceedings against Henry Lord Viscount Melville; viz.

Report from the Committee appointed to draw up Articles of Impeachment against him. ———Articles delivered to the Lords.   Sess. 1805, (206. 221.) vol. 2, pp. 817. 829.

A further Report, and an additional Article of Impeachment.———Reports from Committee on inspecting the Lords' Journals in relation to their proceedings on the impeachment; and on the Bills respecting Witnesses against him.
Sess. 1806, (23. 26. 69. 241.) vol. 2, pp. 61. 81. 107. 83.

Privilege:

Franking, 1735—1764:

4.—⌈Report from the Select Committee respecting the Privilege of Franking by Members; 16 April 1735.   Journals, vol. 22, p. 462.

SUBJECTS.—Commencement of the privilege.—Manner of exercising it.—Checks endeavoured to be imposed by the Post-office.—Effects on the revenue.—Resolutions for the regulations of the privilege.

5.—⌈Report from the Select Committee on Abuses in the Post-office, and relating to Franking.   Journals, vol. 29, pp. 997. 1010.

SUBJECTS.—Inquiry into former proceedings of the House.—Statement of deductions from franked letters in 1714, 1734 and 1762.—Great increase in the latter year.—Cause. —Counterfeiting members' hand-writing.—Other frauds in franking.—Franking by public offices.—List of offices having that privilege; and other accounts.

The Speaker's Warrant, 1771:

6.—⌈Report from the Committee of Inquiry into facts relative to obstructions to the execution of the Orders of the House; 1771.   First Series, vol. III. p. 3.

SUBJECT.—Contempt of his warrant for the apprehension of Mr. Miller, a bookseller of London.—Resistance made to its execution in the city.—Imprisonment of the messenger by the city magistrates.

Military Interference, 1815:

7.—Report from the Select Committee respecting the obstruction of the approaches to the House by a Military Force.   Sess. 1814–15, (131.) vol. 13, p. 3.

SUBJECTS.—Complaint was made that a military force obstructed the passages to the House.—The Speaker stated that several Members had represented to him that they had
been

Privilege—continued.

been insulted by a mob, and threatened with violence unless they voted against the Corn Bill, then before the House, and they had reached the House at the hazard of their lives; that he had directed a civil magistrate to attend with constables; and his power being inefficient, The Speaker had directed him to call in the military.—Magistrates examined. —Insufficiency of the civil force to restrain the mob.

Libel on the House, 1817:

8.—Extracts from the Evidence of the Rev. Thomas Thirlwall, before the Select Committee on the Police of the Metropolis.   Sess. 1817, (231.) vol. 18, p. 267. [13.]
SUBJECT.—On a publication by the Rev. T. Thirlwall, reflecting on the House.

Bargaining for Election Influence, 1818—1834:

9.—Report from the Committee of Privileges.   Sess. 1818, (258.) vol. 3, p. 61. [13.]
SUBJECT.—On influencing a voter.

10.—Minutes of Evidence, taken at the Bar of the House, on the Petition of Thomas William Grady, Esq.   Sess. 1819, (96. 97.) vol. 1, pp. 5. 99. [13.]
SUBJECT.—Complaint against the Hon. W. W. Quin, for bargaining for election influence.

11.—First Report from the Select Committee on Inns of Court.
Sess. 1834, (503.) vol. 18, p. 313.
SUBJECT.—This Committee was appointed to inquire into the circumstances attending the rejection of Mr. D. W. Harvey's claim to be called to the bar.   In the course of their inquiry, some facts transpired which led to an allegation that a sum of money was supplied by the Treasury for election purposes.—A special Report was made by the Committee of this matter.

Intimidating a Witness:

12.—Minutes of a Court Martial on Thomas Stinton.
Sess. 1819, (182.) vol. 17, p. 123. [13.]
SUBJECT.—Punishing a witness by court-martial, for absence occasioned by attending to give evidence before a Committee.

Pecuniary Penalties:

13.—Report from the Committee on the expediency of relaxing the exercise of the right of imposing Pecuniary Penalties.   Sess. 1830–31, (277.) vol. 3, p. 433.
SUBJECT.—Importance of the privilege that all pecuniary aids and burthens should be solely imposed by the Commons.—Expediency of relaxing this rule in respect to penal enactments either originating with the Lords, or by amendments made by that House affecting such enactments, when not involving any breach of the Commons' privilege of levying taxes.

Members :

Union with Ireland:

14.—Report from the Committee appointed to consider the Fourth Article of the Union between Great Britain and Ireland.   Sess. 1801, (63.) vol. 3, p. 139. [13.]
SUBJECT.—On offices in Ireland which disqualify persons from sitting in the House of Commons of the United Parliament.

Holy Orders:

15.—Two Reports from the Select Committee concerning.
First Series, vol. xiv. p. 162, and Sess. 1801, vol. 5, p. 175.
Containing an examination of Journals and Records of Parliament for precedents respecting the eligibility of persons in Holy Orders to sit in the House.   This inquiry was in consequence of the Rev. Mr. Horne Tooke being returned a member.

Expulsion:

16.—Report from the Select Committee appointed to examine the Journals, &c. for Precedents.   Sess. 1806–7, (79.) vol. 3, p. 107. [13.]
SUBJECTS.—*Precedents relative to the Expulsion and Return of Members.*—This Committee was appointed in consequence of the return of Mr. Cawthorne, who had, in the year 1796, been found guilty by a court-martial, for misapplication of the regimental funds of the corps of which he was colonel, and expelled the House.——*This Report is a complete collection of precedents, arranged with great care.*

Lunacy:

17.—Report from the Committee of Privileges on the Petition of the Freeholders of Wexford, respecting Mr. Alcock.   Sess. 1810–11, (122.) vol. 5, p. 1. [13.]
SUBJECT.—On the lunacy of a member.

Quakers:

18.—Report from the Select Committee relating to the right of Quakers to take their seat in Parliament on their solemn affirmation.   Sess. 1834, (6.) vol. 11, p. 1.

Privilege—Members—continued.

19.—Report from the Select Committee on the matter of the complaint of a Paragraph in the Examiner Newspaper, 10 November 1833.
Sess. 1834, (51.) vol. 11, p. 313.

> SUBJECT.—The paragraph contained a report of a speech made by Mr. Hill, a member, out of the House, imputing improper motives to Mr. Sheil, another member. Upon inquiry the representation appears to have originated in a mistake, which Mr. Hill explains.

Arrest:

20.—Report from the Select Committee on Proceedings to be had in respect to several Papers signed 'Francis Burdett,' which related to his Apprehension and Committal to the Tower.   Sess. 1810, (354.) vol. 2, p. 315. [13.]

> SUBJECTS.—*Arrest of a Member for a libellous Publication.*—Sir Francis Burdett was ordered to be committed to the Tower for the publication of a book reflecting on the House; but resisted the Speaker's warrant. After holding the Serjeant some days in defiance, he was forcibly carried to the place of commitment, escorted by a military force. He afterwards instituted processes against the Speaker and Serjeant, with the view of bringing the legality of the Commons' proceedings in question before a court of law.——*These Reports contain a digested account of parliamentary precedents in support of the authority of the House.*

21.—Report from the Committee of Privileges. Sess. 1814-15, (176.) vol. 3, p. 59. [13.]

> SUBJECTS.—*Arrest of a Member in the House.*—The Report states the matter of fact of Lord Cochrane's conviction for a stock-jobbing conspiracy, and sentence of imprisonment in the King's Bench Prison; his escape;—resorting to the House (he having been returned a Member for Westminster); and arrest by the Marshal of the Bench in the House: with an opinion that no breach of privilege had been committed.

22.—Report from the Committee of Privileges.   Sess. 1831, (117.) vol. 4, p. 685.

> SUBJECT.—Commitment of a Member (the Hon. William Long Wellesley) by the Lord Chancellor, for contempt of court, in removing his infant daughter (a ward of the court) out of its jurisdiction.—Collection of cases showing the law and usage of Parliament.

Serving on Juries:

23.—Report from the Committee of Privileges, respecting the summoning of a Member as a Juryman.   Sess. 1826, (71.) vol. 3, p. 37. [13.]

> SUBJECTS.—Resolutions declaring the antiquity and importance of the privilege, that no Member should be called upon to serve on juries.—Authorities cited.

Holding Office:

24.—Report from Committee of Precedents.   Sess. 1816, (239.) vol. 3, p. 227. [13.]

> SUBJECT.—Precedents of naval and military officers accepting offices, and continuing to sit as members.

25.—Report of the Select Committee on the Returns made by Members to the several Orders of the House of the 8th June 1821.
Sess. 1822, (542.) vol. 4, p. 41. [13.]

> SUBJECTS.—*Members holding Offices.*—The Report and Appendix state, under eight classes, the number of members, and the amount of their emoluments, who hold offices under the Crown or otherwise.—The Appendix is formed of abstracts of Returns made by members to the orders of the House.

26.—Report from the Select Committee on the Petitions from Canterbury, relating to the seat of Stephen Rumbold Lushington, esquire, and on Precedents of Members accepting Offices abroad vacating their seats.
Sess. 1829, (307.) vol. 3, p. 357.

> SUBJECTS.—Ineligibility of members accepting offices abroad to continue members.—Doubtful applicability of Act of 6 Anne, c. 7, to appointments in the East Indies.—Recommendation to extend the provisions of that Act to such cases.—Statement of precedents extracted from the Journals.

27.—Report from the Select Committee on the reduction of Salaries of Office held during the pleasure of the Crown, by Members of either House of Parliament.   Sess. 1830-31, (322.) vol. 3, p. 445.

28.—Report from the Select Committee on Members holding Office.
Sess. 1833, (671.) vol. 12, p. 1.

Elections:

Interference of Peers:

29.—Reports from the Select Committee respecting the Interference of Peers, &c. in Elections.   Sess. 1801, (1. 2.) vol. 2, pp. 1. 5. [13.]

Elections—continued.

Westminster High Bailiff, &c.:

30.—Report from the Select Committee on the Office of High Bailiff of Westminster.   Sess. 1810–11, (220.) vol. 2, p. 349. [**13.**]

SUBJECTS.—Grant of the office.—Duties.—Emoluments.—Losses by refusal of candidates to defray the expenses.

31.—Report from the Select Committee on the Liability of the High Bailiff of
Westminster to the Expense of erecting the Hustings.
                                                 Sess. 1813–14, (271.) vol. 3, p. 123. [**13.**]

SUBJECTS.—*Expense of Hustings.*—Sir Francis Burdett was elected a Member, but
had never personally appeared on the hustings, or canvassed for votes. He refusing to
pay any portion of the expense, an action was brought against him by the high bailiff, who,
being nonsuited, petitioned Parliament for redress.

32.—Report from the Select Committee on the Petition of the High Constable
of Westminster, &c.   Sess. 1818, (62.) vol. 3, p. 353. [**13.**]

SUBJECT.—Remuneration for his attendance on Parliament.

Duration of Polls:

33.—Report from the Select Committee on Elections and Duration of Polls.
                                                 Sess. 1817, (393.) vol. 3, p. 69. [**13.**]

34.—Report from the Select Committee on Petitions from Berkshire, for
shortening the Duration of Polls at Elections.
                                                 Sess. 1820, (274.) vol. 2, p. 329. [**13.**]

SUBJECTS.—*On the Practice and Duration of Polling.*—Duty of the returning officer
as to closing polls.—Not obliged to keep the poll open to the extent limited by law, if circumstances justify the close, according to his discretion.—Provisions recommended.

35.—Report from the Select Committee on County Election Polls.
                                                 Sess. 1826–27, (349.) vol. 4, p. 1105.

SUBJECTS.—Polling at stations.—Registering freeholders.

36.—Report from the Select Committee on the mode of taking Polls at City
and Borough Elections.   Sess. 1826–27, (394.) vol. 4, p. 1111.

SUBJECTS.—Providing several polling places.—Shortening the duration of Polls.—Regulating the manner of deciding disputed votes.

Miscellaneous Matters relating to Elections :

Short-hand Writers :

37.—Report from the Select Committee respecting Short-hand Writers.
                                                 Sess. 1802–3, (40.) vol. 3, p. 613. [**13.**]

SUBJECT.—On the employment of short-hand writers on trials of controverted elections.

Recognizances :

38.—Report from the Select Committee on Fees to Examiners of Election
Recognizances and Bills of Costs.   Sess. 1812–13, (330.) vol. 4, p. 731. [**13.**]

39.—Report from the Select Committee on Election Recognizances.
                                                 Sess. 1828, (359.) vol. 4, p. 133.

SUBJECTS.—Resolutions respecting the examination of the sufficiency of sureties named
in the recognizances under the Act for the trial of controverted elections.—Fees to be
taken for the examination.

40.—Two Reports from the Select Committee on Election Recognizances,
Ireland.   Sess. 1819, (88.) vol. 4, p. 291. [**13.**]

Irish Election Law :

41.—Report from the Select Committee on Irish Election Laws.
                                                 Sess. 1817, (281.) vol. 8, p. 1. [**13.**]

Election Expenses :

42.—Report from the Select Committee on Expenses of Sheriffs at Elections,
and on the Laws for regulating Elections in Ireland.
                                                 Sess. 1820, (226.) vol. 3, p. 269. [**13.**]

43.—Returns, from Sheriffs, of Fees paid at the General Election 1818.
                                                 Sess. 1819, (386.) vol. 4, p. 323. [**13.**]

44.—Returns, from Sheriffs of Counties and Cities, of all Charges at the General
Election 1820.   Sess. 1820, (285.) vol. 6, p. 261. [**13.**]

Miscellaneous Matters relating to Elections—continued.

Election Expenses:

45.—Report from the Select Committee of Inquiry into the Expenses at Elections of Members for Counties and Boroughs in England and Wales, at the last General Election. Sess. 1834, (591.) vol. 9, p. 263.

SUBJECTS.—Advantageous to shorten the duration of polls.—Summary of the representation.—Administration of long oaths would prevent elections being completed in one day.—Expense of preparing the different registers of electors very heavy, and in some cases exorbitant.—Payment for registration should be discontinued.—Persons who ought to make out the list of electors.—No means provided by the Reform Bill to ascertain who have the right to vote at elections.—Revising barrister should have the power of awarding expenses to be paid by persons making frivolous and vexatious opposition to registration.—Lists for the use of sheriffs or returning officers should be supplied at the expense of the county, borough, &c.——— Sums paid to revising barristers for England and Wales in 1832 and 1833.—Number of contested and uncontested elections in 1832.—Expenses charged against candidates very high.—Members not liable to pay the expense of returning the writ after election.—Allowance should be made in all contested elections to the returning officer for books, &c.——— Number of voters polled at contested elections in Scotland.—Shortening the notice of the time of election in Scotland recommended.—Limiting the number of persons to vote in respect of any one property recommended.—No qualification in respect of property required on the part of a candidate in Scotland———Present state of the representation in Ireland.—Sums paid revising barristers there.—Uniform scale of expenses to be paid by candidates necessary.—All objections against a voter in Ireland to be made at the time of registration.—Certificate of the right to vote to be granted by the clerk of the peace, and penalty for refusal.—Certificates to be on parchment.—No obstruction to the exercise of the elective franchise to be allowed at the time of the poll.—Penalty for preventing or impeding any elector from voting at an election.—Qualification oaths to be administered (if necessary) at the time of registration.—Time of polling to be shortened.—Polling stations to be increased, and number to be allowed to poll at one booth in the course of the day.—Polling stations to be provided at the expense of the county, &c.—Regulation of fees to be charged candidates by returning officer and others, and penalty for demanding more.—Persons proposing candidates without their consent to be liable for a share of the legal expenses incurred.—Sheriffs may demand a deposit on account of expenses previous to granting a poll, and balance of sums deposited to be returned by the sheriff, &c. to the candidate.—Penalty for refusing to proceed with the poll after receiving security for expenses.

Forms and Proceedings of the House:

Union with Ireland:

46.—Three Reports from the Select Committee on Orders respecting Ireland. Sess. 1801, (1. 10. 136.) vol. 3, pp. 1. 7. 379. [13.]

SUBJECT.—Resolutions relative to proceedings of the House, in consequence of the Union.

Thanksgiving-day:

47.—Report from the Select Committee appointed to consider of the Manner of the House going to St. Paul's Church, on Thanksgiving-day. Sess. 1813–14, (280.) vol. 3, p. 101. [13.]

SUBJECT.—Regulations to be observed on the occasion.

Coronation of William IV.:

48.—Report from the Select Committee on the Accommodations necessary for the House in attending at Their Majesties Coronation. Sess. 1831, (220.) vol. 4, p. 653.

SUBJECTS.—Sufficiency and safety of the seats in the Abbey.—Arrangements for the attendance of the members.

Private Bill Office:

49.—Report from the Select Committee on the Regularity of the Proceedings upon Private Bills. Sess. 1810, (301.) vol. 2, p. 203. [13.]

SUBJECT.—Establishing the Private Bill Office and Register of Proceedings.

Public and Private Bills:

50.—Report from the Select Committee on the means of expediting the introduction of Public Bills. Sess. 1821, (178.) vol. 4, p. 47. [13.]

SUBJECT.—Resolution limiting the number of orders of the day for proceedings on Private Bills.

Fees on Private Bills:

51.—Report from the Select Committee on the Table of Fees. Sess. 1821, (597.) vol. 4, p. 49. [13.]

SUBJECTS.—Amount and appropriation.—Fees not now payable to particular officers, but carried to a common fund—except as to certain clerks.—Sinecure clerkships.—Shorthand writing should be a qualification.—Sale of inferior offices disapproved of.—Good effect of fees in restraining frivolous applications for bills.—Recommendation of certain alterations.—Particulars of the charges for passing several bills.

Forms and Proceedings of the House—continued.

Proceedings on Private Bills:

52.—Two Reports from the Select Committee on Private Business.

Sess. 1824, (432. 468.) vol. 6, pp. 497. 501. [**13.**]

53.—Report from the Committee of the whole House.

Sess. 1824, (453.) vol. 6, p. 507. [**13.**]

SUBJECTS.—*Proceedings on Private Bills.*—On giving notices.—Proceedings before Committees.—On the application of the Standing Orders.—Accommodation of committee rooms. —Expenses attending private bills.

Committees on Private Bills:

54.—Report from the Select Committee on the Constitution of Committees on Private Bills.   Sess. 1825, (457.) vol. 5, p. 103. [**13.**]

SUBJECTS.—*Present Mode of conducting Business.*—Inconvenience arising from matters before a committee being determined by members not present during their discussion.— Committees chiefly attended by members personally or locally interested.—Motives and evils of opening committees by giving "voices" to all who attend.—Recommendation to discontinue that practice.—Consideration of remodelling the Committees.—As to forming them by ballot, and enforcing attendance by compulsory regulations.—Proposed new arrangement of lists of counties.

Fees and Expenses:

55.—Report from the Select Committee on the nature and amount of Fees, Charges and Expenses, attendant on the progress and passing Private Bills.

Sess. 1834, (540.) vol. 11, p. 333.

SUBJECTS.—A more equitable apportionment of fees necessary.—Standing Orders to be revised.—Recognizances for payment of costs to be entered into when required.—Transmission of notice by the post to the owners of property to be considered sufficient.—Proof of compliance with Standing Orders to be taken on affidavits.—Longer notice of going into Committee to be given in certain cases.—House copy to be dispensed with.—System of ingrossment to be continued.—Act containing general clauses inserted in private bills to be passed.—Alteration to be made in the present system of blanking bills.

Public Petitions:

56.—Report from the Select Committee on facilitating the Presentation of Public Petitions.   Sess. 1831–32, (639.) vol. 5, p. 333.

SUBJECTS.—Increase af public petitions.—Practice of former periods.—Proposed plan of presenting petitions.—Select committee to classify all petitions, and to report periodically a summary of their subjects.———History of the ancient course of petitioning, and the powers of Parliament to remedy grievances.—Receivers and triers of petitions.—Character of petitions at early periods.—Nature of the Rolls of Parliament.—Ancient mode of spreading libels by petitioning.

Business of the House:

57.—Report from the Select Committee on the best mode of expediting the Business of the House; and on the most convenient mode of receiving the Petitions of the People.   Sess. 1834, (284.) vol. 11, p. 317.

58.—Second Report from the Select Committee.   Sess. 1834, (350.) vol. 44, p. 1.

SUBJECTS.—Duties of the Committee on public petitions.—Notice to be given by the Votes of the days appointed for presenting petitions.—Petitions to be presented after private business of the day disposed of.—Debate on petitions not to be resumed till a day appointed by the Committee.—The Speaker authorized to set aside arrangement in cases of exigency.—One day in each week to be set apart for miscellaneous petitions.—Members may deliver petitions to the Committee thereon without their having been previously laid before the House.—No private business or petitions to be brought before the House at the evening sitting without special permission.———Advantages to be derived from passing a General Inclosure Act.—Powers for paving, &c. cities, towns, &c. to be vested in inhabitants, without the necessity of applying to Parliament.

Proceedings on Church of Ireland Bill:

59.—Report from the Select Committee on Precedents.

Sess. 1833, (86.) vol. 12, p. 133.

SUBJECT.—The Bill had been brought in on motion for leave, and read a first time. It was then doubted whether such a course was agreeable to the standing orders of the House, which required that every proposition to impose a burthen or charge on the people, should receive its first discussion in a Committee of the whole House. The second reading was therefore deferred. The Committee decided this course should have been observed as to this Bill; and the proceedings thereon were in consequence dropped.

Divisions of the House:

60.—Report from the Select Committee on the mode of securing an accurate and authentic account of the Divisions of the House.

Sess. 1834, (147.) vol. 11, p. 325.

SUBJECTS.—Propositions for securing an accurate and authentic account of the divisions of the House.—Number of names that can be taken down in a given time.

Standing Orders :

61.—Two Reports from the Select Committee on Standing Orders respecting Bills of Inclosure.   Sess. 1801, (38. 50.) vol. 3, pp. 13. 81. [13.]

62.—Report from the Select Committee respecting Commissioners, Surveyors, &c. in Inclosure and Drainage Bills.   Sess. 1801, (77.) vol. 3, p. 205. [13.]

63.—Recommitted Report respecting the Persons to be appointed Commissioners, &c. in Bills of Inclosure and Drainage.
      Sess. 1801, (106.) vol. 3, p. 359. [13.]

64.—Reports from the Select Committee on Standing Orders relative to Bills of Inclosure.   Sess. 1801, (132. 134.) vol. 3, pp. 365. 375. [13.]

65.—Standing Orders relative to Bills of Inclosure and Drainage.
      Sess. 1801, (144.) vol. 4, p. 841. [13.]

66.—Report from the Select Committee on Standing Orders relating to Turnpike Bills.   Sess. 1807, (41.) vol. 3, p. 131. [13.]

67.—Report from the Select Committee on Standing Orders.
      Sess. 1810, (190.) vol. 2, p. 187. [13.]

68.—Second Report.   Sess. 1810, (303.) vol. 2, p. 191. [13.]

69.—Third Report.   Sess. 1810, (321.) vol. 2, p. 195. [13.]
    Subject.—On Notices for inclosing, draining or improving lands, &c.

70.—Report from the Select Committee on Standing Orders respecting Notices and Forms of Applications for Private Bills.
      Sess. 1810–11, (231.) vol. 11, p. 471. [13.]

71.—Report from the Select Committee on Standing Orders relative to Navigation Bills, &c.   Sess. 1813–14, (245.) vol. 4, p. 369. [13.]

72.—General Collection of Standing Orders ; with Table of Fees.
      Sess. 1813–14, (353.) vol. 14, p. 111. [13.]

73.—Report from the Select Committee on the expediency of a Standing Order relative to Bills for regulating Trade, &c.
      Sess. 1820, (193.) vol. 2, p. 229. [13.]

74.—Report from the Select Committee on Bills respecting Trade.
      Sess. 1823, (376.) vol. 4, p. 59. [13.]

75.—Standing Orders with respect to the mode of conducting the Private Business in the House.   Sess. 1824, (469.) vol. 24, p. 663.

76.—Standing Orders of the House relating to Private Bills, and other Matters ; 1685 to 1830.—With a Table of Fees.   Sess. 1830, (692.) vol. 30, p. 113.
    ☞ The Collection printed in 4to. by Messrs. Hansard contains the alterations and additional Orders made by the House subsequent to the preceding Report.

Establishments of the House of Commons :

77.—Report from the Select Committee on Fees, Salaries, &c. received by the Officers and Public Servants of the House of Commons.
      Sess. 1833, (648.) vol. 12, p. 179.

    Subject.—Salary of The Speaker.—Of the Officers of the House ; and account of their duties.— Proposed salaries, and arrangement of duties.—Proposed revision of the Standing Orders, so as to make those of both Houses similar.—Proceedings on private business.— Printing Sessional Papers, and examination of Messrs. Hansard's accounts.—Printing Private Bills.—Course of proceedings to obtain the passing of a Bill, and expenses attending them.—Sale of Parliamentary Papers.—Care of Stores.——Admission to the Gallery. —Fees.—Reporters of debates.—Returns of appointments of officers.—Salaries and emoluments.—Forms of Printing.

Parliamentary Records :
    Printed Journals and Reports :

78.—[Report from the Select Committee on the State of the Printed Journals, General Indexes, and Volumes of Printed Reports. Journals, vol. 58, p. 653. [13.]
    This Report is printed only in the Journals, vol. 58.—On the state of the printed Reports and Papers in 1825, *see* 3d Report on *Committee Rooms, Library, &c.* Nos. 82, 83.

Parliamentary Records— continued.

Votes and Proceedings of the House, 1817 :

79.—Report from the Select Committee on the Printed Votes and Proceedings of the House of Commons.   Sess. 1817, (156.) vol. 3, p. 47. [13.]

SUBJECTS.—On a more convenient and expeditious method of preparing and distributing the printed Votes of the House, and preparing the Journal during the session.

General Index to the Journals, 1818—1825 :

80.—Report from the Select Committee on the General Index to the Journals of the House of Commons.   Sess. 1818, (396.) vol. 3, p. 85. [13.]

SUBJECTS.—Imperfect state of the General Index ; and proposed improvement in preparing the Index to Votes and Journals of each session.

81.—Report from the Select Committee on the General Index to Journals of the House.   Sess. 1823, (541.) vol. 4, p. 61. [13.]

SUBJECTS.— *Continuation of the Series of Indexes.*—Mr. Rickman's statement of progress made.—Improvements in the mode of framing the General Index.—Description of the Sessional and General Index.—Manner of conducting the formation of the Index.— Printing.—Index to each volume to be incorporated with those of former ones. at the end of each session.

82.—Report from the Select Committee on the progress made in the General Index from the Union to the Demise of his late Majesty ; and continuing a similar Form of Index to the present Time.   Sess. 1825, (477.) vol. 5, p. 1. [13.]

SUBJECTS.—*Progress and Completion of the Index.*—Best mode of remunerating index-makers.—Method of annual allowance not expedient.—Such work best accomplished by withholding payment till completion.—Alphabetical index of names, &c.—Improved mode of arranging the head " Supply."—Annual progressive mode of forming and incorporating the index to each volume.—Scale of remuneration recommended.—Reprinting and incorporating Dunn's Indexes.—Approbation of the Committee of the work.

Ingrossing Bills in Parliament, 1823 :

83.—Report from the Select Committee on the present method of ingrossing Bills.   Sess. 1823, (552.) vol. 4, p. 69. [13.]

SUBJECTS.—*Records of Parliament.*—Ancient and present manner of ingrossing bills.— Kinds of writing used.—Depository of ingrossed copies.—Best form of keeping records.— Book-form recommended as preferable to rolls.—Quality of the ink used.—Manuscript journal of the House of Commons—writing most suitable.—Material best for writing on.— Practice of the Ingrossing Office.

Committee Rooms and Library, 1825 :

84.—First Report from the Select Committee on Committee Rooms and Printed Papers.   Sess. 1825, (496.) vol. 5, p. 7. [13.]

SUBJECTS.—*Necessity of Accommodation.—Inadequacy of the present Library.— Selection and Arrangement of Parliamentary Reports.*—Increase of Parliamentary business.— Number of Committees sitting daily.—Want of accommodation.—Additional Committee-rooms recommended.—Inconvenient and contracted state of the Library.—Site proper for the additional buildings pointed out.—A residence to be provided in the room of the present one occupied by Mr. Ley, as Clerk of the House.—Its necessary contiguity.— Other improvements and alterations recommended.

85.—Second Report from the same Committee.   Sess. 1825, (515.) vol. 5, p. 11. [13.]

SUBJECTS.—Minutes of Evidence.—State of the Library.—Contracted capacity.—Contents.—Number of volumes of Sessional Papers printed.—Books in request, but not in the Library.—Custody of the printed Papers.—Sessional Papers, where kept in store.—Manner of selecting the Papers inserted in the Journal Appendix.—Manuscript Journals and printed Papers before the Union.—Books delivered over to the Librarian.

Library and Printed Reports :

86.—Third Report from the same Committee.   Sess. 1825, (516.) vol. 5, p. 21. [13.]

SUBJECTS.—On a Selection of printed Reports.—Arrangement of selected Papers.— Importance of the subjects of the Reports.—The reprinting deserving the consideration of the House at some future period. — A number of perfect copies should be preserved unbroken.—Complete sets should be deposited in public libraries.—Importance of Reports from Commissioners, and should be included in any future selection.—Indexes prepared by Mr. Hansard to be consolidated.—Consideration as to the size of any future reprint.— A classification of Papers to be made.—The fifteen volumes of Reports in request.— Number of Papers remaining on hand.—Deposits of printed Papers—In warehouses under Mr. Hansard's care.—Classification of the Sessional Reports and Reports of Commissioners.—Arranged list.—Plan for combining the sessional indexes.—Plan for digesting the contents of the Reports when formed into volumes.

*Parliamentary Records—*continued.

Library and Committee Rooms, 1826:

87.—Report from the Select Committee on Committee Rooms and Printed Papers.
Sess. 1826, (403.) vol. 3, p. 39. [13.]

SUBJECTS.—*Difficulties in complying with the Directions of the Committee.—Indispensable Necessity of additional Rooms.*—Causes which have prevented the compliance with the address on Report of 1st July 1825.—Objections to removing the dwelling of the Chief Clerk in Cotton Gardens.—Preference of Mr. Soane's plan as recommended by a former Committee.—Necessity of additional committee rooms—of enlarging the Library—Vote-office and other offices.—A more confined plan recommended for immediate adoption.—General Index to Sessional Papers to be completed without further delay.—State of the library.—Accumulation of volumes. — Accommodation required by the different officers of the House.—Opinions of the accommodations necessary for them.—As to the Vote-office, warehousing, and delivering the Papers; and arrangements with Mr. Hansard respecting that business.—Plans of Colonel Trench and Mr. Soane.——*see* No. 93.

Library, 1830—1834:

88.—Report from the Select Committee on the present state of the Library of the House of Commons.
Sess. 1830, (496.) vol. 4, p. 35.

SUBJECTS.—On the regulations proper for its preservation and arrangement.—Advantage would arise from members consulting the papers in the Library, before moving for returns, in order to prevent repeated production of the same paper.

89.—Report from the Select Committee on the present state and future management of the Library.
Sess. 1831-32, (600.) vol. 5, p. 245.

SUBJECTS.—Present state of the Library.—Class of works in which it requires additions.—Interchange of Papers with foreign legislatures.—State of the collections of Parliamentary Papers.—Collections of pamphlets in The Speaker's Gallery.—Reprinting the Catalogue and manner of delivery.——Expediency of farther accommodation for the Library.—Plans for that purpose.—Deposit of the Parliamentary Papers.—Of MS. Papers presented to the House.—Collection of Papers of 1690 in an unexamined bag.—Future regulations of the Library.—Recommendation of a Standing Committee.—Duties and salaries of the Librarians.—State of the printed Reports and Papers.—Classification of them for 1801 to 1826.—A continuation recommended.—Formation of General Indexes recommended.—Insertion of member's name on the indorsement of the paper moved for by him.—Plan and specimen of a General Index to Reports.

90.—Report from the Standing Committee.
Sess. 1834, (463.) vol. 11, p. 329.

SUBJECTS.—Accession to the Library by a present of books from the French Government, in interchange for Papers and Journals sent from England.—Re-arrangement of the Catalogue.—Completion of General Index to the Sessional Papers up to 1832; its utility; to be annually continued for future incorporation.—Index to local and personal Acts.—Arranged series of Reports to be continued to 1834, with a General Index similar to that attached to the 15 vols. of folio Reports.——MS. Papers presented to the House deposited in the Library.—Regulations for the management of the Library as to admission of strangers, and procuring books wanted in the collection.—Recommended accommodation of apartments for the Librarian.

Catalogues and Indexes, 1830:

91.—Catalogue of Books in the Library.
Sess. 1830, (80.) vol. 4, p. 47.

CLASSIFICATION.—General History.—History of England; Wales; Scotland; Ireland; Foreign Dominions.—Parliamentary History, and Treaties.—Ecclesiastical History.—Commerce and Political Economy.—Antiquities and Topography.—Coins.—Heraldry.——History of Northern Europe: France; Netherlands; Germany and Poland; Italy; Spain, &c.; Portugal; Russia; Turkish and Eastern.——Diplomacy.—Records.—Statutes and Parliamentary Proceedings. —— Law: Ancient; English. —— Colonial Legislation.—Law of Elections.—Modern Law of France.—Dictionaries.—Books of Reference.—Maps.—Miscellaneous.

Parliamentary and Commissioners' Reports:

92.—Classification of the Parliamentary Reports, from 1801 to 1826.
Sess. 1830, (81.) vol. 4, p. 143.

THIS contains a short abstract of the principal subjects. This work was executed in pursuance of the directions of the Third Report of the Committee on Committee Rooms and Printed Papers in 1825. The Reports and Printed Papers in the Library are classed according to this arrangement.

93.—Reports of the House of Commons. The preceding work continued to 1834 inclusive.
Sess. 1834, (626.) vol. 50, p. 1.

THIS work comprises the Parliamentary Reports from the earliest period. The following are the heads of classification:—I. Ecclesiastical subjects, Revenues, and Churches.—II. Education and Charities. — III. Judicial. — IV. Parliamentary. — V. Historical. — VI. Agriculture; Corn Trade; Provisions; Cattle.—VII. Malt and Malting; Beer and Brewing; Distillation and Spirits.—VIII. Trade and Manufactures; Factory Regulations; Fisheries.—IX. Commerce, Shipping and Foreign Trade.—X. Finance; Civil List; Public Accounts.—XI. Banking; Coinage; Currency; Exchange.—XII. Revenue from Duties; Land Revenue.—XIII. Annuities; Usury; Friendly Societies.—XIV. East India Affairs.—XV. Colonies and Slavery.— XVI. Emigration. — XVII. Scientific and Literary.—
XVIII. Arts

Parliamentary Records—Classification of Reports to 1834—*continued.*

XVIII. Arts, connected with Trade and Manufactures.—XIX. Public Works; Palaces; Roads; Bridges; Harbours.—XX. Town Improvements and Local Taxation.—XXI. Poor and Poor Laws.—XXII. Crime, Gaols, Police and Punishment.—XXIII. Population; Parochial Registration of Births, Marriages and Deaths.—XXIV. Army and Navy.— XXV. Public Offices.—XXVI. Miscellaneous.

94.—General Index to the Sessional Papers, 1801 to 1832.

Sess. 1833, (737.) vol. 40.

95.—Indexes to the Reports of the House of Commons.   Sess. 1834, (626.) vol. 50.

THESE are Indexes to the subject-matter of the Reports. The following subjects are completed :—Agriculture and Corn Trade.—Colonies and Slavery.—Emigration.—Poor.— Poor in Ireland.—Weights and Measures.—Children employed in Factories, &c.—Foreign Trade.—Malting, Brewing, Distillation.—Salt.—Fisheries.

Printing Parliamentary Papers and Statutes, 1822—1828 :

96.—Report from the Select Committee on Printing and Stationery.

Sess. 1822, (607.) vol. 4, p. 401. [135.]

SUBJECTS.—*Management of the Stationery-office.—Charges for Printing for the Public.*— Manner of conducting the business of the Stationery-office.—Conduct of the officers and printers employed by that establishment.—Parliamentary printing,—for the House of Commons—Journals, Reports, Papers, and Votes :—For the House of Lords, and by the King's printer.—Manner of conducting the Printing Trade,—and Parliamentary Printing. —Rates of wages, and mode of estimation.—Mode of charge, calculations, &c.—Paper used ;—the denominations, qualities, and prices.—Mode of purchasing, and rates of charge. —Recommendations and opinions of the Committee.

97. –Report from the Select Committee on Printing done for the House.

Sess. 1828, (520.) vol. 4, p. 481.

SUBJECTS.—Description of printing for the House of Commons.—Journals, Reports, Bills, and Papers.—The Votes.—Principles of charging by Messrs. Hansard.—Description of the nature of the business; and of Mr. Hansard's manner of conducting the business.—The Committee's opinion thereof.—Mr. Nichols' mode of conducting the Vote printing; its peculiarity, and rate of charge.—Objection to Sunday-working —Recommendation for lessening the Journal Appendix.—Saving by printing from the same types for both Houses.—Collecting and arranging series of Papers by Messrs. Hansard.—Substitution of lithography for engraving by direction of The Speaker.—Patent privilege of Messrs. Eyre & Spottiswoode for printing Acts of Parliament.—Recommendation to revise the mode of charge at the approaching expiration of the patent.—Suggestions for avoiding unnecessary expense, by printing papers only of Parliamentary importance, and not of a private and local nature.—Unnecessary expense of printing petitions of the nature of general disquisitions.—Importance of the Library.—Utility of the classified set of Reports from 1801 to 1826, and its continuation recommended.—Assiduity of Mr. Spiller, the Librarian. —Accumulation of MS. Bills and Papers to be removed.—A numerical Index to be prepared.

King's Printers, 1832 :

98.—Report from the Select Committee on King's Printer's Patent.

Sess. 1831–32, (713.) vol. 8, p. 1.

SUBJECTS.—On the inutility of exclusive privileges in printing Bibles for insuring accuracy.—The exercise of such privilege in printing Acts of Parliament.—The effect on prices.———English patentees.—Printing Acts of Parliament, Proclamations, Bibles, Testaments, &c.—Prices at which sold.—Supply of Acts to the Houses of Parliament and magistrates.—Prices and sale of Bibles, &c.—Plan for printing and selling them at cheaper rates.—Profits of the business.———Scotch patentees.—Description of printing done by them.—Rates of charge.—Origin of their business of printing Bibles, &c.—History of Bibles printed by others than the patentees.—Comparative correctness.———Stationery supplied by patent; and prices charged.—Printing and sale of Bibles and Prayer-books.—Profits of the business.———Irish patentees.—Printing executed by them.———Liability of printing to incorrectness, and means taken to avoid it.—Comparative correctness of Bibles with other books.—Account of typographical errors in various editions of Bibles.—Number and variety of editions of the Scriptures.—Modes of estimating printing and bookselling charges.—On the practice and effect of stereotyping.—Law proceedings instituted by the patentees to restrain infringement of their rights.—Comparative price of Bibles and other books.—Account of various editions of the Bible.———Treasury Minutes relative to the subject of printing, and the prices charged.—On the supply of paper.—Respecting duplicate setting up the press.—Relating to the management of the Stationery-office.—Copies of patents.———Accounts of payments to the King's printers.—Of the expense of printing and reprinting the Journals and Reports of the House of Commons.—Account of Journals delivered and remaining in store.—List of the different sizes and denominations of Bibles and Prayer-books, and the prices for which sold.———On printing for the two Houses of Parliament.—Estimates and comparison of prices.—On contract printing.—On a Government establishment for printing———Printing Bibles in the United States.—Printing the laws of the States.

Parliamentary Records—continued.

Public Documents, 1833:

99.—First Report from the Select Committee on the best means of affording Members information to be derived from Public Documents, with a view to economy, facility of access, and clearness of arrangement.

Sess. 1833, (44.) vol. 12, p 51.

SUBJECTS,—Want of perspicuity in the information on statistics afforded by Accounts laid before the House.—Work compiling by direction of the Board of Trade to remedy this defect.—Utility of Mr. Marshall's Digest, and recommendation that 1,250 copies should be procured for the use of Parliament.—Probable expense.

100.—Second Report from the same Committee.   Sess. 1833, (717.) vol. 12, p. 57.

SUBJECTS.—Heads of arrangement of the Statistical work of the Board of Trade.—Expense of printing.—Recommendations for controling it.—Sale of Parliamentary papers recommended.—Form of printing.—Printing Bills—Journals.—MSS. to be placed in the Library for reference.—On the distribution of Journals to Members.—Proposed sale of them.—Accumulation of papers to be prevented by regulating the number printed.—Expense of House of Commons' printing, 1829 to 1831, under the heads Reports, Bills, Accounts and Papers, &c.—Of volumes of Journals delivered.—Treasury Minutes regulating the charges for Acts of Parliament, and the Votes.

Peerage :

101.—Report from the Lords' Committees on the Dignity of a Peer of the Realm, &c. &c.   Sess. 1826, (391.) vol. 6. [16.]

102.—Appendix, No. 1, Part 1, to the Report.   Sess. 1826, (392.) vol. 7. [17.]

103.—Appendix, No. 1, Part 2, to the Report.   Sess. 1826, (393.) vol. 8. [18.]

104.—Second, Third and Fourth Reports.   Sess. 1826, (394.) vol. 9. [19.]

SUBJECTS.—*On the Dignity of the Peerage, and on the Constitution of the Legislative Assembly of England.*—1, 2, 3, Preliminary Reports.—The 4th is divided into XIII. divisions : from I. to VII. relate to the constitution of the legislative assembly from the Conquest to the reign of Henry the Third ; from VIII. to XII. relate to the constituent parts of the legislative assemblies from the reign of Edward the First to the Unions of England and Scotland, and of Great Britain and Ireland : the XIIIth is a recapitulation of the subject of inquiry.

Reform in Parliament, 1830—1831 :

105.—Report from the Select Committee on the Petitions for Reform in Parliament.   Sess. 1830-31, (263.) vol. 3, p. 421.

THE HEADS OF CLASSIFICATION are : Reform.—Ballot.—Short Parliaments.—Tithes.—Taxes.—Royal Burghs.

Parliamentary Representation :

106.—Report from the Select Committee respecting the Limits of the Borough of Arundel.   Sess. 1831-32, (537.) vol. 5, p. 1.

107.—Letter from the Returning Officer to the Secretary of State.

Sess. 1831-32, (506.) vol. 36, p. 1.

108.—Report and Minutes of Evidence from the Select Committee respecting the Limits of Dungarvon, Youghal and Mallow Boroughs.

Sess. 1831-32, (631. 635.) vol. 36, pp. 3. 5.

109.—Papers respecting Parliamentary Representation, being 1 to x, and all such as are comprised in vol. 36, Sessional Papers 1831-32.

SUBJECTS.—Instructions to Commissioners respecting boundaries of proposed boroughs.—Returns from boroughs of population, houses of 10 l. rental, number of electors.—Memorials from particular boroughs, &c.—Population and assessed taxes of counties and boroughs.—Parochial assessments.—Freeholders and freemen of particular boroughs.

Reform in Parliament—continued.

110.—Reports of Commissioners, and Answers of Returning Officers.—IV. & V.
Sess. 1831–32, (20.) vol. 37.

SUBJECTS.—Instructions given by the Secretary of State for the Home Department with reference to Parliamentary representation; with 70 plans of boroughs. These Reports are the results of the Supplemental Instructions of the 24th October 1831, communicated to the Commissioners by direction of Lord Melbourne. The answers of the Returning Officers to the circular from the Home-office of the 14th November are arranged with them, so as to facilitate reference. The object of these short Reports being entirely distinct from that of the Boundary Reports, no allusion is made to the boundaries recommended for the new boroughs. The plans show all the houses which belonged to the town at the time to which these Reports refer.

England :

111.—Reports from Commissioners on proposed Division of Counties, and Boundaries of Boroughs; with Plans.   Sess. 1831–32, (141.) vols. 38, 39, 40, 41.

Vol. 1. Bedford to Huntingdon.—2. Kent to Somersetshire.—3. Staffordshire to Yorkshire.—4. Wales.

112.—Report on the proposed Divisions of Counties mentioned in Schedule (F.) of the Reform Bill, England ; with Plans.   Sess. 1831–32, (357.) vol. 41, p. 211.

Scotland:

113.—Reports upon the Boundaries of the several Cities, Burghs and Towns in Scotland, in respect to the Election of Members to serve in Parliament ; with Plans.   Sess. 1831–32, (408.) vol. 42.

Ireland:

114.—Similar Reports for Ireland ; with Plans.   Sess. 1831–32, (519.) vol. 43.

Municipal Reform :

Corporations, England :

115.—Report from the Select Committee on the state of Municipal Corporations in England and Wales.   Sess. 1833, (344.) vol. 13, p. 1.

116.—Returns of Charitable Funds in the possession or disposition of Municipal Corporations; and of the names of members who have become Magistrates during the last 20 years.   Sess. 1834, (460.) vol. 45, p. 1.

Royal Burghs of Scotland :

117.—[Report from the Select Committee on the internal government, financial concerns, modes of municipal election and ancient constitution thereof.
1793 : First Series, vol. xiv. p. 1.

118.—Report from the Select Committee to whom the several Petitions from the Royal Burghs of Scotland were referred.   Sess. 1819, (571. 229.) vol. 6, pp. 1. 551. [24.]

SUBJECTS.—Internal government of the burghs.—Mode of electing the magistracy.— Management of corporation funds.—Levying taxes.

119.—Report from the Select Committee to whom the several Petitions from the Royal Burghs of Scotland, in the years 1818, 1819 and 1820, were referred.
Sess. 1820, (277.) vol. 3, p. 95. [24.]

SUBJECTS.—*Constitution, and Abuses.*—Constitution of the councils of the burghs.— Self-elected, and self-continued.—Liabilities of abuse.—Resolutions.

120.—Report from the Select Committee to whom the Petitions from the Royal Burghs, in 1818, 1819, 1820 and 1821, were referred, &c.

SUBJECT.—Same as the preceding Report.   Sess. 1821, (666.) vol. 8, p. 303. [24.]

121.—Minutes of Proceedings of the above Committee.
Sess. 1821, (666–2.) vol. 8, p. 411. [24]

122.—Returns from the Magistrates of the Royal Burghs, specifying what Accounts have been lodged by them annually, in compliance with the 3 Geo. 4, c. 91.   Sess. 1825, (128.) vol. 20, p. 425. [24.]

Controverted Elections :

    Athlone :

123.—Report from the Select Committee.   Sess. 1826–27, (389.) vol. 4, p. 1081.

    SUBJECT.—Forgery of signatures to a petition against the election of Richard Handcock, Esq.

    Aylesbury :

124.—Report from the Select Committee on Petitions complaining of an undue Election and Return.   Sess. 1803-4, (25.) vol. 2, p. 3. [14.]

    Barnstaple :

125.—Report from the Select Committee on the Barnstaple Election ; together with the Special Report from the said Committee, and also the Minutes of Evidence taken before them.   Sess. 1819, (86.) vol. 4, p. 231. [14.]

126.—Report from the Select Committee appointed to inspect the Lords' Journals, with relation to any Proceedings on the Bill for preventing Bribery and Corruption in Barnstaple.   Sess. 1819-20, (28.) vol. 2, p. 49. [14.]

    Camelford :

127.—Reports from the Select Committee on the Camelford Election ; together with the Special Reports from the said Committee, and also the Minutes of Evidence taken before them.   Sess. 1819, (458. 459.) vol. 4, pp. 407. 595. [14.]

128.—Minutes of Evidence taken before a Committee of the whole House, on the Camelford Election.   Sess. 1819, (544.) vol. 4, p. 657. [14.]

    Carrickfergus :

129.—Report from the Select Committee.   Sess. 1830–31, (112.) vol. 3, p. 179.

    SUBJECT.—Forgery of names to a petition against the election.

130.—Report from the Select Committee on the Petition complaining of an undue Election and Return.   Sess. 1833, (181.) vol. 8, p. 1.

    Coventry :

131.—Report from the Select Committee.   Sess. 1826–27, (147. 148.) vol. 4, pp. 1. 2.

    SUBJECTS.—Conduct of the mayor and magistrates censured for inefficiency in preventing riots.—Recommendation to give concurrent jurisdiction to the magistrates of the county of Warwick.

132.—Report from the Select Committee on the Petition complaining of an undue Election and Return.   Sess. 1833, (488.) vol. 31, p. 197.

    Dublin :

133.—Report from the Select Committee.   Sess. 1831, (145.) vol. 4, p. 447.

    Dunfermline :

134.—Extracts of the Minutes of Evidence taken before the Select Committee on Dunfermline Election Petitions.   Sess. 1802-3, (39.) vol. 3, p. 601. [14.]

    Evesham :

135.—Evidence taken before the Select Committee.   Sess. 1830–31, (73.) vol. 3, p. 35.

    Galway :

136.—Report from the Select Committee.   Sess. 1826–27, (264.) vol. 4, p. 953.

    RESOLUTION.—That an organized system of voting prevailed throughout the election.—The House requested to institute further inquiry.

    Grampound :

137.—Minutes of Evidence taken in a Committee of the whole House, on Indictments against Sir Manasseh Masseh Lopes, baronet, and others, for Bribery.   Sess. 1819, (388.) vol. 4, p. 351. [14.]

138.—Proposed Resolutions for preventing Bribery and Corruption at the Elections for Grampound.   Sess. 1819-20, (20.) vol. 2, p. 137. [13.]

139.—Extracts of Indictments for Bribery at Grampound Election in 1818.   Sess. 1819, (340.) vol. 4, p. 295. [14.]

    Great Grimsby :

140.—Report from the Select Committee on Petitions complaining of an undue Election and Return.   Sess. 1802-3, (35.) vol. 3, p. 469. [14.]

*Controverted Elections—*continued.

Helleston:

141.—Report from the Select Committee on the Helleston Election Petition; together with the Special Report from the said Committee, and also the Minutes of Evidence taken before them. Sess. 1812–13, (108.) vol. 3, p. 259. [14.]

142.—Report from the Select Committee on inspection of Lords' Journals, with relation to Helleston Election Bill. Sess. 1814–15, (325.) vol. 3, p. 63. [14.]

Hertford:

143.—Report from the Select Committee. Sess. 1833, (152.) vol. 9, p. 1.

144.—Report from the Select Committee on the best mode of preventing Bribery, Treating, and other corrupt Practices, at Elections for that Borough. Sess. 1833, (449.) vol. 9, p. 463.

Ilchester:

145.—Report from the Select Committee on the Petition of Sir William Manners, Bart., complaining of an undue Election and Return. Sess. 1802–3, (41.) vol. 3, p. 509. [14.]

Knaresborough:

146.—Report from the Select Committee on Petition of Electors concerning the Return. Sess. 1805, (43.) vol. 3, p. 131. [14.]

Limerick:

147.—Minutes of Evidence taken before Select Committee on the Petition of T. S. Rice, Esq., complaining of an undue Election and Return. Sess. 1819, (77.) vol. 4, p. 287. [14.]

148.—Report from the Select Committee on the Limerick Election; together with the Special Report from the said Committee, and also the Minutes of the Evidence taken before them. Sess. 1820, (229.) vol. 3, p. 283. [14.]

Liskeard:

149.—Minutes of Evidence on the Liskeard Return. Sess. 1803–4, (102^1.) vol. 2, p. 205. [14.]

150.—Supplement to the Minutes of Evidence on the Liskeard Return. Sess. 1803–4, (102^2.) vol. 2, p. 221. [14.]

Liverpool:

151.—Evidence taken before the Select Committee. Sess. 1830–31, (307.) vol. 3, p. 301.

152.—Report from the Select Committee on Petitions complaining of Bribery and Corruption, appointed 6 March. Sess. 1833, (139.) vol. 10.

153.—Supplement referred to in page 139 of the Report, being an account of the Expenses of Lord Sandon's Committee. Sess. 1833, (139^2.) vol. 10, p. 199.

154.—Report from the Select Committee appointed to pursue the inquiries of the Committee appointed on the 6th of March last. Sess. 1833, (583.) vol. 10, p. 201.

Londonderry:

155.—Report from the Select Committee on the Petition complaining of an undue Election and Return. Sess. 1833, (180.) vol. 10, p. 411.

Middlesex:

156.—Report from the Select Committee on Petitions complaining of an undue Election and Return. Sess. 1803–4, vol. 2, p. 225. [15.]

Newry:

157.—Report from the Select Committee on the Petitions complaining of an undue Election and Return. Sess. 1833, (76.) vol. 10, p. 573.

Northampton:

158.—Report from the Select Committee. Sess. 1826–27, (158.) vol. 4, p. 341.
  SUBJECT.—Conduct of the corporation in paying election expenses out of the corporation funds.

Nottingham:

159.—Report from the Select Committee on Petitions complaining of an undue Election and Return. Sess. 1802–3, (33.) vol. 3, p. 1. [15.]

Controverted Elections—continued.

Pembroke:

160.—Report from the Select Committee.   Sess. 1831, (262.) vol. **4**, p. 535.

Penryn:

161.—Report from the Select Committee on Petitions complaining of an undue Election and Return.   Sess. 1806–7, (56.) vol. **4**, p. 1. [15.]

162.—Roport from the Select Committee on the Penryn Election; together with the Special Report from the said Committee, and also the Minutes of Evidence taken before them.   Sess. 1819, (72.) vol. **4**, p. 1. [15.]

163.—Report of the Minutes of Evidence taken in a Committee of the whole House, on the Bill for preventing Bribery and Corruption.
     Sess. 1819, (303.) vol. **4**, p. 167. [15.]

164.—Record of Acquittal of Sir Christopher Hawkins on Charges of Bribery in 1807.   Sess. 1819, (216.) vol. **4**, p. 307. [15.]

165.—Report from the Select Committee.   Sess. 1826–27, (176.) vol. **4**, p. 371.
RESOLUTION.—That great bribery had prevailed at Penryn.

166.—Minutes of Evidence taken before the whole House on the Bill for preventing Bribery and Corruption in Elections of Members for Penryn.
     Sess. 1826–27, (365.) vol. **4**, p. 481.

East Retford:

167.—Report from the Select Committee.   Sess. 1826–27, (288.) vol. **4**, p. 757.
RESOLUTION making void the election.—Corrupt state of the borough.—A bribe of 20 guineas given by each successful Member to their voters.

168.—Minutes of Evidence taken before the House on the Bill for disfranchising the Borough.   Sess. 1828, (80.) vol. **4**, pp. 37. 81. 109.

Stafford:

169.—Report from the Select Committee appointed to inquire into corrupt practices alleged to prevail at the last Election for the Borough of Stafford.
     Sess. 1833, (537.) vol. **11**, p. 1.

Tregony:

170.—Report from the Select Committee on the Tregony Election Petition; together with the Special Report from the said Committee, and also the Minutes of Evidence taken before them.   Sess. 1812–13, (76.) vol. **3**, p. 121.

Warwick:

171.—Report from the Select Committee on the Petitions complaining of an undue Election and Return.   Sess. 1833, (295.) vol. **11**, p. 197.

172.—Report from the Select Committee appointed to make further inquiry into proceedings at the last Election, and to consider the best means of preventing Bribery.   Sess. 1833, (556.) vol. **11**, p. 321.

Westminster:

173.—Minutes of Evidence taken at the Bar of the House, on the Petition of James Paull, Esq., one of the Candidates.   Sess. 1806–7, (101.) vol. **3**, p. 421.

Wexford:

174.—Minutes of Evidence taken before the Select Committee on the Wexford Election Petition.   Sess. 1830, (175.) vol. **4**, p. 315.

Weymouth and Melcombe Regis:

175.—Report from the Select Committee on the Weymouth and Melcombe Regis Election Petition; together with the Special Report from the said Committee, and also the Report from the Committee appointed to inspect the said Special Report.   Sess. 1812–13, (65.) vol. **3**, p. 61. [15.]

Worcester:

176.—Report from the Select Committee on Worcester Election Petitions.
     Sess. 1819, (149.) vol. **4**, p. 285. [15.]

V.

Historical.

Foreign Treaties, and Internal Transactions.

Peace of Utrecht, 1711—1713 :

1.—[Report from the Committee of Secrecy appointed to examine the several Books and Papers relating to the Negociation of the Treaty for Peace and Commerce. First Series, vol. 1, p. 1.

> SUBJECTS.—Political transactions of the latter part of Queen Anne's reign, and the commencement of that of King George the First.—Imputed misconduct of the Ministers concerned in the negociations.—Demolition of Dunkirk.—Assiento contract.—Neglect of the interests of the Catalans.—Transactions relating to the Pretender.

Layer's, &c. Conspiracy, 1713—1722 :

2.—[Report from the Select Committee to examine him and others, in relation to the Conspiracy mentioned in His Majesty's Speech at the opening of Parliament. First Series, vol. 1. p. 99.

> SUBJECTS.—Conspiracy to establish the Pretender on the throne of England.—Political transactions of the party supporting the Pretender ; and, implication of the conduct of several persons of eminence ; viz. General Dillon, the Duke of Norfolk, Lord North, the Earl of Ormond, Lord Orrery, the Bishop of Rochester (Dr. Francis Atterbury.)

Seditious Societies, and the State of Ireland, 1799—1801 :

3.—[Report from the Committee of Secrecy on the proceedings of Seditious Societies, and on the State of Ireland. 1799 : First Series, vol. x. p. 789.

4.—[Two Reports from the Committee of Secrecy on the State of Ireland, and on the proceedings of the disaffected Persons in both parts of the United Kingdom. 1801 : First Series, vol. x. pp. 828. 844.

> SUBJECTS.—Political societies instituted in England and Ireland, with a view to over-turn the government, constitution and laws of England ; and to produce a separation of the two countries.—Rise and progress of the different seditious societies in England.—Nature and system of the society of United Irishmen ; its progress till the period of the Rebellion ; its intercourse with France, and with seditious societies in England.—Account of the meeting called the Scotch Convention.—Treasonable correspondence with France ; expedition of General Hoche for the invasion of Ireland.—Account of seditious societies at Hamburgh.—Seditious and impious writings, addresses, speeches and toasts.—The suspension of the Habeas Corpus Act.

Disturbed Counties, 1812 :

5.—Report of the Committee of Secrecy on Papers relating to certain violent Proceedings in several Counties of England. Sess. 1812, (335.) vol. 2, p. 307. [25.]

> SUBJECTS.—Violences committed in Yorkshire, Cheshire and Lancashire.—Murder of Mr. Horsfall.—Destruction of shearing-frames.—Oath of secrecy.—The persons engaged in these outrages were generally known by the name of *Luddites*.

Seditious Practices, 1817, 1818 :

6.—Two Reports from the Committee of Secrecy on Papers which were presented to the House sealed up. Sess. 1817, (34. 387.) vol. 4, pp. 1. 9. [25.]

> SUBJECTS.—The formation of secret societies.—Spence's plan.—Revolutionary schemes.—Assumption of tri-coloured cockades, and other symbols of the French Revolution.—Meetings at Spa Fields on 15th November and 16th December 1817.

7.—Report of the Secret Committee of the House of Lords, appointed to take into consideration the several Papers sealed up in a Bag, and delivered by Command of His Royal Highness the Prince Regent. Sess. 1817, (399.) vol. 4, p. 17. [25.]

> SUBJECTS.—The same as the preceding Reports from the Commons.

Seditious Practices, 1817, 1818—continued.

8.—Report of the Committee of Secrecy to whom the several Papers which were presented (sealed up) to the House, were referred.

Sess. 1819, (69.) vol. 3, p. 49. [25.]

> SUBJECTS.—Succinct description of the proceedings of the disaffected since the last Report (20 June 1817); the trials at Derby of Brandreth and others; and the beneficial effects of the measures adopted by Parliament, authorizing the detention of suspected persons.

9.—Report of the Secret Committee of the House of Lords, appointed to examine into the matter of the several Papers (sealed up), presented to the House by command of the Prince Regent.   Sess. 1818, (95.) vol. 3, p. 55. [25.]

> SUBJECT.—The same as the preceding Report from the Commons.

State of the Country, 1819:

10.—Papers relative to the internal State of the Country.

Sess. 1819–20, (1.) vol. 4, p. 215. [25.]

> SUBJECTS.—Multitudinous assemblages of persons under the pretext of considering the means of procuring reform in Parliament.—Persons travelling from place to place to harangue them.—Military training.—Procuring arms.—Dispersion of the meeting at Manchester on August the 16th.—Conduct of the magistracy.—Seizure of Henry Hunt.— The persons taking part in those proceedings obtained the name of *Radicals*, from their zeal in propagating the notion that nothing but Radical Reform in Parliament could do any good to the State.

State of Ireland, 1816—1822.

11.—Statement of the Nature and Extent of the Disturbances which have recently prevailed in Ireland, and Measures adopted in consequence thereof.

Sess. 1816, (479.) vol. 9, p. 567. [27.]

> SUBJECTS.—Quarrels between parties of people called *Shanavests* and *Caravats*.—So called from one party wearing old waistcoats, and the other from a Shanavest exulting at the place of execution on the *cravat* being placed about the neck of his enemy condemned to be hanged.—Their violence generally confined to private feuds; but sometimes lay aside their private animosities, and unite to resist the laws.

12.—Papers, presented by His Majesty's Command, relative to the disturbed State of Ireland.   Sess. 1822, (2.) vol. 14, p. 741. [27.]

13.—Papers relating to the State of Ireland; viz. Extracts of Despatches from the Lord Lieutenant, enclosing Communications from Magistrates, &c.

Sess. 1822, (423.) vol. 14, p. 757. [27.]

In 1824:

14.—First Report from the Committee on Districts under the Insurrection Acts.

Sess. 1824, (372.) vol. 8, p. 1. [25.]

> *The Evidence subjoined to this Report is part of that taken before the Committee, and which was printed entire in 1825.——See* No. 16, *infra.*

In 1825:

15.—Minutes of Evidence taken before the Select Committee in the last Session of Parliament, on the Disturbances in Ireland,—13 May to 18 June 1824.

Sess. 1825, (20.) vol. 7, p. 1. [25.]

16.—Minutes of Evidence taken before the Select Committee appointed to examine into the Nature and Extent of the Disturbances which have prevailed in those Districts of Ireland which are now subject to the provisions of the Insurrection Act.   Sess. 1825, (200.) vol. 7, p. 501. [25.]

> N. B—See observation on the First Report on the State of Ireland, in last Session, No. 14, *supra.*

> SUBJECTS.—*Character and Objects of the Disturbances.*—Enmity to distraining landlords, and to persons taking farms of dispossessed tenants.——*Cause of the prevailing Discontents.*—Religious feelings.—Expectation of some great change.——*Condition of the Peasantry.*——*Agricultural System, and Mode of letting Land.*—Eager desire of possessing land.—Minute subdivision of land.—High rents.——*State of Religious and Moral Instruction, and Influence of the Clergy.*——*State of the Magistracy, Police, and Administration of Justice.*—Operation of the Insurrection Act.—Mode in which it is administered.——*Political Feelings and Agitation.*—*Population.*—Causes of increase.—*Catholic Clergy.*—Mode of paying them.—Their general character and conduct.—Class of life from which derived.—Education.——*Measures for employing the People.*—Deficiency of roads in Cork, Limerick and Kerry.—Improvements making under the direction of Government.——*Effects of peculiar Tenets of the Roman-catholic Church, and Influence on Political Feelings.*—Prince Hohenlohe's miracles, and Pastorini's prophecies.——*Expected Effects of the Removal of Civil Disabilities of the Catholics.*—Effects of the penal laws on the minds of the lower orders.—Their feeling of inferiority, from laws excluding them from political privileges.——*Mode of exercising the Functions of the Catholic Priesthood, as showing their Influence over the Public Mind.*

*State of Ireland—*In 1825—continued.

17.—First Report from the Select Committee on the State of Ireland.

Sess. 1825, (129.) vol. 8, p. 1. [26.]

SUBJECTS.— *Emigration.*—Encouraged by Government, and calculated to relieve the distressed population of Ireland.—Great extent of the capability of Canada to receive emigrants.—Description of settlers.—Employment.—Arrangements in favour of those sent out by Government.——see *Emigration,* under Head XVI.——*State of the Public Mind—Effect of the Exclusion Laws— and Expectation from Catholic Emancipation.*—Great influence of the Catholic Association.—Ignorance and mistakes of the lower classes as to the advantages of catholic emancipation.—Great mischief of catholic rent.—Catholics not disposed to disturb the right to forfeited property.—Nearly all the landed property has been forfeited.—Orange associations productive of irritation in the public mind.—Defenders Association and Ribbon-men.—Riots between the Orange parties and Roman-catholics.—Account of the parties in the rebellion of 1798.—Effect of exclusion laws on marriages.—On property depending on marriages.——*Power, Influence and Conduct of the Catholic Priesthood.*—Influence of priests at elections.—Their views and expectations from emancipation do not lead them to wish for any interference in the property of the established church.—The catholic gentry have no wish to supplant the protestant hierarchy.—Power exercised by the Pope in nominations to benefices.——*State Provision for the Clergy.*—Present income of the clergy, and proposed allowance by the State.—Would not lessen their wholesome influence.——*State of Manufactures and Commerce.*—*Elective Franchise.*—Effect of abolishing the forty-shilling freeholders.——*Condition and Morals of the People, and Increase of Population.*—Their condition ;—wretched habitations ; furniture.—Promiscuous living together.—*Mode of letting Land, and managing Estates.*—Extent and evil of sub-letting.——*Education ; and Advancement of Knowledge.*—Education at Maynooth preferable to that in foreign countries.—Political feelings of priests arising from foreign education explained.——*Administration of Justice.*—Impartially administered, though all the judges are protestants.—Venality of petty manor courts in corporate towns and boroughs.—Proposed improvements.—Constitution of grand juries.—Administration of criminal law by magistrates.——*Tithes.*——*Proportion of Catholics and Protestants in Population, Wealth and Influence.*—Admission to parliament and the bench would satisfy them.—Proportion of catholics and protestants at the bar.——*Roman-catholic Religious Orders in Ireland.*—Class of persons educated for priests.—Flourishing state of female convents.

18.—Second Report from the Select Committee on the State of Ireland.

Sess. 1825, (129.) vol. 8, p. 173. [26.]

SUBJECTS.— *Ecclesiastical Polity of the Church of Rome, as connected or interfering with Civil Government.*—Authority of the Pope.——*Peculiar Doctrines or Discipline of the Church of Rome, as counteracting the Duty of the Subject.*—As to the alleged power of absolving from oath of allegiance.—Doctrine of marriage and divorce.—Doctrine of absolution, compared with that of the church of England.—Confession.—Heresy, and not keeping faith with heretics, explained.——*As to removing the Objections to the Foreign Nomination of Bishops.*—Proposed arrangement for domestic nomination.——*On giving Stipendiary Allowances to the Roman-catholic Clergy.*——*Present Mode of Paying the Roman-catholic Clergy, and raising Rates.*—Enforce rates by withholding certain rites, and proclaiming defaulters.——*Peculiar Doctrines.*—Image worship explained.—Indulgences explained.—Invocation of saints.—Parading of ceremonies.—Purgatory.—Images, relics, pictures and cross.—Pastorini's prophecies.——*Impediments to the Progress of Knowledge among the Roman-catholic Population.*—Education of ecclesiastics.—Establishment at Paris.—State of Schools.——*Increase of Population, and Comparison of Protestant and Catholic Population.*—Caused by improvident marriages ;—by minute subdivision of land.——*Present Effects, and promised Benefits of removing Disabilities.*—Would tranquillize the public mind ; and by inducing the English to travel in Ireland, would lead to the introduction of English capital.——*Roman-catholic Opinions of Protestant Ordination.*——*Tithes, Church Property and Peerage.*—Catholic clergy not desirous of interfering with church property ;—nor the prelates of sitting in the Lords.——*Elective Franchise.*—Wretchedness of forty-shilling freeholders.——*Conciliatory Conduct of Protestant Clergy.*—Tithes not enforced against Roman-catholic clergy.——*Roman-catholic Establishments in Ireland.*

19.—Third Report from the Select Committee on the State of Ireland.

Sess. 1825, (129.) vol. 8, p. 293. [26.]

SUBJECTS.—*State of the Magistracy and Administration of Justice.*——*Religious Feelings and Sentiments.*—Jealousy between protestants and catholics, from the sense of inferiority of the catholics, produced by their civil disabilities.—Tithe Composition Act beneficial.—Presbyterian church in Ireland.—Income of their clergy.—Management of the *regium donum.*—Approved of by the people and clergy.—Religious character of the Belfast institutions incline to Arianism.——*Effect of the Removal of Disabilities of Catholics.*——*Peculiar Doctrines and Discipline of the Roman-catholic Church, as interfering with the Duties of the Subject.*——*Roman-catholic Establishments.*——*Maintenance of the Roman-catholic Clergy :—Present Income.*—From what the income of the Roman-catholic clergy is derived.—Average amount.—How enforced.——*Proposed Allowance from the State.*——*Conduct of the Roman-catholic Clergy.*——*Education, Religious Knowledge, and Moral Character of the Irish People.*—Roman-catholic clergy object to the reading of the Bible as a part of the plan.—Demoralizing effect of numerous oaths.——*Tenure of the*

State of Ireland—In 1825—*continued.*

the Occupation of Land.—Management of the Duke of Devonshire's estate.—Evils occasioned by sub-letting.———*Agricultural Practice.*—Course of culture, and management of crops.———*Freeholds of Forty Shillings, and manner of exercising the Elective Franchise.*—Frauds in registering.———*Increase of Population, and State of the Peasantry.*—Occasioned by subdividing land by sub-letting.—Advantage of emigration.—Description of persons emigrating.———*Capability of Ireland of affording profitable Employment of Capital.*—Abounds with advantageous spots for mills and factories.—Capitalists deterred from embarking by its unsettled state.—In any scheme for embarking capital, religious distinctions should be avoided.—Workmen inferior in skill.———*Political Parties, Feelings, Events, and Agitations.*—Origin of the rebellion of 1798.—Ignorance of the lower Irish of the party question of emancipation.—Account of the organization of the disturbances in Limerick.—Disputes about dispositions of small properties in land by will decided by violence.———*Influence of Political and Religious Party Writings on the Minds of the Catholic Population.*—Dr. Doyle's Letter under the signature of J. K. L.—Of catholic newspapers.—Proceedings of catholic associations.—Pastorini's prophecies.

21.—Fourth Report from the Select Committee on the State of Ireland.

Sess. 1825, (129.) vol. 8, p. 457. [26.]

SUBJECTS.—*Cause of Disturbances and Discontented Feelings.*—Feelings transmitted from the rebellion of 1798.—Disturbances in Cork—arising from disputes about tithes.—Collisions on the occasion of burials.———*Influence of the Roman-catholic Priesthood.*———*Authority and Power of the Pope.*—Power of the Pope resulting from his claiming the sole prerogative of interpreting Scripture.—Spiritual and temporal power of the Pope.—Origin of the Pope's supremacy in Ireland.—Deposing power of the Pope extinct.———*Doctrines and Practice of the Roman-catholic Church as affecting their Civil Duties to a Protestant State and Community.*—As to keeping faith with heretics.—Civil and spiritual allegiance of the Roman-catholics.—Doctrine of indulgences.—Oath of allegiance.———*Practices and Institutions of the Roman-catholic Church offensive to Protestant Feelings.*—Privileged altars.—Religious orders.—Purgation societies in Ireland.—Indulgences.—Absolution.—Catholic festivals.—Prayers against enemies of the church—against heresy.—Adoration of the cross, and omission of the second commandment explained.—On the substitution of the word penance in the catholic Bible, where the word repentance is used in the protestant.———*Expectations of Catholics of the Effects of the Removal of Disabilities, and Apprehensions of the Protestants.*—As to restitution of temporalities and forfeited property.—Seats in the Peers.———*Education and Progress of Knowledge.*—Catholics educated at Trinity College, Dublin.—Character of priests educated at Maynooth.—Objections of catholics to circulating the scriptures.—Bible societies.—Influence of political publications.—Arian bias of the Belfast Institutions disputed.—More inquiry among the catholics.—Discussions in Bible societies beneficial.—On the plans of general education.—Effect of party publications.———*Administration of Justice, State of Magistracy, Grand Juries and Presentments.*—Prevalence of perjury.—Multiplied oaths.—Abuse of manor courts.—Inferior rank of attornies.—Inadequate fees.—Utility and practice of the Assistant Barristers' Court.—Abuses in presentments.———*Catholic and Protestant Population.*—Relative property.—Employments.———*Provision by the State for the Support of the Catholic Clergy.*—Comparative income of the Protestant and Roman-catholic clergy.—Arrangement of the *regium donum* to the presbyterians.———*Securities to be required from the Catholics.*———*Condition of the Peasantry.*—Good effects expected to result from catholic emancipation.—Diet—Causes and progress of increase of population.—Effect of absenteeship.———*Abuses in exacting Tolls and Market Dues.*———*Elective Franchise.*—Miserable condition of forty-shilling voters.———*Opinions and Practices peculiar to the Roman-catholic and Protestant Churches explained.*———*Poor Laws.*—On their applicability to Ireland.———*Religious Distinctions affecting Catholics in Government Appointments.*———*Tithes.*—Origin explained.—Beneficial effect of Composition Act.———*Management of Estates.*—Overstocked with tenants.—Mode of letting and management.———*Probable Success of the Establishment of Manufactories by English Capital.*

22.—Minutes of Evidence taken before the Select Committee of the House of Lords, appointed to inquire into the State of Ireland; 18 February to 21 March, and 24 March to 22 June. Sess. 1825, (181. 521.) vol. 9, pp. 1. 249. [27.]

SUBJECTS.—The same as the preceding.

In 1826 :

23.—Report from the Select Committee of the House of Lords, appointed to inquire into the State of Ireland. Sess. 1826, (40.) vol. 5, p. 659. [27.]

SUBJECTS.—*Catholic Disabilities.*—*Education.*—*Sub-letting of Land.*—*Elective Franchise.*—The Committee decline giving any opinion of the Roman-catholics' civil disabilities,—but collect information.—Importance of education.—Evils of sub-letting, and the laws of distraining.—Abuses of grand jury presentments.—Administration of justice.—Evils of the present state of the elective franchise.—Want of provision for the poor.—Encouragement of industry.

State of Ireland—continued.

In 1832 :

24.—Report from the Select Committee on the State of Ireland.

Sess. 1831–32, (677.) vol. 16, p. 1.

> SUBJECTS.—Character of the disturbances recently occurring.—Conduct of agitators.—Party distinctions.—Organization of Blackfeet and Whitefeet.—Violence committed on process-servers.—Effect produced by ejecting tenantry from estates for the purpose of increasing the size of farms.—Effect of the Insurrection Act.—Peace Preservation **Act.** ——Unlawful associations; and associations for protecting property.—Necessity of suppressing assembling by night.—Combinations bound together by illegal oaths.——Resistance to the payment of tithes.—Difficulty of collecting tithes.—Resolute endeavours to effect their complete extinction.—Effect of the Composition Act.—Object of tithe meetings, and conduct of the catholic priests.——State of the peasantry.—Low rate of wages.—Their great distress.—State of the colliery districts.—Ill effect of the system of middlemen.——Effect of absenteeism.—Dissatisfaction of the manner of forming grand juries; and of grand jury presentments.—Manner of letting lands.—Conacre system.—Condition of the poor.—Opinions on a legal provision for them.——Quantity of arms in the possession of the disaffected peasantry.—Necessity of disarming them.——Conduct of the magistracy and police.——Conduct and condition of the Protestant clergy.——Conduct of the Roman-catholic clergy during the disturbances.—Their influence.——State of education, and unsatisfactory feeling towards the existing system.—Insufficiency of funds for establishing schools.——Proposed improvements of navigable rivers—the Shannon, Barrow, Bresna.—Improvement of roads.—Importance of finding employment as the means of suppressing the disposition to disturbance.
>
> A map is inserted, showing the capabilities of improvement.

In 1834 :

25.—Papers respecting the State of Ireland.   Sess. 1834, (459.) vol. 47, p. 415.

26.—Papers relating to the Proclamation of the Baronies of Farnbill, Delvin, Moyachel, and Magheradernon, in the county of Westmeath, as under the Disturbances Act.   Sess. 1834, (292.) vol. 47, p. 361.

27.—Papers respecting the declaring the Baronies of Ballyboy, Ballybrit, Eglish, and Garrycastle, in the King's County, to be in a state of disturbance and insubordination.   Sess. 1834, (241.) vol. 47, p. 381.

> *See* likewise, *Poor in Ireland,* under Head XXI.; *Education,* under Head II.; and *Public Works,* under Head XIX.

VI.

Agriculture and Corn Trade;

Bread : Provisions and Cattle.

Agriculture :

   Waste Lands, 1795—1800 :

1.—[Three Reports from the Select Committee appointed to take into consideration the means of promoting the cultivation and improvement of the waste,
uninclosed and unproductive Lands in the Kingdom.

First Series, vol. IX. pp. 199. 217. 227.

   SUBJECTS.—Expense of passing bills of inclosure through the House, and difficulty of
obtaining consent to them.—The origin, extent and value of common lands; and the
benefits of dividing and inclosing them.—Inadequacy of the cultivation of corn to its consumption by the country.

   Returns of Averages, 1820 :

2.—Report from the Select Committee on Petitions complaining of Agricultural
Distress, &c.   Sess. 1820, (255.) vol. 2, p. 101. [31.]

   SUBJECTS.—Returns of average prices.—Manner in which the returns of average
prices are taken.—Irregularities in making the returns.—Fraudulent returns.—Proposed
regulations.

   Depression of Prices, 1821 :

3.—Report from the Select Committee on the Petitions complaining of the
depressed state of the Agriculture of the United Kingdom.

Sess. 1821, (668.) vol. 9, p. 1. [31.]

   SUBJECTS.—*Causes of Agricultural Distress.*—Depression of prices of agricultural produce.—Sufferings of persons engaged in agriculture.—Expenses of cultivation, and inadequate returns.—Diminution of rents.—Supposed effect of the changes in the currency on
the rents.—Effects on the prices by the abundance of the harvests, extension of tillage, and
importation.—Retrospect of similar difficulties in former times.—Tendency of agriculture,
as well as all objects of industry, to change.—Interference to be cautiously undertaken.—
Similarity of sufferings in other countries.—Fluctuations in the price of corn.—Periodical
seasons of abundance and scarcity.—Foreign trade in corn.—Proposal to substitute a duty
instead of the present import regulations.—The idea of a free trade considered.—Ancient
compulsory laws.—Progressive advancement of agriculture from 1773 to 1814.—Commercial and general improvements.—Supposed effects of taxation.—The present corn laws.—
Warehousing foreign corn.

   Proposed Loans, 1822 :

4.—Report from the Select Committee on the several Petitions complaining of
the depressed state of the Agriculture of the United Kingdom.

Sess. 1822, (165.) vol. 5, p. 1. [31.]

   SUBJECTS.—*Plans of Relief.*—Necessity of temporary relief.—Objectionable suggestions
to lay out 1,000,000 *l.* by Government purchasing corn for store.—Advance by loan on
corn to be laid up in store : this recommended.—Foreign warehoused corn.—Advance to
parishes on rates, proposed; but objectionable.—Restrictive laws on importation to be
continued.—To be modified by lowering the import price, and imposing a duty.

   Warehousing Foreign Corn, 1822 :

5.—Second Report from the same Committee.   Sess. 1822, (346.) vol. 5, p. 9. [31.]

   SUBJECTS.—Warehousing foreign corn.—Possibility of clandestinely withdrawing quantities from the stores, and bringing it into market.

Agriculture—continued.

State and Employment, 1833:

6.—Report from the Select Committee on the present State of Agriculture, and of Persons employed in Agriculture, in the United Kingdom, and to whom several Petitions on the subject were referred.   Sess. 1833, (612.) vol. 5, p. 1.

> SUBJECTS.—Depressed state of arable land.—Outgoings contrasted with change of prices.—Increased depression in agriculture since 1821.—Burthens on land have changed places between rent and poor-rates.—Mr. Burke's opinion on agriculture.—Mr. Jacob's opinion on the growth of wheat.—Produce of wheat unequal to the consumption.—But present growth of bread-corn insurance against famine.—Dependance on importation.—Increase of burthens not compensated for by reduction of money payments.—Legislature cannot meddle with rent and wages.—Burthen of the county-rate, tithes and poor-rates, on the land.—Evils of paying wages out of the poor-rates.—Effect of a labour-rate.—Evils of the law of settlement.—Adam Smith's opinion.—Improved condition of the labourer.—Benefit of the allotment system.—Condition of the agriculturalists in Scotland and Ireland.—Contract for salt provisions ceased with the war.—Effects of emigration on parishes.—Depressed condition of the yeomanry.—State of tradesmen in rural districts.—Reduction of rents.—Improvements in agriculture.—Evils of fixed incumbrances and family settlements on land.—Alteration of the currency.—Reluctance to purchase land.—Uncertainty of the existing corn laws.—Returns of the prices of corn.—Variation of prices formerly.—Average price of wheat.—Extent of the imports of wheat.

Seeds, Wool, and Tobacco:

Wool Trade, 1816:

7.—First Report from the Select Committee on the Importation of Foreign Seeds; on the Laws relative to Woollen Goods and the Wool Trade; and also to the Growth of Tobacco in Great Britain.   Sess. 1816, (272.) vol. 6, p. 145.

> SUBJECT.—Influence of the prices of British wool on agricultural distress, and the expediency of making any alteration in the laws relating to woollen goods and the trade in wool.

Rape Seed imported, 1816:

8.—Second Report from the same Committee.   Sess. 1816, (272.) vol. 6, p. 161.

> SUBJECTS.—Use of rape-oil in making woollen cloth.—Importation, and price.—Home growth, and price.—Comparative advantages and disadvantages.—Use of gallipoly, and its use and price compared with rape-oil.—Use and value of rape cake, and its use as rape-dust in agriculture.—Effect of duties on foreign rape-seed.—Cultivation of the plant, and its estimation as an agricultural crop.—Effect of the low price of rape-oil made from foreign rape-seed, on the price of whale oil.—Expediency of increasing the duty on foreign rape-seed.

Linseed and other Seeds; and Tobacco; 1816:

9.—Third Report from the same Committee.   Sess. 1816, (272.) vol. 6, p. 209.

> SUBJECTS.—Effect of the importation of linseed, clover-seed, and smaller seeds, on agriculture.—Not sufficient to justify any restraint on their importation.—Advantage of allowing the free importation of rape and linseed-cake——Growth of Tobacco in France and Holland.—Capable of being grown in this country.—Nature of soil required.—Quality produced.—Inexpediency of altering laws to permit its growth, in consequence of the difficulty of collecting the duty.

Clover and Trefoil Seeds imported, 1821:

10.—Report from the Select Committee on the Adulteration of Clover and Trefoil Seeds.   Sess. 1821, (595.) vol. 4, p. 305. [31.]

> SUBJECTS.—*Adulteration of Seed.*—Spurious seed *doctored* by certain process, so as to appear good.—Brimstone, or some chemical process, used.—A distinct trade.—Injurious to the vegetating quality of the seed.—Process of artificial colouring described.—Chiefly practised on imported seed.

Tobacco, 1830:

11.—Report from the Select Committee on the Growth and Cultivation of Tobacco within the United Kingdom.   Sess. 1830, (565.) vol. 10, p. 547.

> SUBJECTS.—The expediency of encouraging the home-growth.—Extent of growth in Ireland.—Mode of culture, and cure.—Produce.—Quality and value.—Effect on the revenue; and difficulty of excise superintendence.—Effect on the home-trade, and manufacture in London.—General quality of tobacco of European growth.—Extensively grown in France and Holland.—Mode of culture and curing in America.—In Virginia; and effect on land where grown.

Labourers' Wages, 1824:

12.—Report from the Select Committee on Labourers' Wages.
                                            Sess. 1824, (392.) vol. 6, p. 401. [87.]

> SUBJECTS.—*Inadequacy of Wages.*—*Ill effects of paying for Labour out of Poor-rates.*—*Condition, Habits, and Morals of Agricultural Labourers.*—Low wages compel labourers to apply for parochial relief.—Abuse from supplying agricultural labour to persons claiming parochial relief.—The claim for parochial aid being uniformly acknowledged, the
>   labourer

*Labourers' Wages—*continued.

labourer is sure of subsistence from that source; and then when sent to work as rounds-man, becomes idle.—Origin of the practice of paying labourers out of the poor-rate in 1795.—Rates of wages in several counties.—Abuses in the administration of the *Poor Laws.*—Insufficient mode of accounting for expenditure.—Where labour is found, it should be less acceptable, and at a lower rate than regular labour.—Observations on the utility of the Act 59 Geo. 3, c. 12.—Mode of employing labourers thrown on the parish of Putney.—Utility of select vestries, and paid assistant overseers.—Character of agricultural labourers not improved.—Habits and mode of living.—Marriage. —System of roundsmen described :— its evil effects.—Labour-rate tried in some parishes : its operation described.—Inadequacy of wages.—General information on the condition, habits, and morals of agricultural labourers.

13.—Abstract of Returns respecting Labourers' Wages.

Sess. 1825, (299.) vol. 19, p. 363. [87.]

see Head XII. for *Salt* used in Agriculture.

CORN TRADE, &c.

Jobbers and Factors, 1766 :

14.—⌈Report from the Select Committee respecting the state of the Corn Trade.

Journals, vol. 30, p. 762.

SUBJECT.—The practices of jobbers and factors.—Table of prices, from 1661 to 1765.

Importation and Deficiency of Crops, 1793 :

15.—⌈Two Reports from the Select Committee on the Importation and Exportation of Corn and Grain, and on the Scarcity thereof.

First Series, vol. IX. pp. 27. 37.

SUBJECTS.—Regulations of the importation and exportation.—Scarcity of wheat, barley and oats, from the deficiency of the crops.—Effects of distillation.—Distress in Scotland.

High Price, 1795–1796 :

16.—⌈Five Reports from the Select Committee on the High Price of Corn.

First Series, vol. IX. pp. 43. 47. 51. 61. 63.

SUBJECTS.—Deficiency in the crops.—Measures recommended to counteract the consequences; as,—by importation and bounty ;—by economizing the consumption of bread; and by using a mixed kind.—Experiments on various kinds of grain ; and on making bread. —and see *infra*, Nos. 42, 43.

Trade with Ireland, 1802 :

17.—Report from the Select Committee on the state of the Corn Trade between Great Britain and Ireland.

Sess. 1801–2, vol. 2, p. 121 ; and vol. IX. of First Series, p. 161.

SUBJECTS.—Existing restrictions on, and regulations of, the corn trade, and the necessity of alterations.—Different modes of ascertaining the average prices of grain in England and Ireland.—Bounties.—Duties on the export and import of grain from the two countries regulated and reconciled.

Importation and Exportation, 1803—1805:

18.—Report from the Select Committee on Petitions relating to the Importation and Exportation of Corn.   Sess. 1803–4, (96.) vol. 5, p. 699. [32.]

SUBJECTS.—Regulating the importation and exportation.—Duties on foreign corn.— Expectation of the home supply becoming equal to the demand.

19.—Report from the Select Committee on re-committed Report respecting the Corn Trade.   Sess. 18c3–4, (127.) vol. 5, p. 779. [32.]

SUBJECTS.—Same as the preceding.

20.—Resolutions respecting the Corn Trade.   Sess. 1803–4, (183.) vol. 8, p. 953. [32.]

These are according to the recommendations of the preceding Report.

21.—Report from the Select Committee on Petitions respecting the Act of last Session regulating the Importation and Exportation of Corn.

Sess. 1805, (154.) vol. 3, p. 181. [32.]

Trade of the United Kingdom :

22.—Report from the Select Committee appointed to inquire into the Corn Trade of the United Kingdom.   Sess. 1812–13, (184.) vol. 3, p. 184. [32.]

SUBJECTS.—Value of imports.—Capability of increasing the supply by home cultivation. —Laws regulating importation and exportation.

Corn Trade—continued.

Corn Laws, 1813:

23.—Report and Evidence from the Select Committee on Petitions respecting the Corn Laws.   Sess. 1813–14, (339.) vol. **3**, p. 195. [**32.**]

SUBJECTS.—Improvement in agriculture.—Increased produce.—Price requisite to remunerate the grower.—Importation.

Growth, Commerce and Laws, 1814:

24.—Reports from the Lords' Committees on the state of the Growth, Commerce and Consumption of Grain, and all Laws relating thereto.

SUBJECTS.—Same as the preceding.   Sess. 1814–15, (26.) vol. **5**, p. 1035. [**32.**]

Foreign Trade and Agriculture, 1826—1828:

25.—Mr. Jacob's Instructions, and his Report on the Trade in Corn and on the Agriculture of the North of Europe.   Sess. 1826, (159.) vol. **21**, pp. 311. 315. [**32.**]

SUBJECTS.—*Supply of Corn from Northern Europe.—State of Agriculture.—Condition of Cultivators, &c.*—Proceedings in executing them.—Districts chiefly possessing the commerce in corn.——THE VISTULA.—Jews possess the whole commerce.—Ill treatment of them.—Landed proprietors dependent on the Jews.—Warehousing system on the banks of the Vistula.—Mode of conveyance on that river.—The growth of the grain in consequence of exposure to rain, which forms a matting of roots, and shelters the remainder.—The trade not profitable.—Stocks of wheat in warehouses at the North Sea ports.—Supposed quantity of corn in European countries.——Warehouses on the Vistula.—Scanty quantities in store.—Russian provinces of Podolia and Volhynia.—Summary statement of wheat in store.——THE MARATIME PROVINCES OF PRUSSIA. — Tenure of land. — Peasantry—not known in our sense of the word.—Land worked by people more like slaves—who are sold with the land.—Change in their condition not yet productive of benefit.—Value of land.—Soil.—Stock of cattle.—Increase of corn.—Course of cultivation.—Wheaten loaf never seen.—Small rolls only at the tables of foreigners at hotels, &c.—Rotation of crops.—Diminished cultivation of wheat.—Potatoes—Use in distillery—Treacle extracted from them.—Distressed condition of proprietors. — Labourers. — Privations. — Wages.—Food. Poor—formerly supported by the large proprietors.—Working cattle and agricultural implements—their rude construction.—Little iron used in their ploughs, and none in their harrows.—Value of stock.—Taxes.—Tithes.—Military services.—Quartering soldiers.—Scale of living in the classes of agriculturists.—Food, and utensils for domestic use.—Fuel.—Dwellings.—Honey and chicory substituted for sugar and coffee.—Sufferings of the peasantry from scarcity.—Increase of population.—King of Prussia's reply to an address respecting the expected change in the English corn laws.—Decrease in the cultivation of wheat.—Manufactures.—Attempt at woollen manufacture.—Wages.—Cost of wheat to the grower.—Average prices from 1791 to 1825.——*Poland* under Russian dominion.—Soil.—Extent of estates.—Subdivision of nobles' estates.—Minimum of income enabling their children to assume titles.—Rent paid by labour.—Condition of peasantry.—Attachment to their homes.—Manner of living.—Huts.—Food.—Inebriety.—Ignorance.—Operations of husbandry ill performed.—Course of cultivation.—Live stock.—Poland well adapted to breeding sheep; but neglected, from poverty and ignorance.—Rotation of crops.—Produce.—Not profitable.—Parts most productive.—Corn trade impeded by transit duties.—Rents.—State of society.—Aversion of the gentry to trade:—Poverty and pride.—Artizans and merchants all Jews.—Buildings on estates—for housing cattle.—Wolves numerous; and destroy sheep by undermining the buildings where housed.—Value of the land.—Incumbrances on estates.—Interest of money.—Interchange of commodities without money intervening.—Prices of live stock.—Burthens on land.—Tithes.—Low origin of the clergy.—Duties on foreign commodities.—Taxation.—Military service.—Manufactures.—Mines.—Cost of wheat to the grower, and on importation in London.—Stock of wheat in Russia, Austria and Poland.—Power of supply diminished.—Quantity imported into England, and proportion it bears to our whole consumption.—Probability of any increased production, if the corn laws were repealed.

26.—Mr. Jacob's Second Report.   Sess. 1828, (258.) vol. **8**, p. 107. [**199.**]

SUBJECTS.—Report of William Jacob, esq., Comptroller of Corn Returns, respecting the Agriculture and Trade in Corn in some of the Continental States of Northern Europe.——Route taken by Mr. Jacob.—State of roads, and their effect on the trade in corn.—Cost of land carriage.—Agricultural condition of East Friesland; of Oldenburg; of Bremen; of Mecklenburg; of the Danish dominions; of Hamburg; of Hanover.—Value of land.—Rates of labour.—Mode of living.—Taxes and Rent.—Cost of raising wheat.—Stock of wheat on hand.—Consumption of corn in Great Britain.—Information obtained by individuals extensively engaged in the corn trade.—Estimates of the productiveness of certain periods.—Estimate of stock on hand, produce and importation, and consumption.—Increased consumption from improved state of the lower orders.—On the degree of supply to be drawn from abroad.—Causes of the depressed state of prices.—On speculations in corn.—Probability of an increased production of corn on the Continent.—Increase of inhabitants in Europe.—Storing of corn.—Expense of consignments to London.

Price of Foreign Grain, 1827:

27.—Report from the Lords' Committees on the Price of Shipping Foreign Grain from Foreign Ports.   Sess. 1827, (333.) vol. **6**, p. 633.

SUBJECTS.—Comparative effect of the different modes of taking averages.—The demand for English manufactures abroad would not increase in proportion to the demand for foreign corn.—The Russian tariff acts as a prohibition to the importation of British manufactures

there

there.—Capital employed in the corn trade very considerable.—Portion of public taxes allowed to be paid in corn by the Danish government.—A graduated scale of duty would prevent the importation of corn.—Exchanges are affected by the importation thereof. —Effect of navigation laws on importation.—Port dues in this country extremely burthensome.—Prices of corn (British and Foreign) at different places.—Quality of that imported.—Places from which imported.—Odessa wheat subject to quarantine.—Ship-building less expensive abroad.—Steam-vessels not applicable for the conveyance of corn from Odessa.—Present system of warehousing corn very beneficial.—Very little barley imported that is fit for malting.—The produce of this country quite sufficient for the demand.—Mode of paying for foreign corn.

Sale of Corn, 1834:

28.—Report from the Select Committee on the present Practices of Selling Corn throughout the United Kingdom, with a view to the better Regulation thereof.

Sess. 1834, (517.) vol. 7, p. 1.

SUBJECTS.—Systems under which corn is sold.—Causes to which diversities in different systems are attributable.—Evils arising from the different systems.—Quotations of prices unintelligible from the diversities in the mode of sale.—Want of uniformity a sufficient ground for legislative interference.—The introduction of improved methods entirely frustrated by the resistance of the ignorant and the prejudiced.—Three of the standards now in use are in themselves incomplete for their purpose.—Systems proposed to be established. —Weight and measure indispensable to give the quality.—Different systems considered in regard to the sale of corn.—Objection of corn factors to a system of measure combined with weight cannot be sustained.—More flour produced from corn of greater specific gravity than from inferior corn.—Accuracy the first condition of a standard.—Course of traffic between the different parties engaged in the corn trade traced from the farmer to the consumer.—Advantages to the agricultural interest from an improved system of selling corn.—Condition of corn varies from changes in the atmosphere.—Frauds practised to obtain better prices for an inferior description of corn.—Comparison between the systems of weight and measure.—London system of metage should be adopted in all ports where corn shipped.—Comparison of the operations of measuring and weighing, as to time and expense.—Use of imperial bushel should be everywhere enforced.—Measure more generally used than weight.—Measure universally used throughout the Continent as the standard of quantity.—Effect which the substitution of weight for measure would have upon the machinery for computing averages.—Objection to the proposition for making the standard, measure combined with weight.—Advantages from making the standard a combination of measure with description of the weight per measure.—Objections made to the use of weight and measure combined.—Outline of the leading provisions of a bill for establishing an uniform standard for the sale of corn by measure combined with weight.

BREAD.

Assize of Bread, 1767;

29.—[Report from the Select Committee respecting the Assize of Bread; dated 16 April 1767.

Journals, vol. 31, p. 319.

SUBJECTS.—Number of loaves than can be made out of three quarters of wheat.— Statement of the cost of manufacturing.—Cost of the quartern-loaf according to the prices of wheat.

Assize, 1772:

30.—[Report from the Select Committee respecting the Assize of Bread.

First Series, vol. III. p. 55.

Flour, Bread and Assize, 1774:

31.—[Report from the Select Committee on the Methods of making Flour from Wheat; the Prices thereof; and on the expediency of putting the same under the regulation of the Assize.

First Series, vol. IX. p. 1.

In 1800:

32.—[Two Reports on the Act of 13th of His present Majesty, "For regulating the Assize and making of Bread;" and on the Deficiency of the last Crop of Grain.

First Series, vol. IX. pp. 65. 81.

SUBJECTS.—The best modes of ascertaining the assize of bread.—The methods of making flour.—Information respecting the baking trade.—Importation of corn, wheat, &c.—Bounties.—Method of making bread, and the most nutritious as well as economical sorts.— Quantity consumed.—Comparative wholesomeness of household and wheaten bread.— Substitutes for bread in time of scarcity.—Prices of wheaten flour.—Influence of the millers' trade.—Deficiency of crops, and high price of corn, in 1783, 1795, 1796, and 1800.

London Bakers, 1804:

33.—Report from the Select Committee on the London Bakers' Petition.

Sess. 1803-4, (76.) vol. 5, p. 329. [32]

SUBJECTS.—Respecting the operation of the regulations under the assize laws.—Cost of labour and materials in the baking trade, and the profits accruing.

Country Bakers, 1813:

34.—Report from the Select Committee on the Petition of certain Country Bakers.

Sess. 1812-13, (82.) vol. 3, p. 401. [32.]

SUBJECTS.—On the laws establishing regulations affecting them.

Bread—continued.

35.—Minutes of Evidence taken before the Select Committee on the Bill for altering Laws relating to the Price and Assize of Bread to be sold out of London, &c.   Sess. 1812–13, (259.) vol. 5, p. 417. [32.]

36.—Report from the Select Committee on Petitions of Country Bakers.
          Sess. 1818, (345.) vol. 9, p. 227. [32.]
          SUBJECTS.—On the laws establishing regulations affecting them.

Making and Assize, 1814—1821 :

37.—Report from the Select Committee on Laws relating to the Manufacture, Sale and Assize of Bread.   Sess. 1814–15, (186.) vol. 5, p. 1341. [32.]
          SUBJECTS.—On the assize laws.—Bakers' allowance.—Returns of prices.—The flour trade.—Repeal of the assize laws recommended.

38.—Report from the Select Committee on the existing Regulations relative to the Making and Sale of Bread.   Sess. 1821, (426.) vol. 5, p. 1. [32.]
          SUBJECT.—Inefficacy of restrictions on the manner of selling bread.

Bakers' Allowance, 1824 :

39.—Report from the Select Committee on Allowances granted to Bakers by the Act 53 Geo. 3, c. 116, in those places where an Assize of Bread is set.
          Sess. 1824, (212.) vol. 6, p. 465. [32.]

CROPS, PROVISIONS AND CATTLE.

Price of Provisions, 1764 :

40.—⌈Report from the Select Committee respecting the High Price of Provisions.
          SUBJECTS.—Price of beef and mutton.—Beef at 4 *d.* and 4½ *d.*—Cause of the high price.
          —Forestalling the market by buying on the road.   Journals, vol. 29, p. 1046.

Price and Forestalling, 1766–1768 :

41.—⌈Report from the Select Committee on the High Price of Provisions, and on Forestalling Cattle.   Journals, vol. 30, p. 787 ; and vol. 31, p. 587.
          SUBJECTS.—Practices of jobbers.—Comparative prices of meat.

Deficiency of Crops ; Substitutes for Wheat, 1800–1801 :

42.—⌈Six Reports from the Select Committee appointed to consider the present high Price of Provisions.   First Series, vol. IX. ; and Sess. 1801, (174.) vol. 2.

43.—⌈Seven Reports from the same Committee.   Ibid - - - Ibid.
          SUBJECTS.—Deficiency of the crops.—Methods recommended to obviate the consequent evil :—by reducing the consumption of corn ; by the introduction of other kinds of bread than fine wheaten ; by the use of rice, and the mixing it with flour in making bread : by the cultivation of potatoes.—Experiments in dressing wheat in various ways.—The substitution of other food, as fish, &c.—Nature and extent of corn-jobbing.—Regulations wanted in the corn-market.

Deficiency of Crops in Orkneys and Shetland, 1804 :

44.—Report from the Select Committee on the Petition of the Owners of Lands in Shetland.   Sess. 1803-4, (42.) vol. 5, p. 215. [134.]

45.—Report from the Select Committee on the Petition of Thomas Lord Dundas, and other Land-owners of the Orkneys.   Sess. 1803-4, (117.) vol. 5, p. 775. [134.]
          SUBJECTS.—*Distress of the Inhabitants from Failures of Crops.*—Deficiency of the crops, and necessity of Parliamentary aid to relieve the inhabitants.

Sheep and Cattle Jobbing, 1755 :

46.—⌈Report from the Select Committee on the Petition of several Breeders and Feeders of Sheep in the County of Lincoln.   First Series, vol. XI. p. 379.
          SUBJECTS.—Jobbing of sheep detrimental to improvement in the breeding.—Graziers and feeders unable to buy with advantage, being forestalled by the jobbers.—Distempered sheep more easily sold by the practice of jobbing.

Cattle-Jobbing and Forestalling, 1796 :

47.—⌈Report from the Select Committee on the Petition of the Butchers respecting the Practice of Jobbing and Forestalling Cattle ; dated 29 April 1796.   Journals, vol. 51, p. 636.
          SUBJECTS.—The practice of jobbing described.—Its effects on the price of cattle.—The jobbers stand between the graziers and the market.—The drovers collect the cattle from all parts.—Description of the transactions between the grazier, jobber and salesman.—Cattle bought and resold in the same market.—Intercepted on the road.—Carcase-butchers buy before the cattle reach town, and kill as the market demands supply.

VII.

Malting, Brewing and Distillation.

MALT AND MALTING.

Malt, Barley, and Bigg :

1.—Report from the Select Committee on the re-committed Report respecting the Rate of Duty payable on Malt made from Barley of the growth of England, and from Barley and Bigg of the growth of Scotland.

Sess. 1803-4, (129.) vol. 5, p 787. [33.]

SUBJECTS.—History of the duty.—Kinds of barley used for malting.—Natural history.—Bigg.—Place of growth.—Culture.—Bigg of indispensable use in Scotland.—Its adaptation to northern and mountainous districts. – Unfavourable nature of the Orkneys and Shetland to agriculture.—Apportionment of the duty.

Malting :

2. - Papers relating to Experiments made by order of the Commissioners of Excise for Scotland, to ascertain the relative Qualities of Malt made from Barley and Scotch Bigg, &c.   Sess. 1806, (202.) vol. 2, p. 425. [33.]

SUBJECTS.—A series of experiments are here detailed, conducted in pursuance of d rections of the Lords of the Treasury, and under the superintendence of men of scientific knowledge and practical ability at Edinburgh.——The plan of experiments emanated from the suggestions of a Report of the House of Commons, dated 15 June 1804, on petitions to reduce the duty on malt made from bigg, in compensation for its inferiority to that made from barley.——Extensive scale of experiments —Brewhouses and distilleries provided for that purpose.——I. Account of grain.—Bigg hardier than barley.—Ripens ten days earlier, though sown ten days later.——II. Malt : – 1. Steeping.—2. The couch.—3. The floor.—Vegetation ; plumula, future stem, or acrospire,—shooting of the radicals or roots.—Changes of the kernel,—becomes of a starchy substance. – The malt destroyed by the acrospire piercing through the grain.—4. The kiln.—Degrees of heat. – Pale and brown malt.—Diminution of weight.——III. The Brewing:—1. Mashing.—2. Cooling.—Temperature.—3. Fermenting.—Yeast.—Temperature of wort when let into the back for fermenting.—Increased by fermenting.—Continues to ferment five or six days, and completely subsides on the ninth or tenth.——IV. Distillation :—1. Grinding.—2. Brewing.—3. Temperature of fermentation, 50°.—4. Distillery.—Soap used to prevent violent ebullition.——Result :—Malt made from bigg is from 8 to 14 per cent. less productive than malt made from barley.—The experiments were made by Drs. Hope, Thompson and Coventry ; they are referred to by all recent writers on the practice of brewing and malting, and are considered as established authority.

3.—Report from the Select Committee on the several Petitions relative to the making of Malt.   Sess. 1806, (224.) vol. 2, p. 335. [33.]

SUBJECTS.—On the process of making malt, and on the mode of levying the duty.—Kinds of barley.—Different methods of malting.—Facility of defrauding the revenue in particular methods of conducting the process.—Scientific rationale of the process.—Quality of malt sprinkled or steeped.—Kinds of malt made, and to what uses applied. – Process ; steeped 48 to 50 hours ; lies 26 on the couch ; spread on the floor and turned ; about the sixth day sprinkled, to revive the languid vegetation, which becomes complete about the twelfth, by the acrospire shooting to the whole length of the grain : then dried in the kiln.

4.—Papers respecting the Sprinkling of Malt on the Floor.

Sess. 1806, (235.) vol. 2, p. 547. [33.]

SUBJECTS.—Reports from experienced revenue officers on the practice of maltsters ; with the opinions of the Commissioners of Excise.

Duty on Malt :

5.—Report from the Select Committee on Petitions complaining of the additional Duty on Malt in Scotland.   Sess. 1821, (598.) vol. 8, p. 211. [33.]

SUBJECTS.—*Comparative Capability of Scotch and English to bear an increase of Duty* — Variations in the quality of grain from soil and climate.—Comparative value of barley grown in the northern and southern parts of the island.—Illicit distillation.—Barley dried in kilns rendered capable of keeping a long time uninjured.—Bigg, a variety of barley.—Utility in northern climates.—Ripens three weeks earlier than barley.—Recommended to be allowed to be malted at a reduced duty.—Idea of bonding malt before paying duty.

Malt and Malting—continued.

Malt Drawback:

6.—Report from the Select Committee on the effect of allowing a Malt Drawback on Spirits.   Sess. 1831, (295.) vol. 7, p. 341.

SUBJECTS.—Operation of drawbacks on the revenue by giving opportunities of frauds.—Disadvantageous to honourable distillers.—Effects unequal from the different qualities of grain and mode of malting.—Effect of drawback on capital.—Advantageous to the small distiller.—Effect of drawback on illicit distillation.—Distillation and distillery regulations.—Illegal distillation.—Distillers of England, Scotland and Ireland, compared as to their practising fraud ; the advantages from material, mode of manufacture, and expenses.——Malt and malting.—Inefficiency of excise regulations to prevent illicit practices.—Mode of manufacture, and methods practised in various stages to obtain undue advantages: by substituting raw-grain for malt; by the working for the drawback : by the arrangement in charging the duty; in the process of grinding; by smuggling.—Different quality of grain as suited to malting—Bere and bigg compared with barley.—Practice of imperfect malting grain used for distillation.—Excise regulations ineffectual for preventing fraud.—Quality of spirits produced by distillation from malt and grain ; from raw-corn; from imperfect malted grain; from barley, bere and bigg, and oats.—Consumption, duty, and price of spirits.—Produce of spirit from given materials.—Manufacture of Irish and Scotch whiskey.—Highland and Lowland whiskey.—State of the revenue arising from the distillery laws.—Qualification and character of revenue officers.

BEER AND BREWING.

Dublin Brewers:

7.—Report from the Select Committee on the Petition of the Brewers of Dublin and Waterford.   Sess. 1810–11, (222.) vol. 5, p. 17.

SUBJECTS.—Resolutions of the Committee.—Use of spirituous liquors in Ireland very much increased, and cause thereof.—Illicit distillation very prevalent in Ireland.—Drunkenness more prevalent in the county of Wicklow than when spirits were dearer.—Price of whiskey now and formerly.—People employed on the River Liffey more depraved than people employed in another way.—Great fluctuation in the price of whiskey within the last five years.—Wages in Dublin regulated by the demand for labour.—Drunkenness much more prevalent when there is plenty of work, and spirits are cheap, than when there is a scarcity of work, and spirits dear.—Considerable increase in the number of patients admitted to the Fever Hospital in Dublin.—Apprehension among the poorer classes that they would not be well treated in the Hospital made them less desirous of being admitted.—Use of spirits in Louth not carried to any great extent.—Increase of intoxication caused by the cheapness of the liquor.—Great difficulty would be experienced in carrying on illicit distillation in Louth.—Intoxication causes idleness, and produces combinations among workmen.—Annual sales of malt liquor from nine of the principal breweries in Dublin, for 1810 and 1811, and affidavits in support thereof.—Certificate of the lord mayor and magistrates of the city of Dublin, relative to the increase of profligacy amongst the lower orders of that city and its neighbourhood, and cause thereof.—No increase in the price of beer in Dublin.—Extract from the Medical Report of the House of Recovery and Fever Hospital in Dublin, respecting the great increase of fevers, and causes to which it was to be attributed.—State of the House of Recovery in Waterford for years ending 1st January 1808 to 1811.—Number of patients relieved at the Waterford General Dispensary, from 1808 to 1811.—Amount of malt duty paid in the district of Waterford, from 1808 to 1811.—Account of the quantity of home-made spirits brought coastways into Waterford in the years 1807 and 1810.—Certificate of the coroners of Dublin, that the number of deaths from excessive drinking have greatly increased within the last twelve months.—Number of persons tried at the quarter sessions for breaches of the peace within the last year much more considerable than for several years preceding.—No persons charged with caravatism tried at the last quarter sessions.—Prices of spirits at different periods, from 1805 to 1810.—Extracts from Report of Committee on the distillation of sugar in 1808.

Beer and Breweries:

8.—Report from the Select Committee on Public Breweries.

                          Sess. 1818, (399.) vol. 3, p. 295. [33.]

SUBJECTS.—Prices at which beer supplied to the consumer during a considerable period has not yielded more than a fair profit to the brewer.—Profits to the brewer have not been extravagant or unfair.—Large capital invested by brewers in the purchase or mortgage of freehold or leasehold estates in public-houses.—No deleterious ingredients in use by any of the great brewers in the metropolis, with one exception.—Drugs of a very nauseous and pernicious quality are vended by persons as a trade.—Practice of mixing strong beer with table beer very prevalent among lesser brewers and publicans.—Licensing system subject to very great abuse in country districts.—Maltsters and spirit merchants in country districts, as well as brewers, frequently purchase free public-houses, and compel their tenants to take their articles.—Practice of purchasing licensed houses condemned by two of the principal metropolitan brewers.—Magistrates should be empowered to refuse the licences of such houses as by any new contract shall have become the property of any brewer.

Beer and Breweries—continued.

9.—Minutes of Evidence taken (in Session 1818) before the Select Committee on Public Breweries.   Sess. 1819, (220.) vol. 5, p. 453. [33.]

> SUBJECTS.—On the cause of the high price of beer.—Quality.—Alleged use of dele-terious ingredients.—Manner of conducting the trade.—Expenses attending prosecutions for irregular practices, and for using and selling drugs.—Statement of drugs used by unlawful brewers.—Effect of licensing.
> *See likewise* on *Licensing*, in the Reports on *Police*, Head XXII.

Sale of Beer:

10.—Report from the Select Committee on the Sale of Beer by Retail.
       Sess. 1830, (253.) vol. 10, p. 1.

> SUBJECTS.—Licences for sale of beer, and regulations for persons licensed.—Objections to the present system of licensing.—Monopoly of brewers.—Intermediate and retail brewers.—Adulteration.—Duty.—Sale of coffee, wine and spirits.—Malt duty.—Value of public-houses.—Injury that will take place by opening the trade.—Mode of regulating the price of beer.—Effect of loans to publicans.—Detection of adulterations in beer.—Effect of the gin trade on public-houses.—Acts of Parliament relative to licences.—Inconveniences sustained by the laws respecting private breweries.—Power of magistrates in granting licences.—Wish of retail dealers for allowing consumption on premises.—Manner opening the trade might be made to fall easy on vested interests.—Dissatisfaction of the public at the prices of beer since the war duties on corn ceased.—Premiums on sale of houses.—Abolition of the beer duty.—Free trade in beer in Cornwall.—Capital employed by country brewers.—Value of spirit licences to publicans.—Suspension of licences by magis-trates, particularly in Middlesex and Surrey.—Advantage of the large porter brewers in brewing over a private brewer.—Order and regularity in gin-shops.—Drunkenness not increased.—Effect of increasing the spirit duty, and abolishing that on malt liquor, on the wholesale dealer and the public.—Increase in the gin trade, in what proportion.—Acts of Parliament have confirmed the value of licensed property.—Price of spirits as retailed.—Tap-rooms encourage drunkenness.—If trade opened, beer should not be drank on the premises.—Licences are for protection of the public.—Circulation of silver.—Con-sumption of beer in coffee houses if the trade opened.—Licensing system in Scotland.—Effect of Act 9 Geo. 4, c. 58.—Abstract of male population, and number of publicans, in the western district of Perthshire.—Number of public-houses in England and Wales in certain collections, 1801, 1821 and 1829.

11.—Report from the Select Committee on the state and management of Houses in which Beer is sold by Retail, under Act 1 Will. 4, c. 64.
       Sess. 1833, (416.) vol. 15, p. 1.

> SUBJECTS.—Evils arising from the present management and conduct of beer-houses.—Characters of persons keeping and those frequenting them.—Alterations to be made in the mode of granting licences, and the qualification necessary to obtain it.—Magistrates in petty sessions to have the power of suspending licences in addition to penalties imposed by Acts 11 Geo. 4 and 1 Will. 4.—Period of keeping open beer-houses at night may be beneficially extended in town and contracted in country districts.—Assimilation of all the regulations as to hours and management (to which every description of house licensed to sell beer or spirituous liquors by retail is subjected) very much required.

Victualling Licences:

12.—Report from the Select Committee on allegations relative to the conduct of certain Magistrates, in the Holborn Division of Middlesex, in granting Licences for Victualling-houses.   Sess. 1833, (585. 664.) vol. 15, p. 261.

> SUBJECTS.—The vestry of St. Giles-in-the-Fields have frequently sent recommendations to licensing magistrates respecting the increase or decrease of the number of public-houses there.—Public-houses too numerous in that parish.—Accusations against, and suspension of, Mr. Thomas, the police superintendent.—No corrupt motive actuated magistrates in granting licence to Mr. Williams.—Subordinate officer of the licensing magistrates guilty of irregularities in taking bribes from persons applying for licences.—Present system of licensing prejudicial to the public interests.

DISTILLATION OF SPIRITS.

Distillery in Scotland, 1798, 1799:

13.—[Two Reports from the Select Committee on the Distillery in different parts of Scotland, and on the best mode of levying and collecting the Duties upon the Distillation of Corn Spirits in Scotland.
       First Series, vol. XI. pp. 319. 804.

> SUBJECTS.—Various modes of levying and collecting the excise duties on spirits.—Account of the systems of survey and licence, and of the comparative effects on the revenue, and on the quality of the spirits.—Rapid distillation introduced in consequence of the licence system.—Methods of promoting the most rapid process—its ill effects.—Illicit distillation, and contrivances to elude detection by the manner of constructing the apparatus.—Smuggling.—Structure of stills.—Scientific principles of distillation.—Ingre-dients used for flavouring.—Methods of disguising spirits of inferior quality.—Methods of distillation in foreign countries.—Agriculture, as influenced by the consumption of grain.

Distillation of Spirits—continued.

Distilleries in Ireland, 1812–1816:

14.—Report from the Select Committee on the increase and extent of Illicit Distillation of Spirits in Ireland.   Sess. 1812–13, (269.) vol. 6, p. 1.

SUBJECTS.—Tendency of repealing the laws imposing fines on townlands and parishes where illegal stills were found, and necessity of reviving those laws.—Expediency of allowing legal distillers to use small stills, to put them on equal terms with the illicit distiller.—On imposing an extra duty on the excess of spirits produced above the chargeable contents of the still.—On improving the quality of legal-made spirits.—On warehousing and bonding spirits made in small stills.

15.—First Report from the Select Committee on the causes and extent of Illicit Distillation of Spirits in Ireland.   Sess. 1816, (436.) vol. 9, p. 9.

SUBJECTS.—Inexpediency of altering the principle of law in force in Ireland, imposing fines for illicit distillation on the vicinage where the offence is committed.—But to modify the law to prevent hardships arising in its operation.

16.—Second Report from the same Committee.   Sess. 1816, (490.) vol. 9, p. 13.

SUBJECTS.—Effects of the present laws for the suppression of illicit distillation of spirits in Ireland.—Injurious to agriculture, revenue and morals.—Proposed modifications of the law ; and reduction of duty on spirits.——Increase of illicit distillation.—Effects of the fining system.—Collusion of officers in bringing fines on townlands, by leaving stills in districts.—Cause of the increase.—Amount of profit made by the illicit distiller.—Advantage of legalizing small stills.—Extensive use of spirits in private families.—Contests between the people engaged in illicit distillation, and the military and revenue officers employed in suppressing it.—Effect that might be produced from a reduction of duty.—Description of people who carry on illicit distillation.—Seclusion and secrecy in which they conduct it.—Effect on the morals of the people.—Inquiry whether and to what extent the price of barley is influenced by the prevalence of illicit distillation.—Exertions of the excise officers to suppress the practice and enforce the fines.—Assistance of military necessary.—Great amount of fines on some counties.—Quantities of illicit and legal spirits, and reasons for the difference.—Effect of the reduction of duty, or of any change of system, on the revenue.

Spirits ; Reciprocity of Intercourse; 1809:

17.—Report from the Select Committee appointed to inquire into the Regulations which govern the Drawbacks and Countervailing Duties on the Importation and Exportation of Spirits the manufacture of Great Britain or Ireland, from one Country to the other respectively.   Sess. 1809, (199. 235.) vol. 3, p. 197. [33.]

SUBJECTS.—Comparison of amount of English, Scotch and Irish duties.—Advantages of Irish distillers from miscalculation in proportioning the duties.—Necessity of an uniformity of standard of the strength of spirits, &c.—Plan for regulating the intercourse of spirits.

Experiments in Distillation, 1821:

18.—Copy of the Reports made to the Commissioners of Excise of Ireland, by Officers appointed to superintend the Experiments in the process of Distillation carried on at Carrickfergus.   Sess. 1821, (538. 606.) vol. 19, pp. 369. 389. [33.]

SUBJECTS.—*Ascertaining the Strength of Wash,* &c.—Description of a process of distillation by which the quantities of wash used, and of the spirit drawn off, are recorded by a self-registering system of machinery.

Distillation from Corn, 1745:

19.—[Report from the Select Committee respecting the Distillation from Corn ; dated 27 March 1745.   Journals, vol. 24, p. 833.

SUBJECT.—Effect on agriculture, by allowing the use of unmalted corn ; the best is used, and the wash applied to feeding hogs ; so that the farmers can neither get purchasers for their damaged corn, nor feed swine with it, to so much advantage as the distillers can use their wash for the same purpose.

Distillation from Sugar and Molasses :—In 1807, 1808:

20.—Report from the Select Committee appointed to consider the expediency of permitting the Distillation from Sugar, and on the Distress of the Sugar Colonies.   Sess. 1806–7, (83.) vol. 2, p. 71. [33.]

SUBJECTS.—Depressed state of the West India market.—Expediency of permitting distillation.—Relative product of sugar and malt in saccharine matter.

21.—Four Reports from the Select Committee on the expediency of confining the Distilleries to the use of Sugar and Molasses only ; and on the relief to the Growers of Sugar in the West India Colonies.   Sess. 1808, (178. 278. 300. 318.) vol. 4, pp. 1. 319. 343. 389. [33.]

SUBJECTS.—1st Report.—Continued distress of the sugar colonies.—Revenue derived from the distilleries.—Comparative product of corn and sugar wash.—Supposed ill effect on agriculture if sugar be used, by diminishing the consumption of barley.—Comparative yieldings

Distillation of Spirits—continued.

yieldings of sugar and molasses.—Mode of supplying yeast from London :—a distinct trade between the brewer and distiller, called Yeast-men.—Duty.—System of agriculture as to the cultivation of barley and oats.—[*Appx.* B. *in this First Report is the preceding Report of* 1806-7 ; *and Appx.* C. *is the Report on the commercial state of the West Indies,* 24*th July* 1807.——— 2d Report.—Discusses the subject of substituting the use of rum for foreign brandy and spirits.———3d Report.— Relates to the intercourse subsisting between the West India Colonies and the United States ; the nature of that trade, and the manner of payment.— The adoption of measures are recommended, calculated to put the Colonies on a more advantageous footing.———4th Report.—On permitting refining of sugar in the Colonies. —On applying sugar for fattening cattle.—Necessity of some general regulation of duty.— A series of experiments by Mr. Parkes, chemist, to ascertain what would be best to mix with sugar used for feeding cattle, and to prevent its use for any other purpose.

In 1831 :

22.—Report from the Select Committee on the expediency of admitting the use of Molasses in Breweries and Distilleries.　　　Sess. 1831, (109. 297.) vol. **7**, p. 1.

SUBJECTS.—Distressed state of the West India Colonies.—Extent to which molasses and sugar might be used in breweries and distilleries.—Effect of the use on the consumption and price of West India produce.—Would supersede foreign barley.—Quantity of molasses and sugar imported ; quality and price ; and extent to which it could be imported. —Under what circumstances and in what proportions molasses and sugar might be used.— Advantages and disadvantages.———Effect of the use of molasses on the agricultural interests.—On the consumption and price of barley and corn.— Diminution of food for cattle, as the spent wash of molasses would not be a substitute for grains.———Inquiry whether the use of molasses will facilitate the use of drugs for adulterating beer.— Articles generally used for that purpose.———Description of ale and beer brewed from molasses.— Quality and fitness for keeping.— Proportions that may be used with advantage. —Experiments thereon.———Practice of distillation —Quantity of spirits produced from corn and malt in certain proportions.—Advantage of using molasses mixed with grain.— Qualities of spirit produced from malt, sugar, and molasses.———Theory and practice of malting, fermentation, distillation and brewing.—Products.—Saccharine matter contained in sugar, molasses, and malt.—Scientific principles explained, and experiments stated, to show the comparative value of malt and molasses used in brewing.— Equivalent quantities and value stated.———Increase of frauds on the revenue from the use of molasses in breweries and distilleries, by affording opportunities to illicit distillation.—Frauds by using raw-grain and mixed with molasses.—Excise regulations and checks on brewers and distillers.— Several apparatus for that purpose.—Colouring matter used in making beer.—Fraudulent construction of stills.

VIII.

Trade and Manufactures;
Fisheries.

Masters and Servants :

1.—Report from the Select Committee on the state of the Laws between Masters and Servants.   Sess. 1801, (62.) vol. **3**, p. 135.

> Subjects.—Defective state of the existing laws.—Should not be confined to husbandry servants.—Should be extended to menial and domestic servants.—Magistrates should have power to settle disputes between masters and artificers, and labourers.

Artizans, Machinery, and Combination Laws :

2.—Six Reports from the Select Committee on Artizans and Machinery.
Sess. 1824, (51.) vol. **5**. [20.]

> Subjects.—*Laws relating to Machinery—Emigration of Artizans—and Combinations.*—On the inexpediency of the laws prohibiting the exportation of machinery, and prohibiting artizans from leaving the kingdom, and for preventing combinations.—Improvement in knowledge and morals of workmen.—Information as to the manner of conducting several trades.—Prohibition laws against exporting machinery evaded.—Establishments formed in France, and large orders said to be executed there, which were declined in England.—On the supposed effect of removing the restrictions on exportation of machinery.—Machine-makers in England now unable to execute the orders in hand.—Facilities of transmitting information of mechanical improvements to foreign countries.—On the relative fitness of English and Swedish iron in making steel.—Bobbin-net lace machines introduced into France.—Proportion of materials, labour and profit in the price of machinery.—Injurious effects on manufactories by the exportation of machinery.—Contra evidence that it is better policy to allow the exportation.———Laws against the emigration of artizans evaded by high premiums and promises of large wages.—French manufactures carried on by them.—Inaptitude of French workmen to learn from the English artizans.—Comparison of the habits of industry in English and French workmen.—Treatment and manner of living of workmen in France not congenial to English habits.—Police regulations.—Few likely to remain long there.———Comparative state of manufactures in England and foreign countries; and of mechanical arts.—Superiority of machinery.———Instance of importance in trade from seemingly trifling articles.—Extensive trade in glass toys and dolls' eyes.—Beads.—Process of making a particular kind secret.—Subdivision of labour carried to a greater extent here than abroad.—Birmingham manufactories.—Dies and presses let out on hire.———Instance of the mischief of combinations, and the necessity of the laws against them in the button trade.———Inefficacy of the combination laws.—Supposed to habituate men to illegal associations.—Produce great distrust between the masters and men.—Men obliged to combine to resist unjust proceedings of the masters.—Effect of repealing them.—Sometimes those laws are made use of for oppressively reducing wages,—and preventing just advances.—Resistance of framework knitters of Leicester, &c. to an excessive reduction of wages in 1817.—Prevalence of combinations at Liverpool.—Ship-building combinations there.—Control the masters.—Sawyers.—Systematic and organized combination of the tailors' trade.—Iron-works in Staffordshire.—Shoemakers,—their prices.—Combinations for imposing restrictions on masters in the employment of men,—in preventing particular masters from carrying on a trade ;—for raising wages;—for resisting reductions ;—for destroying work ; for intimidating other men from working.—Manner of effecting strikes ;—Combinations mutually supported by different trades or society of trades.—Prosecutions and punishment of men in Dublin for combinations.—Rate of wages of several trades.

3.—Report from the Select Committee on the Combination Laws, particularly as to Act 5 Geo. 4, c. 95 ; together with Minutes of Evidence.
Sess. 1825, (437. 417.) vol. **4**, pp. 499. 565. [20.]

> Subjects.—*Evils of Combination.—Present Laws impolitic.—Proposed Improvements.*—General existence of combination in manufacturing parts.—Proceedings of workmen in particular trades considered.—Objects of their combinations.—Coopers.—Formidable combination of seamen in the North.—Weavers in Yorkshire.—Constitution of presidents and officers.—Power exercised over the masters.—Reprehensible connivance of some masters, in promoting the views of the society, in order to distress rivals in the trade.—Shipwrights.—Unsubstantial grounds of their hostility to the masters.—Violence committed by the shipwrights in Ireland.—Manner of supporting the associations.—Trades mutually assist each other.—Inadequacy of the 5 Geo. 4 to prevent these evils.—Proposed amendments of the law.—Masters and workmen to be at liberty to concert about wages, &c. ; but the use of intimidation to be prevented.—Observations on the evils of combinations.

*Artizans, Machinery, and Combination Laws—*continued.

4.—Report from the Select Committee on the Laws relating to the Export of Tools and Machinery. Sess. 1825, (504.) vol. 5, p. 115. [20.]

SUBJECTS.—*Policy of exporting Machinery.*—Inefficacy of the prohibitory laws.—Difficulty of detecting prohibited machinery by the Custom-house officers.—Discrepancies in the laws describing prohibited tools and machinery.—On the policy which dictated the prohibitory laws. – History of those laws.—Framework-knitters.—As to the woollen and silk trade.—As to linen and cotton.—As to iron and steel manufactures.—As to the button and buckle trade.—Complete loss of the buckle trade.—Diminution of the button trade.—Impolicy of frequent changes in the laws of import and export, and advantage of a settled principle.—Difficulty of understanding why the export of machinery for coining is prohibited.—Diversity of opinions on the policy of the prohibitory laws.—Arguments to remove the objections.—Effect of low wages of the Continent considered.—Superiority of English manufactures owing to machinery.—The possession of English machinery by foreigners would not advance their superiority, from their want of skill.—Permanency of our superiority, from capital, skill and enterprize.—Foreign countries, if restrained from having machinery from England, will be driven to make it themselves, from the drawings published here.

Butter Trade, Ireland:

5 —Report from the Select Committee on the Butter Trade of Ireland.
Sess. 1826, (406.) vol. 5, p. 135. [31.]

SUBJECTS.—*Manner of conducting the Trade.*—*Operation of Parliamentary Regulations.*—Expediency or inexpediency of Parliamentary regulations.—Nature and peculiarity of the trade.—Existence of illegal practices and unauthorized fees.—Practice of branding and tasting, and weighing.—Method of packing.—Manner of conducting the markets.—Making of casks.—Inutility of the practice of official tasting.—Collusive marks put on as to the quality of the butter.—The best butter produced by the largest maker.—Exportation trade impeded by the laws of inspection, tasting and weighing.—Statement of charges on butter at the public crane.—Description and character of persons employed as tasters.—Open to bribery.—Parliamentary regulations not necessary.—Restrictions on the size of casks.—Advantage of small ones.—Impositions on the buyers, by using fictitious brands.—Advantage and disadvantage of public markets.—Amount of fees on weighing, &c.—Larger fees exacted than allowed by law.—Description by a farmer and butter-maker of the practice of the markets.—Practice of the Cork market.—Prices, and quantities exported.—Importance of parliamentary regulations in conducting the trade.—Practice of the English butter trade.—Plan of removing compulsory parliamentary regulations, and establishing optional inspection and weighing.—Opinions in favour of an open market on such plan.—Regulations should be uniform in all the markets.—Description by a London butter merchant of the manner of carrying on the trade.

Calico Printers:

6.—Minutes of Evidence on the state of their Trade, and on Disputes concerning the Rate of Wages. Sess. 1803-4, (150.) vol. 5, p. 887. [34.]

SUBJECTS.—Complaints of the workmen of the system of apprenticeships; and the inadequacy of their wages.

7.—Report from the Select Committee on the Minutes of Evidence respecting the Calico Printers, printed 4th July 1804. Sess. 1806, (319.) vol. 3, p. 1127. [34.]

SUBJECTS.—This is a Report on the Evidence mentioned in the preceding article. It condemns the system of apprenticeships, and considers the earnings of the journeymen inadequate.

Cambrics, 1749:

8.—[Report from the Select Committee respecting the prohibition of the Importation of Cambrics. 1749: Journals, vol. 25, p. 1066.

SUBJECTS.—Clandestine importation of French cambrics.—Nature of the fabric.—Similarity of Silesia lawns.—Other articles manufactured in imitation.—Long lawns.—Success in smuggling.—Similarity of the British manufacture.—French cambrics and German lawns not easily distinguished by the custom-house officers.—Prices of the different articles stated.—Many particulars are mentioned relating to the linen trade.

Coal Trade:

Price and Supply, 1800:

9.—[Two Reports from the Select Committee on the present state of the Coal Trade of this Kingdom. First Series, vol. x. pp. 538. 640.

SUBJECTS.—Causes of the late increase in the price of coals.—Frauds in the measurement of coals.—The coal-exchange not an open market, and the consequences of preventing a competition.—Agreement among the coal-owners in the North, called the " Limitation of Vends," and its effects.—The possibility of supplying London with inland coal.—Insufficiency of meters and lighters in the port of London.

Coal Trade—continued.

Admeasurement, 1806 :

10.—Report from the Select Committee on the Petition respecting the Admeasurement of Coals.   Sess. 1806, (40.) vol. 2, p. 135.

> SUBJECTS.—Act of Anne respecting the admeasurement of coals.—Uncertain practice of measuring and heaping.—Plans to ascertain the extent of heaping.—Difficulty of selling by weight.—Necessity of regulating the measure to prevent frauds by retailers.

Sale by Measure and Weight, 1830 :

11.—Report from the Select Committee of the House of Lords on the state of the Coal Trade.   Sess. 1830, (9.) vol. 8, p. 405.

> SUBJECTS.—On sale by measurement and weight.—Effect of breaking down the coal before sale by measurement.—Advantages of selling by weight, from the coal being brought in a better state to market.—Quality and uses, as brought to the London market. —Different state of coal occasioned by the mode of sale.—Waste by skreening.—Destruction of small coal.——State of the coal trade.—Importance as a nursery of seamen.— Profits of coal-owner.—Expense of sinking coal-pits.—Their depth.—Rate of wages.— Names and description of collieries.—Manner of working.—Valuation of.—Accidents.— Importance of Davy's safety-lamp.—Diagrams showing the manner of working.—Map of coal district.—Price of coals at collieries.—Charges of shipment.—Duties.—At the mines and places of shipment.—On delivery in the Thames and in London.—Impositions in the sale.—Amount of consumption in various places, and by manufactories.—Exportation.— Quality used for steam-engines and furnaces.——Geological map of coal districts.— Diagrams showing the manner of working mines.

Sale by Weight and Measure, 1830 :

12.—Report from the Select Committee on the state of the Coal Trade.
                    Sess. 1830, (663.) vol. 8, p. 1.

> SUBJECTS.—Mode of sale and delivery of coals in the port of delivery in London.—At the port of shipment.—Price of coal at the ports of shipment and delivery.—Land-meters. —Sums paid to coal-meters and wages of whippers.—Difference between the number of chaldrons of coals shipped and delivered.—Inducement to break coals.—Weight recommended instead of measure.—Charges on shipping, payable out of the freight.—Compact between coal-owners in the North, and competition with other parts.—Charges on coals in the port of London.—Land-coal metage Acts.—Establishment of the coal-market.—Principal meters' salaries.—Revenue and expenditure of the coal market, and application of balance. —Why penny duty not reduced.—Warehousing and mixing coal.—Regent's canal is not under meterage.—Frauds against meters.—Bribing meters.—Quantity of coal imported into the port of London in 1829.—Quantity consumed in Surrey.—Increasing weight by wetting coals.—Merchants selling by Pool measure should be done away with.—Metage in Westminster.—Frauds upon Government relative to drawback and duty.—Charge by merchants above the Pool price.—Price and quality of coals at Stockton, and quantity exported.— Business of coal-factors.—Supply of the London market.—Complaints by coal-whippers against undertakers, masters and publicans.—Engine for unloading ships.—Mode of delivering coals by weight in Dublin.—Duties payable to Government, and charges payable to the City.—Payments on account of the approaches to London-bridge.—Right of the City to the metage of 4 *d.* per chaldron.—Suggestion for measuring the exact quantity of tons in weight a ship has on board.—Probable extent of produce of the coal-field in Northumberland and Durham.—Skreening coals at the pit's mouth should be prohibited.—Working collieries in the north, and regulations as to price.—Welsh culm. —Terms of leases, and amount of royalty.—Expense of sinking a colliery.—Origin of the Richmond shilling.—Sir H. Davy's safety-lamp.—Steel-mills.—Capital invested in mines. —Profits thereon.—Keel dues of the river Tyne.—Changing the name of coal.—Experiments upon the weight of coal.—Port dues at Newcastle.—Manner in which the freedom of Newcastle obtained.——And see *Cox's Unloading Engine*, under Head XVIII.

Copper Trade, 1799 :

13.—[Report from the Select Committee on the state of the Copper Trade and Copper Mines of this Kingdom, and on the Petitions from various Persons concerned in the Copper and Brass Manufactories.
                    First Series, vol. x. p. 653.

> SUBJECTS.—Great advance in the price of copper and copper ore, and proposed means of reduction.—Advantages or disadvantages of laying the copper trade completely open.— The exportation of copper by the East India Company considered as to its effects on the copper trade.—The importation of copper from foreign countries considered as to its effects on the copper-mines of this kingdom.

Cotton Trade :

Inadequacy of Wages, 1808 :

14.—Report from the Select Committee on Petitions of several Cotton Manufacturers and Journeymen Cotton Weavers, &c.   Sess. 1808, (177.) vol. 2, p. 95. [34.]

> SUBJECTS.—State of the trade.—Inadequacy of wages.—The chief feature of the subjects urged in the Evidence is the proposition for fixing a *minimum of wages*.

Cotton Trade—continued.

Minimum of Wages, 1809:

15.—Report from the Select Committee on the Petition of the Journeymen Cotton Weavers resident in England, and of the Cotton Manufacturers of Scotland.   Sess. 1809, (111.) vol. 3, p. 331. [34.]

SUBJECTS.—The preceding Report is referred to the Committee, who declare the idea of a *minimum of wages*, and any attempt to effect an uniformity of prices, to be inadmissible and impracticable.

Remedies for inadequate Wages, 1811:

16.—Report from the Select Committee on the Petition of the Cotton Weavers of Manchester, &c.   Sess. 1810–11, (232.) vol. 2, p. 389. [34.]

SUBJECTS.—The distress of the workmen is fully admitted.—Schemes proposed by the petitioners for remedying their grievances : *i. e.* diminishing the number of hands—minimum of wages—tax on steam-engines—advances by Government.—The Report decidedly condemns all such schemes.———See No. 29.

Duties, 1818:

17.—Report from the Select Committee on the Duties payable on Printed Cotton Goods, &c.   Sess 1818, (279.) vol. 3, p. 301. [34.]

SUBJECT.—Repeal of the Excise duties on printed calicoes.
see likewise *Children employed in Manufactories*, No. 59, *infra.*

Flax and Hemp :

Importation of Bad Seed, 1802:

18.—Report from the Select Committee on the Importation of Flax Seed into Ireland, and on the Acts of Parliament relative to the Linen and Hempen Manufactures.   First Series, vol. x. p. 532 ; and Sess. 1801–2, vol. 2, p. 319.

SUBJECTS.—Frauds committed in the quality of flax and hemp-seed sold in Ireland as good and fit for sowing.—Regulations necessary for securing an adequate and sufficient examination of flax-seed.—Inspectors should be appointed by the Linen Board of Ireland for the examination of seed, and for branding casks.

Flax :

Mode of preparing, 1813—1817:

19.—Report from the Select Committee on the Petition of James Lee, respecting his Mode of preparing Hemp and Flax.   Sess. 1812–13, (67.) vol. 3, p. 393. [34.]

SUBJECT.—The principle of this method is to produce the hemp or flax completely dressed, by passing it through a kind of hand-mill, without first subjecting the plant to the tedious and injurious process of steeping and fermenting.

20.—Report from the Select Committee on Machinery for manufacturing Flax.

SUBJECT.—Same as the preceding.   Sess. 1817, (311.) vol. 3, p. 99. [34.]

Framework Knitters :

Management of the Trade, 1753:

21.—[Report from the Select Committee respecting the Trade ; dated 19 April 1753.   Journals, vol. 26, p. 779.

SUBJECTS.—Incorporation of the trade, not of the *masters*, but of the *journeymen.*—Bye-laws and regulations, imposing restraints on the masters, and binding the men into combinations against them.—Limitations as to apprentices ;—as to persons with whom the men may or may not work.—Appointment of deputies.—Endeavours to prevent non-admitted members from carrying on the business.—Enforcement of contributions.—Scheme in 1720 by the incorporated journeymen to raise a joint stock fund of 2,000,000 *l.*—and subscription actually obtained to some amount.

Regulation of Wages, 1778, 1779:

22.—[Reports from the Select Committee respecting the Regulation of the Wages of Framework Knitters.

1778 and 1779: Journals, vol. 36, p. 740, and vol. 37, p. 370.

Inferior Manufactures, 1812—1819:

23.—Two Reports from the Select Committee on the Framework Knitters' Petitions.   Sess. 1812, (247. 349.) vol. 2, pp. 203. 267. [34.]

SUBJECTS.—Grievances of the workmen from deceitfully-manufactured goods.— Lace trade.—Of stockings made in the square piece, and cut into shape, called *cut-up stockings.*— *See likewise* the following Report of 1819.

Framework Knitters—continued.

24.—Report from the Select Committee on the Framework Knitters' Petition.

Sess. 1819, (193.) vol. 5, p. 401. [34.]

> SUBJECTS.—This Report relates to a mode of making stockings called *cut-up.*—These *cut-up stockings* are not wove into shape, but cut out of a square piece. The workmen allege this practice to be injurious to them, as producing rapidly a quantity of an article for the making of which low wages are paid, and of more inferior quality than the price for which they are sold. And as their inferior workmanship cannot be readily observed, the public receive no advantage, but are liable to deception, and the workmen injured.

Gold and Silver Trade:

Assay Offices at Sheffield and Birmingham, 1773:

25.—[Report from the Select Committee respecting establishing an Assay Office at Sheffield and Birmingham.   1773: Journals, vol. 34, p. 190.

> SUBJECTS.—Increase of the silver manufacture in Sheffield and Birmingham.—Inconvenience of sending plate to London for assaying.—Manner of carrying on the trade between London and Sheffield; and nature of the Birmingham trade.—Description of the London trade.——See *Bullion and Coinage,* under Head XI.

Assay Offices throughout the Kingdom, 1773:

26.—[Report from the Select Committee on the manner of conducting Assay Offices throughout the Kingdom, and on Frauds in the manufacture of Plate.

1773: First Series, vol. III. p. 59.

Standard used by Jewellers, 1781:

27.—[Report from the Committee respecting the Standard of Gold and Silver used by Jewellers and Toymen;—dated 9 April 1781.   Journals, vol. 38, p. 394.

> SUBJECTS.—Different standards in use in other countries.—Detriment to trade by the English manufacturers being restricted to the use of standard gold, &c.—Consequent advantage to foreigners.—Less pure gold takes the highest polish, and best adapted to the efforts of workmanship.—Many gold-workers in France.—Comparative advantages of the silver manufacture, from the standard being less fine than in France.——See *Bullion,* under the Head XI.

Gum Senega:

28.—[Report from the Select Committee respecting the Importation of Gum Senega;—dated 18 February 1752.   Journals, vol. 26, p. 441.

> SUBJECTS.—Use of Gum Senega in the printing manufacture of silks, linens and calicoes. —Other gums not found to be a fit substitute.—Whence imported.—Incidental mention of particulars relating to the linen trade, and the arts connected therewith.

Hand-loom Weavers:

29.—Report from the Select Committee on Petitions from the Hand-loom Weavers.   Sess. 1834, (556.) vol. 10, p. 1.

> SUBJECTS.—State of distress and its results.——Causes of distress.—Reduction of wages.—Over production.—Competition at home and abroad.—No combinations among the workmen.—Machinery. — Taxation. — Corn Laws. — Currency.—Embezzlement and smuggling.——Remedies for the distress.—A minimum rate of wages.—Boards of Trade for regulating wages.—Taxation of machinery, and reduction of taxation on the necessaries of life.—Prohibitory duties on importation.—Emigration not a proper remedy.——State of the hand-loom weavers in Scotland; their distress, and proposed remedies.——See No. 16.

Hat Manufacture:

State of the Trade, 1752:

30.—[Report from the Select Committee on Petitions relating to the manufacture of Hats.   First Series, vol. II. p. 371.

> SUBJECTS.—State of the manufacture.—Its perfection in England.—Decline, and causes. —Increasing superiority of the French manufacture, and reasons.—Scarcity of beaver in England.—Other materials used.

Foreign Trade, 1764:

31.—[Report from the Select Committee relating to the Foreign Trade in Hats.

Journals, vol. 29, p. 905.

> SUBJECTS.—State of the trade from 1750 to 1763.—Exports.—Evil effect on the trade from the great export of beaver skins.—Decline of the trade.—Hats cheaper in France, but not equal in quality to the English.—Annual exports to Portugal from 1750 to 1762.— Decline of trade to Spain, and to other parts.

Hat Manufacture—continued.

Disputes of Masters and Journeymen, 1777:

32.—[Report from the Select Committee relating to the internal management of the Hat Trade.   Journals, vol. 36, p. 192.

    Subjects.—Diminished number of journeymen;—owing to restraints on taking apprentices.—Combinations.—Their meetings called *congresses.*—Wages exacted from the masters. —Contributions levied by the men on each other.—Compel masters to discharge men not paying thereto.—Control exercised over the men by their committees.—8 Eliz. limiting the number of apprentices to two to each master.

Hides and Skins :

33.—Minutes of Evidence taken before the Committee on the Bill for repealing Acts 39, 40 & 41 of his late Majesty, relating to the use of Horse Hides in making Boots and Shoes, and for better preventing the damaging of Raw Hides and Skins in the flaying thereof.   Sess. 1824, (323.) vol. 7, p. 183.

    Subjects.—Operation of the Acts.—Power of the inspector to fine for skins injured in flaying.—Manner of enforcing the regulations.—Value of skins and hides.—Manner of flaying, and difficulties to do it without damage.—Inutility of the law.—Remained dormant for many years, till a tanner became mayor of Canterbury, and enforced it.—Improper conduct of inspectors.———Opinions on the benefit of the inspection and fines in preventing damage.

Leather Trade :

34.—Three Reports from the Select Committee on the state of the Laws relating to the Leather Trade.   Sess. 1816, (386.) vol. 6, pp. 1. 93. 133.

    Subjects.—Expediency of encouraging the export trade, by increasing the drawbacks. —Propriety of removing the restrictions on tanners preventing them shaving in the ooze.— Restraint to be put on curriers using shumac, except for colouring.———Injurious effects of the restrictions on the tanner.—Articles used in tanning; and merits of new ones.— Inquiry whether it would be advantageous to allow the tanning and currying trades to be carried on together.—Effect it might have on the revenue.—Manner of carrying on the tanning business.—Effect of the excise regulations on convenience of conducting the business.—Use and merits of larch bark.—Use of shumac in making leather for boot-tops. —Beneficial to imperfectly tanned leather.—Comparative qualities of English, Irish and Foreign leather.—Practice of splitting hides by engine, and their use and comparative value.———Effect of duty and restrictions on the manufacture of tanned leather.—State of the glove-trade.—Loss on leather used, by the process of preparing.—Nature of leather-dressers trade.—Ill effects of the revenue restrictions.—Effect of duties and drawbacks on exportation.———Shoe-trade.—Amount of duty on a given quantity of shoes.———State of the art of tanning.—Improved application of materials checked by the revenue restrictions.—Explanation of the mode and chemical principle of tanning.———See *Hides and Skins,* No. 33, and *Tanners,* No. 45.
    See *Revenue Reports,* under Head XII.; and *Elm Bark,* under Head XVIII.

Linen Trade :

Home Trade, 1744—1751:

35.—[Report from the Select Committee on the Petition of the Dealers in, and Manufacturers of, Linens, &c.; 1744.
    Report from the Select Committee appointed to examine the Petitions respecting the Linen Manufactory; 1751.   First Series, vol. 11. pp. 65. 287.

    Subjects.—Increase of the linen manufacture in England, Scotland and Ireland.—Discouragement of it, by the drawback allowed on exporting foreign linens.—Nature of the trade to the Plantations.—Capability of the British manufactures, equal to the supply of that trade.—Chequed and striped linens, made for the African and Plantation markets.— Progressive increase of the linen trade.—Rise and progress of the cotton trade.—Impediments arising from the difficulty of procuring yarn and cotton-wool.—Successful competition of the French, Dutch and Germans.

Foreign Trade, 1773:

36.—[Report from the Select Committee relative to the state of the Linen Trade in Great Britain and Ireland.   First Series, vol. 111. p. 99.
    Subjects.—Its decline in England.—Improvement in Germany.—Emigration of workmen.—Description of the manufacture.

Linen Trade of Ireland, 1822:

37.—Report from the Select Committee on the Laws which regulate the Linen Trade of Ireland.   Sess. 1822, (560.) vol. 7, p. 449. [34.]
    Subjects.—*Linen Board.—Laws.—Premiums.—Bounties.*—The subjects of the inquiries of the Committee are thus enumerated in the Report :———1st, The constitution of the Board of Trustees.—2d, Their proceedings in the distribution of premiums, &c.—3d, Duty and utility of the provincial and county officers.—4th, Operation of the existing laws for the regulation of the trade.—5th, Bounties paid on the exportation of linen.

Linen Trade—continued.

Linen Trade of Ireland, 1825:

38.—Report from the Select Committee on the Linen Trade of Ireland.

Sess. 1825, (411. 463.) vol. 5, pp. 657. 667. [34.]

SUBJECTS. — *Condition of the Trade ; Claims to Encouragement.* — Importance of the inquiry.—Inapplicability of many of the laws.—Proposed consolidation.—Irish-grown flax not properly prepared for market :—Would be sufficient for home consumption, if properly attended to.—Proposed regulations of inspection.—Mode of management of the manu facture better in Scotland.—Importance of attending to improvements in the spinning of yarn.—Weaving more beneficially carried on in England, from the division of labour.— Utility of an authorized superintendence.—Utility of the annual parliamentary grant for the encouragement of the linen manufacture.——Resolutions.—Origin of the annual par‐ liamentary grant.—Of the linen manufacture in Ireland.—Woollen trade formerly and natu‐ rally the staple manufacture.—Considered to interfere with the English trade in wool.— The linen trade contrived to take the place of the woollen.—Statutes subsequently made with this view.——The Report of 6 June 1825, above mentioned, is reprinted as part of the Report dated 22 June 1825.——And see No. 28.

Manufacturers' Employment, 1830 :

39.—Report from the Select Committee on the means of lessening the evils arising from the fluctuation of Employment in Manufacturing Districts.

Sess. 1830, (590.) vol. 10, p. 221.

SUBJECTS.—Fluctuations in employment.—Sufficiency of earnings, and plan for insti‐ tuting benefit clubs for providing for support during the want of work.—Fluctuations occasioned by change in fashions.—Change of place of manufactures.—Introduction of machinery.—Statement of the amount of earnings in several trades.—Associations in Lon‐ don for supporting men out of work ; their tendency, and want of beneficial success.—— Plan proposed of forming societies, under legal sanction, to be called " Employment Fund Societies."—Observations and reasonings, stating the objections and advantages of the plan.

Paper and Paper-making :

Koops' Method of Re-manufacturing, 1800 :

40.—[Report from the Select Committee on the Petition of Matthias Koops and others, for establishing a Company for Re-manufacturing Paper.

Journals, vol. 55, p. 647.

SUBJECTS.—Proposed establishment of a " Regenerating Paper Company."—Plan for extracting the printing-ink from waste paper.—Great advantage expected from increasing the quantity of raw material, in reducing the price of paper.

Paper and Book Trade, 1802 :

41.—[Report from the Select Committee on the state of the Book Trade.

First Series, vol. xiv. p. 164.

SUBJECTS.—Declining state of the trade.—Attributed to the effect of the duties.—Other causes of decline.—As to the competition with the foreign market.——Appendix, con‐ sisting of estimates, accounts of duties, drawbacks, prices, foreign book trade, &c.

Ribbon Weavers :

42.—Report from the Select Committee on the Petitions of the Ribbon Weavers and Silk Manufacturers.   Sess. 1818, (398.) vol. 9, p. 1.

Minutes of Evidence taken before the Committee.

Sess. 1818, (134. 211.) vol. 9, pp. 7. 53.

SUBJECTS.—Distressed state of the workmen, from inadequate wages, particularly in Coventry.—State of the trade.—No want of work.—Evil of the system of half-pay appren‐ ticeships.—Advantage of the " Spitalfields Acts" to the London workmen.—The extension of them recommended.

Silk Trade, 1765–1773 :

43.—[Reports from the Select Committee on the state of the Silk Trade.

Journals, vol. 30, pp. 208. 724 ; and Journals, vol. 34, p. 239.

SUBJECTS.—Decline of the trade : ascribed to the importation of French silks.—Rates of wages at home and abroad.—Peculiarities in conducting the trade.—Prices of raw silk. —Evils of a prohibition duty on French silks ;—would exclude new designs.—State of the art of designing in England and France.—Execution best in England, but the French excel in taste.—Account of the qualities of silks produced in different countries.—Terms in rearing silk ;—in manufacturing.—Framework knitting trade.—Silk stockings made in England equal to those of France.—Encouragement of the silk manufacture in Prussia.

44.—Report from the Select Committee on the present state of the Silk Trade.

Sess. 1831‑32, (678.) vol. 19, p. 1.

SUBJECTS.—State of the trade in England.—Distressed condition of the manufacturer.— Effect of the admission of French goods.—Increased consumption of silk.—Description of goods manufactured.—Importation of raw and thrown silk.—Number, extent and value of throwing mills.—Comparison of the silk and cotton trades.——Importation and exporta‐ tion.—Effect of importation on the English manufacture.—Quantity and value of imports. —Value of exports.—Nature of goods generally exported.—Effect of drawback.—— Smuggling.—

Silk Trade, 1765—1773—*continued.*

Smuggling.—Its extent and manner of carrying on.—Rates of insurance for smuggling.—Means of prevention.—Custom-house regulations, and mode of transacting business.——State of the ribbon-trade.—Its depression.—Capability of the English manufacturer to produce articles equal to the French.—Difficulties to contend with in dearness of living.—Extent of the consumption of foreign ribbons.——Condition of operatives.—Number of persons employed in throwing-mills.—Description of persons employed, method of hiring and rate of wages.—Their distressed and demoralized condition.—Distressed state of the weavers.—In manufacturing towns: In England;—In France;—their condition compared with that of the English weavers.—Rate of wages in England and foreign countries.——State of the trade in France.—Comparison of advantages with the English trade.—Production of silk.—Restrictions on the exports of unmanufactured silk.—Description of French goods exported.—Comparison of French and English manufacture.—Universal preference to French fashions and deference to French taste.——Designs and designers.—Nature of their employment.—Chiefly Frenchmen.—Description of the various kinds of looms in use.—Number employed.—Introduction and effect of machinery.—Exportation to France.—Comparison of English and French machinery.

Tanners:

45.—Report from the Select Committee on Acts relating to Tanners, Curriers, Shoemakers, and other Artificers occupying the cutting of Leather, &c.

Sess. 1807, (40.) vol. 2, p. 295. [**35.**]

SUBJECTS.—Regulations established by Act of Parliament concerning those trades; the buying and selling of leather and of bark.——see *Hides* and *Leather*, Nos. 33, 34.

Watchmakers:

46.—Report from the Select Committee on the Petitions of the Watchmakers of Coventry, &c.

Sess. 1817, (504.) vol. 6, p. 285. [**35.**]

SUBJECTS.—Although this is a Report of Evidence only, yet it contains full information on the subject of this trade; and is rendered complete by the Report of the following session, which refers to it.

47.—Report from the Select Committee appointed to consider of the Laws relating to Watchmakers.

Sess. 1818, (135.) vol. 9, p. 203. [**35.**]

SUBJECTS.—Refers to the preceding Report.—Comparative state of the trade from 1796 to 1816.—Its distressed state.—Apprenticeships.—Emigrations.—Forgery of makers' names ——This Report contains a digest or index to the Evidence printed in 1817, and a list of Acts relating to clocks and watches.

Woollen Manufacture:

Rates of Wages, 1757:

48.—[Report from the Select Committee respecting the Laws for regulating the Wages of Cloth-Workers; dated 24 February 1757.

Journals, vol. 27, p. 728.

SUBJECTS.—Laws regulating the wages of the workmen;—with particular reference to the woollen trade.—Violence of workmen to compel justices to make rates.—Obstacles in making the rates according to law.—Technical mode of rating the work, and describing it.—Amount of wages that can be earned;—generally 1 s. per day.

Width and Stamping, 1765, 1766:

49.—[Reports respecting the Standard Breadth of Cloths, and Laws for Stamping them; dated 19 March 1765, and 4 March 1766.

Journals, vol. 30, pp. 262, 263.

SUBJECTS.—Difficulty of weaving to a certain width.—Standard width 1 yard 13½ inches.—Stretched cloth may be discovered by wetting.—The width of cloth stamped on the piece.—Practice of the trade as to stamping the width.—Abuses and impediments arising from it.—Mode of dealing between the draper and clothier.

Wool, Live Sheep, Worsted and Yarn, 1786–1788:

50.—[Reports from the Select Committee on the Illicit Exportation of Wool, Live Sheep, Worsted and Yarn; and on the Laws relative to the Exportation of Live Sheep and Lamb's Wool, Wool Fells, &c. First Series, vol. XI. pp. 300. 303.

SUBJECTS.—Method and extent of illicitly exporting wool and sheep to France.—Bad consequences of this practice to the British manufacturers.—Necessity of the British wool to the French.

Wool Combers:

Effects of Machinery, 1794:

51.—[Report on their Petition, complaining of the use of the "Gig-mill;" dated 13 March 1794.

Journals, vol. 49, p. 322.

SUBJECTS.—Effects of the introduction of machinery by lessening the number of hands employed.—Limitation of the number of apprentices.—The machine will do the work of 30 men in a given time.—Its work done as well as by hand.—Object of the clubs.—Support the men when out of work.—Fund raised by contribution on the men.

Woollen Trade :

Apprenticeships, 1803:

52.—Report from the Select Committee on Woollen Clothiers' Petition.

Sess. 1802–3, (30.) vol. 5, p. 243. [: 5.]

SUBJECT.—The practice and effect of taking apprentices.

53.—Report from the Select Committee on Petitions from the Yorkshire Woollen Manufacturers.   Sess. 1802–3, (71.) vol. 5, p. 305. [**35.**]

SUBJECT.—The state and mode of conducting the trade by the domestic practice and factory system.

Laws relating to the Trade, 1803:

54.—Minutes of Evidence taken before the Select Committee on the Bill respecting the Laws relating to the Woollen Trade.

Sess. 1802–3, (95.) vol. 7, p. 495. [**35.**]

Apprenticeships, 1804 :

55.—Report from the Select Committee on the Petition of the Manufacturers of Woollen Cloth in the County of York.   Sess. 1803–4, (66.) vol. 5, p. 325. [**35.**]

SUBJECTS.—The above relate to apprenticeships— they are chiefly evidence.—The gist of the subject is, the masters' endeavours to get rid of the statute of Elizabeth, the penalties of which the men were endeavouring to enforce against them for employing unapprenticed workmen.

Machinery and Apprenticeships, 1806:

56.—Report from the Select Committee on the state of the Woollen Manufacture of England.   Sess. 1806, (268. 268 ª.) vol. 3, pp. 567. 595. [**36.**]

SUBJECTS.—Prosperous increase.—Value of exports nine millions of pounds.—Opposition of the workmen to the use of the gig-mill.—Penalties of old statutes enforced.—Endeavours to prevent the use of other machinery.—Advantage to the quality of cloth from its use.— Hands employed not diminished, but increased by an increased demand.—Advantages of an unrestrained exercise of talent and capital.—Importance of machinery.— Master-clothier system of the west ; the Factory system ; the Domestic system ; markets and halls at Leeds, &c. of the latter.—*Apprenticeships.*—Associations of workmen.——This Report gives a connected history of the trade, and of the peculiarity of its various departments and subdivisions ; and discusses principles applicable to the mode of conducting manufactories generally.

Stamping, 1821 :

57.—Report from the Select Committee on the Laws relating to the Stamping of Woollen Cloths.   Sess. 1821, (437.) vol. 6, p. 435. [**36.**]

SUBJECTS.—*Stamping Laws—Practice of Stretching—Manner of conducting the Trade, —Description of Articles manufactured.*—Laws relating to the woollen manufacture, particularly as to the abuses of stretching the cloths, and stamping laws.—Doubtful benefit of those laws.—Other provisions recommended.—The Report is contained in five pages.—— *Evidence to show the inutility of Stamping.*—Manner of carrying on the trade.—Domestic manufacturers.—Allowance of stretching.—Description of articles manufactured—Coatings, duffils.—Course of business at Leeds' hall.—Supposed abuse by overstretching.—Stamping useful, for ascertaining the claims for drawback on soap used.—Process of manufacture before stamping.—Routine of stamping.—Stamping no criterion of the accuracy of the admeasurement.—Colours affect the length.—Proposed appointment of a sworn measurer.— Power of dipping or troughing.—Pirching.——*Evidence in Support of the Stamping Laws.* —Use of the seal.—Evidence of a *domestic* clothier in favour of the stamping law.—Convenience of a public measurer.—Use or misuse of the thumb in measuring.—Use in stamping, in settling disputes.—Accuracy of the stamp measurement.—Protection afforded by the laws to the manufacturer.—Seals generally correct, and useful.—When wet, the proper time for measuring.—Stamp, however, not a guide for payment.—Duty of a supervisor.— Frauds in obtaining drawback for soap used.—Explanation of the laws.

Price of Wool, 1828 :

58.—Report from the Select Committee of the House of Lords on the state of the British Wool Trade.   Sess. 1828, (515.) vol. 8, p. 445.

SUBJECTS.—State of the growers of wool.—Probability of change, and the state of the stock in hand.—Depression in the prices of wool, and its causes.—State of agriculture as dependent on the breed of sheep.—Supposed change in the quality of wool produced.— Various uses and application of wools.—Export and import of woollen cloths.—Effects of duties.—Proportion between home and foreign markets.—Change in the demand for finer articles.—Value of cloths manufactured solely from British wools, and from any mixture with foreign ;—of cloths made wholly from foreign wools.—Manufacture of articles mixed with cotton and wool.—Importation and use of woollen rags.—Supply of wool from Australia.

Employment of Children :
In Manufactories :

59.—Report of Minutes of Evidence taken by the Select Committee on the state of Children employed in the Manufactories of the United Kingdom.

Sess. 1816, (397.) vol. 3, p. 235.

SUBJECTS.—Chiefly relates to the state of children employed in the cotton manufactories. —Their extreme youth.—Manner of employment.—State of health.—Morals.——It is entirely a Report of Evidence, and of considerable interest.

Chimney-sweeping :

60.—Report from the Select Committee on the employment of Boys in sweeping Chimnies. Sess. 1817, (400.) vol. 6, p. 171. [87.]

SUBJECTS.—On the sufferings of those so employed;—and the practicability of substituting machines for that purpose.

In Mills and Factories :

61.—Report from the Select Committee on the " Bill to regulate the Labour of Children in Mills and Factories." Sess. 1831–32, (706.) vol. 15.

SUBJECTS.—Employment of children in cotton-factories.—Effect on their health and morals.—Diminishing the vigour of body and incapacitating the mind.—Necessity of regulating their employment and treatment.—Limiting the hours of work, and providing for their education.—Practice of labour in cotton-factories.—Hours of work.—Objection to the number of hours.—Practice of night-work.—Sets of hands alternately working and sleeping. —Its injurious effect.—Inadequate allowance of meal-time.—Liability to accidents from the machinery of the mills not being sufficiently guarded.—Age at which children are put to work.—General treatment.—Chastisements and cruelties.—Effect of factory-labour at an early age, on the health in advanced life.—Deficient state of education of factory children. —Attempt to be provided for by Sunday-schools and night-schools.—Children unfit to attend them from fatigue.—Opinions of medical men on the effect of the practice of factory-labour.—Diseases and deformities likely to be produced.—On the incapacity of children to receive instruction after a hard day's labour, or at night.—Bad effects of a polluted atmosphere, and of an artificial temperature.—Evil effects on the female constitution.—Females become unfit for domestic duties.—Inquiry into the effect on the duration of life on a factory population.

62.—First Report of the Commissioners for inquiring into the Employment of Children in Factories. Sess. 1833, (450.) vol. 20.

63.—Second Report of the same Commissioners. Sess. 1833, (519.) vol. 21.

64.—Supplemental Report (Part I.) of the Central Board for collecting information as to the Employment of Children, and as to the curtailing the hours of their labour. Sess. 1834. (167.) vol. 19, p. 253.

65.—Supplemental Report (Part II.) of the same Commissioners.

Sess. 1834, (167.) vol. 20.

66.—Report, &c. of the Factory Inspectors to the Secretary of State.

Sess. 1834, (596.) vol. 43, p. 413.

A Map of Districts is inserted.

FISHERIES.

Pilchard and Herring Fisheries, 1785, 1786 :

67. — [Two Reports from the Select Committee on the state of the Pilchard Fisheries, and the most effectual means of securing and improving the same.

First Series, vol. x. pp. 3. 7.

68. — [Seven Reports from the same Committee on the state of the British Fisheries, and of the most effectual means for their improvement, encouragement and extension. First Series, vol. x. pp. 11 to 198.

SUBJECTS.—The herring fisheries described, and the methods of taking and curing the fish detailed.—Duty on herrings for home consumption inexpedient.—The pilchard fishery very beneficial; an additional bounty on it recommended.—The cod and ling fisheries, where and how carried on.—The turbot fishery might be carried on by the English, instead of the Dutch, for the supply of the London markets.—Fisheries on the coasts of Scotland on the decline : fishermen require the stimulus of a bounty.—Bait contracted for to a prejudicial extent by the Dutch.—How their competition in the fisheries might be guarded against.—The present salt laws intricate and perplexing, and the necessity of their revision.—Particulars relating to the natural history of several fish which are objects of commerce.

Fisheries—continued.

British Herring Fishery, 1798-1800:

69.—[Six Reports from the Select Committee on the state of the British Herring Fishery, the most effectual means of its extension and improvement, and on the means of procuring a plentiful supply of Fish during the high price of Provisions. First Series, vol. x. pp. 201 to 323.

> SUBJECTS.—Manner of conducting the herring fisheries, and the design of Government in encouraging them.—Bounties considered as to their effects on the fisheries.—On the buss or boat fishery.—The best manner of curing herrings; causes of their spoiling by exportation and other means, and in what the superiority of the Dutch method of curing consists.—Mode of supplying and conducting Billingsgate market.—On the manufacture of salt, and the intricacy of the laws concerning it.—The revenue, how probably affected by the proposed abolition of the salt laws.—Particulars of the natural history of several fish which are objects of commerce.

South Devon Fisheries, 1817:

70.—Report from the Select Committee on the condition of the Fisheries on the South Coast of Devon. Sess. 1817, (394.) vol. 3, p. 113.

> SUBJECTS.—Ancient laws for the preservation of the spawn of sea-fish.—Necessity of further measures.—Start-bay, Torbay and Exmouth-bay should be preserved during the spawning season.—Legal protection should be afforded to baskets, nets or lines set to catch fish.—Regulations recommended for the size of the mesh of nets.

Newfoundland Fishery, 1817:

71.—*See* Report from the Select Committee on the Trade and Settlement of Newfoundland. Under Head XV. *Colonies*, Sess. 1817, (436.) vol. 6, p. 465. And under Head. XIX. Sess. 1817, (436.) vol. 6, p. 465.

British Channel Fisheries, 1833:

72.—Report from the Select Committee appointed to inquire into the present state of the British Channel Fisheries, and the Laws affecting the Fishing Trade of England, with a view to their amendment. Sess. 1833, (676.) vol. 14, p. 69.

> SUBJECTS.—British Channel fisheries, and the various interests connected therewith, in a very depressed and declining state.—Capital employed therein does not yield a profitable return.—Extensive interference and aggressions of French fishermen on the coasts of Kent and Sussex.—Large quantity of foreign-caught fish illegally imported and sold in the London markets.—Very great decrease, and comparative scarcity, of fish in the Channel.—Stow-boat fishery causes extensive injury to the spawn and brood of fish, and suggestions for limiting the time of its continuance.—Present system of granting licences very injurious and oppressive to the fishermen, and unnecessary for the protection of the revenue.—Exempting carriages laden with fish from turnpike tolls would greatly assist the fishermen.—Clerk of the London market has not sufficient powers to prevent the sale of improper fish.—Tithes taken on fish caught at sea very much complained of.—Extension of the Acts 31 Geo. 3, c. 51, and 43 Geo. 3, c. 144, for regulating oyster fisheries, recommended.—Devon and Cornwall pilchard Seine fisheries of very great importance.—Fishing interests at Harwich in very great distress.—Great want of capital for carrying it on.—Yarmouth fisheries in rather a prosperous state, but suffer greatly from the heavy duty levied at Naples on herrings exported thither, and also from the competition of French fishermen, and the illegal importation of those fish.—Yarmouth and Lowestoffe fishing-boats compelled to pay towards the support of Greenwich Hospital.—Number of fishing vessels, number of men, and amount of capital employed therein.

Salmon Fishery, 1834:

73.—Report from the Select Committee on the state of the Salmon Fisheries of the United Kingdom, and on the modes of improving them. Sess. 1824, (427.) vol. 7, p. 1. [81.]

> SUBJECTS.—*Decrease of the Fisheries, and proposed modes of Improvement.—Methods of Fishing.—Natural History of the Salmon.*—Endeavours made to procure information.—Extensiveness of the subject.—Present inquiries form a ground for future investigation.—Rental of the Tweed, from Coldstream to its mouth, 10,000 *l.* to 12,000 *l.*—Taking fish by attracting them by a light and spearing them, called burning the river.—Modes of fishing in practice, and which are most beneficial or least destructive.—Various kinds of nets used.—Varieties of salmon.—Process of spawning described.—Seasons of unwholesome fish a month before and after spawning.—Time of spawning.—Salmon return to the river where bred.—Angling more successful as to unwholesome fish, they taking the fly with avidity —Stake-nets destructive.—Diseases which infect the fish.—Destroyed by the grampus, porpoise and seal in the Tay.—Management of fishing property.—Produce and rentals.

74.—Reports from the Select Committee on the Salmon Fisheries of the United Kingdom. Sess. 1825, (173. 393.) vol. 5, pp. 283-315. [81.]

> SUBJECTS.—The subject of the Report of 1824 continued.—Obstructions in rivers.—Various modes of taking fish.—Drawings of weirs, cruives, dams, and other contrivances for catching salmon.—Progress of the spawn of the salmon from the egg.

Fisheries—Salmon Fisheries—*continued.*

75.—Minutes of Evidence on the Bill for the preservation of the Breed of Salmon.   Sess. 1826–27, (417.) vol. 6, p. 261.

SUBJECT.—Continuation of the preceding.

Fisheries in Scotland, 1809–1829 :

76.—Annual Reports of the Commissioners under Acts 48 & 55 Geo. 3, from 1809 to 1829.

SUBJECTS.—Management of the fishery.—Regulations for enforcing a proper mode of curing.—Vessels employed.—Quantities cured.—Effect of bounties.—Provisions for repairing piers, quays and boats.—Plans of piers and harbours:—For 1809; Sess. 1810–11 (18.) IV. 409.——For 1810; Sess. 1814–15 (219.) VI. 2045.——For 1811; Sess. 1814–15 (220.) VI. 2057.——For 1812; Sess. 1814–15 (221.) VI. 2069.——For 1813; Sess. 1814–15 (30.) VI. 2083.——For 1814; Sess. 1816 (185.) VIII. 387.——For 1815; Sess. 1817 (82.) IX. 223.——For 1816; Sess. 1818 (83.) X. 321.——For 1817; Sess. 1819 (57.) XI. 289.—— For 1818; Sess. 1819–20 (73.) II. 403.——For 1819; Sess. 1821 (481.) X. 473.——For 1820; Sess. 1822 (39.) VIII. 415.——For 1821; Sess. 1823 (574.) VII. 155.——For 1822 ; Sess. 1824 (25.) IX. 343.——For 1823; Sess. 1825 (8.) XV. 133.——For 1824; Sess. 1826 (9.) XI. 27.——For 1825; Sess. 1826–27 (11.) VII. 153.——For 1826; Sess. 1828 (16.) IX. 369.——For 1827; Sess. 1829 (29.) V. 49.——For 1828; Sess. 1830 (39.) XV. 155.——For 1829; Sess. 1830–31 (51.) IV. 339.

77.—Report of Commissioners, and Letter from the Irish Board, respecting Bounties on Fisheries.   Sess. 1824, (330.) vol. IX. p. 361.

Naval Stations and Fisheries :

78.—*See* the Fourth Report of the Select Committee on the Survey of the Central Highlands of Scotland.   Under Head XIX.; and Sess. 1803, (118.) vol. 4, p. 129.

Fisheries in Ireland, 1821–1830 :

79.—First Report of the Commissioners of the Irish Fisheries, appointed under Act 59 Geo. 3.   Sess. 1821, (32.) vol. 11, p. 5. [83.]

SUBJECT.—Proceedings in the year 1819.

80.—Second Report of the Commissioners.   Sess. 1821, (646.) vol. 11, p. 13. [83.]

SUBJECT.—Proceedings in the year 1820.

81.—Third Report of the Commissioners.   Sess. 1822, (428.) vol. 14, p. 687. [83.]

SUBJECT.—Proceedings in the year 1821.

82.—Fourth Report of the Commissioners.   Sess. 1823, (383.) vol. 10, p. 367. [83.]

SUBJECTS.—Proceedings in the year 1822.—Improvement in fishing stations.—With several plans.

83.—Fifth Report of the Commissioners.   Sess. 1824, (283.) vol. 12, p. 427. [83.]

SUBJECT.—Proceedings in the year 1823.

84.—Sixth Report of the Commissioners.   Sess. 1825, (385.) vol. 15, p. 177. [83.]

SUBJECTS.—*Proceedings in the year* 1824.—*Encouragement of the Fishery, and Assistance of the Fishermen.*—Measures taken to promote the fisheries.—Construction of small piers, harbours, &c.—Building of boats ;—done by loan to the fishermen, the boats ultimately becoming theirs.—Repairs of boats.—Establishing small fishing companies.—Diminution of the white fishery; but increase of the herring fishery.—Coast survey.—Protective powers of the Commissioners against disturbance of the fishery.—Improvement of the fisheries.—Increased number of persons employed.—Six plans of proposed improvements in harbours and piers.

85.—Seventh Report of the Commissioners, pursuant to Acts 59 Geo. 3, c. 109, and 5 Geo. 4, c. 64.   Sess. 1826, (395.) vol. 11, p. 537. [83.]

SUBJECTS.—*Survey of Coasts.—Improved Fishing-Boats.—Loan-Fund for Repairing Boats.*—Progress of the Commissioners.—Impediments from not being able to procure contributions for repairs.—Progress of coast survey.—Construction of improved fishing-boats.—Utility of the loan-fund for repairing boats.—Suppression of disorders and irregularities by employing a protecting boat.—Returns and accounts of the fishing trade, and state of funds vested in the Commissioners.

86.—Eighth Report of the Commissioners, pursuant to Act 59 Geo. 3, c. 109.
                                          Sess. 1827, (487.) vol. 11, p. 719.

SUBJECTS.—Revision of state of funds.—Formation of a general fishery loan fund.—Object and management.—Progress in the improvement of fishery piers.—Condition of fishing-stations.—Fourteen plans of improvements in piers and harbours.

Fisheries in Ireland—continued.

87.—Ninth Report of the Commissioners of the Irish Fisheries, appointed under
Act 59 Geo. 3.   Sess. 1828, (465.) vol. 12, p. 431.

SUBJECT.—Beneficial effect of the loan fund for assisting fishermen in supplies and
repairs of boats.

88.—Tenth Report of the Commissioners.   Sess. 1829, (329.) vol. 13, p. 499.

SUBJECTS.—Utility of the loan fund.—Erection of piers and quays.—Good effect on the
habits of the people, in the maritime districts, from the encouragement of industry.—Statement of expenditure.—Many plans and sketches of proposed and executed works are
inserted.

89.—Eleventh Report of the Commissioners.   Sess. 1830, (491.) vol. 15, p. 183.

SUBJECTS.—Precautions necessary on the expiry of the fishery laws.—Completion of
fishery piers.—Advantages derived therefrom.—Necessity of encouraging the Irish fisheries.

IX.

Foreign Trade, Commerce, and Shipping.

FOREIGN TRADE.

1.—Report from the Select Committee on improving the Foreign Trade of the Country. Sess. 1820, (300.) vol. 2, p. 365. [37.]

SUBJECTS.—*Restrictions on Foreign Trade—Navigation Laws—Warehousing System—Port and Pilotage Dues—Information on the subject of Trade.*

REPORT.—Inquiry as to the policy of restrictions and protections.—Complexity of mercantile laws.—Proposed alterations. — Warehousing system. —Port and harbour dues.—Regulations of the Customs improved.—Restriction on British-built ships being sold to foreigners.—Advantages of a temperate and gradual change of system.

APPENDIX.—Summary of prohibitions and exemptions.—Comparative advantages and expenses of British and Foreign shipping.—Levant ships share the freight between the navigators.—Their cheapness.—Intricacy of the laws relating to trade, induces the employment of Custom-house agents.—American trade.—Rates of freight.—Loss on ship-building.—Commendation of American ships, as being well found.—Premiums of insurance of English and Foreign ships.—Revision and simplification of the laws of trade.—Navigation laws explained.—Opinion on removal of restrictions.—Comparison of Foreign and English provisions.—Continental ships navigated in shares.—Pilot dues ;—Ballastage. — Bonding system, why more successful in England.—German linens preferred in South America.—South American trade carried on by aliens.—Proposed extension of the warehousing system, to the general admission of foreign goods. — Warehouse and Customs regulations, alterations necessary.———— Linen Trade.—Comparative durability of cotton.—German and Foreign linens.—Imitation of foreign linens.—Continental trade. — Warehousing foreign linens.—Brazil trade.—Foreign warehousing system.—Possible improvements in the warehousing system.— Nuremberg toy trade.—Bounties.—Assorted cargoes for Spanish America.—Transit duties in foreign ports.—Irish linen trade. — Wine trade.— Silk trade.—Comparative value of Foreign and Irish linens.

2.—First Report from the Select Committee appointed to consider of the means of improving and maintaining the Foreign Trade of the Country.

SUBJECT.—*Timber Trade.* Sess. 1821, (186.) vol. 6, p. 1. [37.]

3.—Second Report from the same Committee. Sess. 1821, (535.) vol. 6, p. 187. [37.]

SUBJECTS.— *Trade with the East Indies and China.*—Stating the difficulty of making a Report embracing the whole of the subjects before them, from the great extent of the evidence ; and recommending the granting to British subjects the privilege of trading between India and foreign countries, in the same manner as foreigners now can do, with exception to the tea trade, and to any trading with the United Kingdom.

4.—Third Report from the same Committee. Sess. 1821, (746.) vol. 6, p. 191. [37.]

SUBJECT.—*Trade with the East Indies and China.*

5.—First Report from the Select Committee of the House of Lords, appointed to inquire into the means of extending and securing the Foreign Trade of the Country, &c. Sess. 1820, (269.) vol. 3, p. 381. [38.]

SUBJECTS.—*Timber Trade.*—Comparative durability of European timber and American.—State of the European and American trade.

6.—Report from the Select Committee of the House of Lords, appointed to inquire into the means of extending and securing the Foreign Trade of the Country, &c. Sess. 1821, (476.) vol. 7, p. 1. [38.]

SUBJECTS.—*Trade with the East Indies and China.* — Restrictions. — Increased consumption of European manufactures. - Smaller ships than allowed by restrictions advantageous. — Native governments less adverse to foreign commerce than formerly. — Tea trade with foreign Europe might be made free.—Difficulties apprehended from the conduct of undisciplined crews.—Increase of American trade with China.—Regulations possible to obviate dangers apprehended.———— Manner of conducting the China trade.—Hong merchants.————Description of trade carried on in the Eastern Islands.—Population of the Indian Archipelago. —Japan trade.—Supposed prejudice of Indian nations to European trade diminishing.

Foreign Trade—continued.

diminishing.—Produce of Japan.—Java trade.—English manufactures correctly imitate the Indian, which they supersede.—Fur trade.—Sealskin trade.—State of navigation in Indian seas.—Pirates.—Chief articles of trade.—Accounts of teas imported by the Americans into Holland.—Exports of Americans from Canton.—Russian trade with China.—Superior quality of tea imported through Russia.—British manufactures carried from St. Petersburgh 5,000 miles to China!—Nature of restrictions in the licences granted by the East India Company.—Effect of a free trade on the Company.—Smuggling would be promoted by a free trade to Europe. — Apprehended evils from unruly conduct of seamen at Canton, likely to be introduced by a free trade.—Supposed profit of captains of Company's ships trading to Canton, 10,000 *l.*—Instances of the severities of Chinese law in case of death of natives happening in affrays with foreigners.—Detailed account of the Company's trade with China and the Indian Seas,—and of the method of transacting the Chinese trade with the Hong merchants.—History of the intercourse with China.—A summary account of the attempts, from early to the present times, to open trading intercourse with the Chinese, and with other places in the Eastern seas.—Accounts of imports and exports.

see likewise *East India Affairs*, under Head XIV.

7.—Second Report from the Select Committee of the House of Lords, appointed to inquire into the means of extending and securing the Foreign Trade of the Country, &c.   Sess. 1821, (703.) vol. 7, p. 421. [**38.**]

SUBJECT.—*On the Improvement of the Silk Manufactures, and Importation of Wine.*— Increased supply and quality of raw silk from Bengal.—Probable beneficial effect on the manufacture in England.—Difficulties in the way of competition with foreign manufactures. —Superiority of workmanship in some cases.—Lyonese machinery.—Injurious effects of the laws regulating the trade and journeymen.———Diminished importation of wine.—Propriety of altering the duties doubted.——And *see* under Head VIII.

8.—Report from the Select Committee on improving and maintaining the Foreign Trade of the Country.   Sess. 1822, (591.) vol. 5, p. 107. [**39.**]

SUBJECTS.—*Lights, Harbour Dues, and Pilotage.*—Authority under which light-dues are collected.—Origin of the Trinity-house incorporation.—History of its charters.—Light-dues.—Lighthouses and floating lights.—Impolicy of exacting dues from foreign ships passing only the lights. — Expense of collection. — Remuneration to elder brethren.— Amount of expenditure for lights.—Objection to letting lights on lease.—Improvements recommended.—Ramsgate Harbour dues.—Burthensome effect on foreign ships.—Amount of cost of that harbour;—estimated expense of completing it —Proposed reduction of rates. —Dover Harbour.—State of funds.—Nature of the harbour.

9.—Report from the Select Committee appointed to consider of the means of improving and maintaining the Foreign Trade of the Country.
                                          Sess. 1823, (411.) vol. 4, p. 489. [**40.**]

SUBJECTS.—*West India Docks. — Claim of exclusive Privileges.* — Advantages to the trade and revenue from the docks.—Grounds of claim to continuation of exclusive privileges.—Comparative security of the West India and London Docks to the property of merchants and revenue. — Does not justify their claim to exclusive privileges. — Open system of competition among the dock establishments recommended.—Accumulation of surplus fund.—Payment of income tax out of it.—Ought to have been applied in reduction of the rates.—The privilege of landing and bonding recommended to be extended to other warehouses.—Exclusive privileges of all the docks to expire in 1827.———*see likewise* under Head XIX.

10.—First Report from the same Committee.   Sess. 1824, (416.) vol. 6, p. 1. [**40.**]

SUBJECTS.—*Pilotage.— Post-office Regulations.—Ramsgate Harbour Dues.—Light Dues. —Ballast.*—Acts regulating pilots and pilotage.—Rates of pilotage.—Proposed reduction. —Rotation of duty necessary.—Boarding-money to be continued.— Summary decision of disputes in London :—Power for that purpose to be given to a committee of the Trinity-house.—Proposal of allowing pilots to take ships upwards as well as outwards, and *vice versa,* not thought eligible.—Ships trading to Ireland not to be considered foreign.———Post-office regulations as to letters on shipboard.———Ramsgate Harbour dues.—Reduction.— Regret that the remission has not taken place of those on vessels not capable from their draught to enter the harbour.———Reduction of other harbour and light dues.—Reduction of commissioners on collecting.———Ballast establishments.—Improvements in management commended.——See *infra,* Nos. 14, 15.

11.—Second Report from the same Committee.   Sess. 1824, (417.) vol. 6, p. 165. [**40.**]

SUBJECTS.—*On the Nature of the Plague,—Contagion,—and Quarantine.*—Interest and delicacy of the subject of quarantine.—Report on the doctrine of contagion of 1819 referred to.—That doctrine considered correct, generally.—Whether any improvements in the quarantine laws can be made, consistent with security.—Proceedings in 1810, &c. respecting the lazaretto on Chetney Hill, and its abandonment, stated.—Bills of health described.— Quarantine regulations explained.—Expensiveness of the charges.—Opinions of eminent medical men.—Proposed amended regulations.———The evidence contains an account of foreign lazarettos, and quarantine regulations.—Statements of persons employed in those establishments in England.—Opinions of medical men, and persons who have been resident in the Levant, on the necessity of such regulations.—On the manner in which the contagion is supposed to be communicated, and on the method of guarding against it.

see *likewise* under Head XVII.

Foreign Trade—continued.

12.—Third Report from the Select Committee appointed to consider of the means of improving the Foreign Trade of the Country.

Sess. 1824, (431.) vol. 6, p. 287. [40

SUBJECTS.—*Appropriation of Advances by Government for the Improvement of the Port of London.*—London Port duty.—Proceedings in 1796 and 1799 for improving the port of London.—Clause in Act then passed, laying a certain duty for making compensation under the provisions of that Act.—Transit duty to defray the expense of Isle of Dogs' canal.— Acts for making wet docks.—Compensations to owners of wharfs, &c. — Transactions respecting the Canal.—Its failure, and conversion to a wet dock.—The port duty laid on to defray the expense is therefore not reimbursed, and becomes a permanent burthen.— Amount of payments from Consolidated Fund towards the improvement of the port of London.—Payments to Mr. Tyrell for law charges and salary, and under the commission for- compensations. — Summary statement of payments and receipts on account of the London Port improvement.—Harbour-masters.—Sale of the Isle of Dogs' canal recommended.—Reductions to be expected in London Port establishment.—Partiality of relieving the burthen of duties on the port of London at the national expense, unless the same liberality be shown to other ports.——*See* under Head XIX.

Commerce and Manufactures:

13.—Report from the Select Committee on the present state of Manufactures, Commerce and Shipping in the United Kingdom.

Sess. 1833, (690.) vol. 6.

SUBJECTS —Trade in an unusually sound and healthy state.—No want of capital.— Large supplies of cash from agricultural districts.—Usury laws inoperative from the low value of money.—Over-production and want of capital the cause of the failures in the East Indies.—Difference between capital and circulating medium, and how far the abundance of the latter, and the low rate of interest, accounted for by the return from war to peace.— Advantages of the improvements in machinery in enabling the English manufacturer to enter into competition with the Foreign manufacturer.—Capabilities of foreign countries to extend their cotton manufacture, and effect of competition in lowering prices.—Americans can compete with the English in the manufacture of coarse cottons with regard to price without the protection granted by the tariff.—Middlemen in all sorts of business much diminished.—Considerable rivalry to be expected from Belgium in the manufacture of woollen goods.—Power-looms have not superseded the use of hand-looms in Scotland.— The great facility in obtaining discounts and accommodation in Glasgow has led to speculation.—Great increase in the importation of Australian wool since 1821.—Woollen manufacturers of America are in a very bad state.—Condition of retail dealers better than formerly.—Losses by bad debts considerably less than formerly.—Wages in Spitalfields as high as they have been for the last two years, though not so high as before the admission of French goods and the extension of the silk trade in Manchester and the northern districts.—The cultivation of cotton in the United States increasing.——*See* under Head VIII.

Cinque Ports' Pilots:

14.—Report from the Select Committee on the existing Laws and Regulations respecting Cinque Ports' Pilots.   Sess. 1833, (636.) vol. 7, p. 523.

SUBJECTS.—Services and present deplorable condition of the Deal boatmen and their boats.—Present system of supplying homeward-bound ships with pilots.—Establishment of pilot-cutters by 48 Geo. 3.—Consequent injury to the boatmen.—Fails in answering the intention of the Act.—Expediency of encouraging the services of the boatmen.—Usefulness of the Deal boats and men;—their services in saving lives in cases of shipwrecks— and in saving ships run on shore.—Necessity of encouraging the men, and preserving their boats.—Hardship to boatmen, when conducting a ship, in being superseded by Cinqueport pilots without any remuneration.—Scale of the remuneration recommended.—Folkstone to be a pilot station.—Surveys of French coast should be transferred from the pilots to the Admiralty.—Necessity of an uniform system of pilot-regulation.—Partiality in appointing the Cinque-port pilots.—Inequality of the charges for pilotage.—Necessity of exempting certain description of trading vessels from pilotage.—Recommendation of a settled mode of rewarding boatmen for services and losses.

Lighthouses:

15.—Report from the Select Committee on the state and management of the Lighthouses, Floating Lights, Buoys and Beacons, under the charge and management of the Corporation of the Trinity-house; of the Commissioners of Northern Lighthouses; of the Corporation for improving the Port of Dublin; and of all those in the hands of any other Corporation, Public Body or Private Individual.   Sess. 1834, (590.) vol. 12.

SUBJECTS.—Reduction of light dues recommended.—Number of public general lights in England.—Comparison of lights.—State of lighthouses, and amount of dues under the management of the Trinity-house.—Sums expended in repairing certain lighthouses.— Efficiency of the lights depends upon the quality of the stores.—Supplies of stores not purchased by contract.—Contract prices of sperm-oil for the service of the lighthouses.— Trinity-board have proceeded with great regularity and precision in carrying on new works, &c.—Evils of the way in which the light dues are collected by agents.—Value of

Argand

Lighthouses—continued.

Argand-lamp in comparison to others.—Constitution of the Dublin Ballast Board.—Suggestions for the formation of a board for the management of lighthouses.—Efficiency of the Bristol pilots.—Seamen are best qualified to judge of the placing of beacons, &c.—Cost of building Burnham lighthouse.—Extent of the right of Cinque-port pilots.—Collection of light-dues.—Per-centage allowed for the collection of light dues.—Custom-house officers should collect light dues as part of their public duty.—Greater intensity of the Drummond-light over others.—Ships pay nothing towards the maintenance of French lights.—Renewal of the lease of the Harwich light highly detrimental to the shipping interest.—Acts under which the Irish lights were transferred to the Ballast-board.—Leases of lighthouses.—Comparison between lenses and reflectors.—Light dues press very heavy on the shipping trade.—Method of illuminating lighthouses.—The Mumbles lighthouse of no service as a Channel light.—Expense of building the Northern lighthouses, and inspection thereof.—Quality of the oil depends much on the character of the contractor.—Intensity of the light from oil-gas—Objection to surplus light dues being paid as pensions.—Present system of private lighthouses, and the collection of their dues, very vexatious.—Claims on the Consolidated Fund for carrying into effect reciprocity treaties.—Manner in which the revolving light is produced.—Trinity Corporation have no control over the Skerries or Spurn lights.—Payment of light dues by steam-vessels.—Use of steam-vessels for lighthouse purposes.—Constitution of the Trinity Board.—Trinity-house lighthouses are sometimes built by contract.—Lights on the Yarmouth coast are well and properly exhibited.

Marine Insurance :

16.—Report from the Select Committee on Marine Insurance.
Sess. 1810, (226.) vol. 4, p. 247. [134.]

SUBJECT.—On the inexpediency of continuing the exclusive privileges granted to the Royal Exchange and London Assurance Companies.

Merchant-Law :

17.—Report from the Select Committee on the Law relating to Merchants, Agents or Factors, &c. Sess. 1823, (452.) vol. 4, p. 265. [23.]

SUBJECTS.—*Insecurity of Loans to Agents on Goods entrusted to them for Sale.*—The subjects of the Report are thus stated by the Committee :—I. To *bonâ fide* advances made to agents or factors upon the security of merchandize, in ignorance of their not being the owners of the property —II To purchasers of merchandize from agents or factors not invested with the power of sale, although that fact is unknown to the purchaser.—The liability, under the existing law, of the person advancing money, in the first case, to lose his security ; and the purchaser, under the second, of having to pay twice.—Cases of the law of principal and factor as decided by the courts of law.—Extensiveness of the practice of making advances on consignments.—Manner of conducting such transactions in various branches of trade.—Law in foreign countries different.—Proposed alteration of the law.———*The Appendix contains a collection of cases determined in the courts of law relating to the subject of the Report.*

Admeasurement of Shipping :

18.—Report of the Committee appointed by the Admiralty to consider the mode of Measuring the Tonnage of Ships. Sess. 1834, (43.) vol. 49, p. 577.

SUBJECTS.—Principle of admeasurement.—Rules to be observed.—Formula, and examples of applying them.—Proposed methods of calculation by several persons.—Mr. Cradock's method and calculations.—Professor Inman's observations —Mr. Davies Gilbert's method.—Methods at present in use by England, France, America, and other States.

Steam Navigation to India :

19.—Report from the Select Committee on the means of promoting Communication with India by Steam. Sess. 1834, (478.) vol. 14, p 363.

SUBJECTS.—Importance of a communication between Great Britain and India by means of steam-vessels.—Expense of conducting steam-vessels to be equally divided between His Majesty's Government and the East India Company.—Practicability of steam navigation between Bombay and Bussora.—Extension of the line of Malta packets recommended.—To what extent the Arabs could be bound.—Climate of Bagdad, and trade carried on there.—Advantages of bitumen and wood being mixed together for furnaces.—Size, power and capacity of steam-vessels necessary for a voyage round the Cape.—Coal found in India not applicable to steam purposes.—Advantages from steam navigation on the Euphrates.—Difficulties in the way thereof.—Necessity for an experimental voyage, and estimate thereof.—Comparative advantages and disadvantages of the route by the Euphrates and the Red Sea.—Survey of the Euphrates.—Superiority of the iron over the wooden steam-boats.———Ten Maps and Plans.

Shipwrecked Mariners :

Greathead's Life-Boat :

20.—Report from the Select Committee on Mr. Greathead's Invention of a Life-Boat. Sess. 1801-2, (37.) vol 2, p. 169 ; and First Series, vol. x. p. 730.

SUBJECTS.—Originality of the invention claimed by Mr Greathead.—Whether any remuneration has been received by him, and to what extent.—Utility of the life-boat.

*Shipwrecked Mariners—*Greathead's Life-Boat—*continued.*

21.—Another Report from the Select Committee on Mr. Greathead's Invention of a Life-Boat. Sess. 1810–11, (230.) vol. 2, p. 387.

Manby's Plans for Saving Lives :

22.—Report from the Select Committee on Captain Manby's Petition. Sess. 1810, (163.) vol. 4, p. 5. [135.]

SUBJECTS.—*Method of Communication with stranded Vessels.*—Contrivances and experiments for saving the lives of shipwrecked persons.

23.—Report from the Committee of Field Officers of Artillery, containing an Account of the Experiments made at Woolwich, on Captain Manby's Invention for saving the Lives of Shipwrecked Mariners. Sess. 1810–11, (215.) vol. 11, p. 111. [135.]

24.—Report from the Committee on Captain Manby's Experiments. Sess. 1813–14, (227.) vol. 3, p. 343. [135.]

SUBJECTS.—This Report, after noticing a former one, states the progress made in a survey of the coasts under the direction of Government, by Captain Manby ; and recommends him to be rewarded.

25.—Report from the Select Committee on Captain Manby's Apparatus for saving the Lives of Shipwrecked Seamen, &c. Sess. 1823, (351.) vol. 4, p. 153. [135.]

SUBJECTS.—*Claim for Reward.*—Reference made to the Report of 1810, containing resolutions in favour of the contrivance.—Continued success since that time.—Recommendation to render the apparatus more effectual at the places where stationed.—Bounty on lives saved recommended.—Grant of 2,000 *l.* recommended.—The evidence contains many instances of the application of the apparatus, and explaining the manner of using it. —Account of several wrecks where the apparatus has been useful in saving lives, and others where lives have been lost for want of it.

26.—Papers relating to Captain Manby's Experiments for effecting a Communication with Ships stranded. Sess. 1809, (255.) vol. 10, p. 389. [135.]

27.—Further Papers on the same subject. Sess. 1813–14, (48.) vol. 11, p. 415. [135.]

These Papers are the most complete on the subject. They contain sketches of headlands, coasts, and signals, represented by wood-engravings.

28.—Further Papers on the same subject. Sess. 1816, (409.) vol. 19, p. 193. [135.]

These Papers contain engravings of the apparatus used, and of forms shewing the manner of applying it.

29.—Return of Vessels lost, through Shipwreck ; and the Number of Lives that were preserved. Sess. 1816, (529.) vol. 19, p. 231. [135.]

Mallison's :

30.—Report from the Select Committee on the Petition of William Henry Mallison. Sess. 1810–11, (206.) vol. 2, p. 375. [135.]

SUBJECTS.—Construction of cork jackets.—Use.—Experiments.—Three pounds of cork gives a sufficient buoyancy to support a man afloat.

31.—Correspondence between the Master-General of the Ordnance ; between the Board of Ordnance ; and between the Board of Admiralty, and Mr. Mallison ; respecting his Apparatus. Sess. 1818, (272.) vol. 13, p. 341. [135.]

Whitfield's Plans for Saving Lives :

32.—Report from the Select Committee on the Petition of Elizabeth Whitfield, late Bell. Sess. 1813–14, (309.) vol. 3, p. 347. [135.]

SUBJECT.—Mrs. Bell claims, for her late husband, the priority of the merit of suggesting the method of forming a communication with the shore and a wrecked vessel, by projecting a rope by means of a shell and mortar.

Trengrouse's :

33.—Papers respecting Mr. Trengrouse's Apparatus for preserving Lives and Property in cases of Shipwreck. Sess. 1825, (415.) vol. 21, p. 361. [135.]

34.—Report of the Committee of Pilotage and Examination, to whom was referred the Invention of Mr. Henry Trengrouse, for saving Seamen from Shipwrecked Vessels. Sess. 1825, (489.) vol. 21, p. 363. [135.]

X.

Finance, Civil List, and Public Accounts.

Public Expenditure, 1763 :

1.—[Report from the Select Committee on Accounts relating to the Public Expenditure since the commencement of the late War.

Journals, vol. 29, p. 635.

Public Debt and Annuities, 1782:

2.—[Report from the Select Committee on the amount of the Sums raised by Annuities towards the Supply granted between 1776 and 1782.

First Series, vol. XI. p. 3.

Subjects.—Amount of the public debt as it stood from 1776 to 1782.—Annual interest of annuities and of the public debt.—Expenses of the seven years' war.—Methods of keeping the accounts of the Customs, and suggestions for limiting the period of passing them. —Produce of the taxes and duties from 1774 to 1782.——and see under Head XIII.

Income and Expenditure, 1786—1791 :

3.—[Two Reports from the Select Committee on the Public Income and Expenditure ; on the future Annual Income and Expenditure; and on the state of the Public Debt.   First Series, vol. XI. pp. 39. 81.

Subjects.—Accounts of the various branches of income and expenditure.—State of the public debt.—Produce of all the taxes.— Probable expense of a permanent peace establishment.

Finance, 1797—1803 :

4.—[Thirty-six Reports from the Select Committee on Finance ; and proceedings and measures of Government on these Reports.

First Series, vols. XII. & XIII.

Subjects.—1. Debt and Taxes.—2. Collection of the public revenue.—3. Expenditure, and auditing accounts.—4. Revenue, debt and expenditure.—5. Civil establishment.— 6. Military establishments.

Public Expenditure of the Kingdom, 1807—1812:

5.—First Report from the Select Committee on the Public Expenditure of the Kingdom.   Sess. 1807, (61.) vol. 2, p. 313. [42.]
Subject.—Pay Office.

6.—Second Report from the same Committee.   Sess. 1807, (108.) vol. 2, p. 379. [42.]
Subject.—The Bank.——and see *Bank*, under Head XI.

7.—Third Report from the same Committee.   Sess. 1808, (331.) vol. 3, p. 257. [42.]
Subject.—Pensions, Sinecures, Reversions, &c.

8.—Supplementary Report to the Third Report from the same Committee.

Sess. 1809, (200.) vol. 3, p. 61. [42.]

Subject.—Pensions, Sinecures, Reversions, &c.——See *infra*, No. 27 ; and *Sinecures*, under Head XXV.

9.—Resolutions 1 and 2, on Third Report from the Select Committee upon Public Expenditure.   Sess. 1810, (135. 136.) vol. 2, pp. 353. 355. [42.]

10.—Resolutions 3 and 4, on Third Report from the Select Committee upon Public Expenditure.   Sess. 1810, (137. 138.) vol. 2, pp. 359. 363. [42.]

11.—Resolutions of the House of Commons, on the Third Report from the Select Committee on Public Expenditure.   Sess. 1810, (334.) vol. 2, p. 365. [42.]

Public Expenditure of the Kingdom, 1807–1812—continued.

12.—Fourth Report from the Select Committee on the Public Expenditure, &c. of the United Kingdom.   Sess. 1809, (99.) vol. 3, p. 105. [42.]
 SUBJECT.—Commissioners for Dutch Prizes.

13.—Fifth Report from the same Committee.   Sess. 1810, (216.) vol. 2, p. 369. [42.]
 SUBJECT.—Office of Paymaster of Marines ; and Audit of Accounts.

14.—Second Part of Fifth Report from the same Committee.
                                                   Sess. 1810, (371¹.) vol. 2, p. 381. [42.]
 SUBJECT.—Audit of Public Accounts.——and see Nos. 13. 19. 42.

15.—Sixth Report from the same Committee.   Sess. 1810 (369.) vol. 2, p. 567. [43.]
 SUBJECT.—Collection of Taxes in Scotland.

16.—Seventh Report from the same Committee.
                                                   Sess. 1810, (370.) vol. 2, p. 523. [43.]
 SUBJECT.—Buildings, Civil and Military.——and see *Public Works,* under Head XIX.

17.—Eighth Report from the same Committee.
                                                   Sess. 1810, (371².) vol. 2, p. 543. [43.]
 SUBJECT.—Linen Board, Ireland.——and see *Linen Trade,* under Head VIII.

18.—Ninth Report from the same Committee.   Sess. 1810, (373.) vol. 2, p. 551. [43.]
 SUBJECT.—Printing and Stationery.——see likewise *Parliamentary Printing,* under Head IV.

19.—Tenth Report from the same Committee.
                                                   Sess. 1810–11, (253.) vol. 3, p. 1001. [43.]
 SUBJECT.—Audit of Accounts.——and see Nos. 13. 14. 42.

20.—Eleventh Report from the same Committee.
                                                   Sess. 1810–11, (257.) vol. 3, p. 1055. [43.]
 SUBJECT.—Continuation of the Fifth, Sixth and Seventh Reports.

21.—Twelfth Report from the same Committee.   Sess. 1812, (339.) vol. 2, p. 489. [43.]
 SUBJECT.—Balances, and Defaulters.

22.—Thirteenth Report from the same Committee.
                                                   Sess. 1812, (340.) vol. 2, p. 529. [43.]
 SUBJECTS.—Proceedings in consequence of commissions of inquiry.—Proceedings relating
 to regimental accounts.—Commissioners sent to the West Indies.

      Of Ireland, 1811—1815 :
23.—Report from the Select Committee on Accounts and Papers relating to the Public Income and Expenditure of Ireland.
                                                   Sess. 1810–11, (262.) vol. 5, p. 99. [43.]

24.—Second Report from the same Committee.   Sess. 1812, (376.) vol. 5, p. 1. [43.]
 These Reports consist of results stated in figures.—The Appendixes consist of accounts.

25.—Report from the Select Committee on Accounts and Papers relating to the Public Income and Expenditure of Ireland.
                                                   Sess. 1812–13, (309.) vol. 6, p. 173. [43.]
 A collection of Accounts.

26.—Report from the same Committee.   Sess. 1814–15, (214.) vol. 6, p. 1597. [43.]
 Chiefly Accounts.

 Income and Expenditure, 1817—1821 :
27.—First Report from the Select Committee on Finance.
                                                   Sess. 1817, (159.) vol. 4, p. 23. [44.]
 SUBJECT.—On Sinecures.——and see *Sinecures,* under Head XXV., and 3d Report on
 Public Expenditure, No. 8, *supra.*

28.—Second Report from the same Committee.   Sess. 1817, (162.) vol. 4, p. 43. [44.]
 SUBJECT.—On the Army.——and see Nos. 33. 39 ; and Head XXIV.

Income and Expenditure, 1817–1821—continued.

29.—Third Report from the Select Committee on Finance.
Sess. 1817, (275.) vol. 4, p. 87. [44.]
SUBJECT.—On the Ordnance.——and see Nos. 35. 41. 45.

30.—Fourth Report from the same Committee.   Sess. 1817, (318.) vol. 4, p. 137. [44.]
SUBJECT.— On Public Income and Expenditure.

31.—Fifth Report from the same Committee.   Sess. 1817, (366.) vol. 4, p. 191. [44.]
SUBJECT.—On Irish Civil Estimates.

32.—Sixth Report from the same Committee.   Sess. 1817, (410.) vol. 4, p. 203. [44.]
SUBJECT.—On the Navy.——and see Nos. 34. 40; and Head XXIV.

33.—Seventh Report from the same Committee.   Sess. 1818, (57.) vol. 3, p. 99. [44.]
SUBJECT.—On the Army Estimates.

34.—Eighth Report from the same Committee.   Sess. 1818, (97.) vol. 3, p. 143. [44.]
SUBJECT.—On Navy Estimates.——and see Nos. 32. 40; and under Head XXIV.

35.—Ninth Report from the same Committee.   Sess. 1818, (133.) vol. 3, p. 173. [44.]
SUBJECT.—On the Ordnance.——and see Nos. 29. 41. 45.

36.—Tenth Report from the same Committee.   Sess. 1818, (269.) vol. 3, p. 197. [44.]
SUBJECT.—On Civil Contingencies.

37.—Eleventh Report from the same Committee.
SUBJECT.—On Income and Expenditure.   Sess. 1818, (355.) vol. 3, p. 213. [44.]

38.—First Report from the Select Committee on Finance.
SUBJECT.—On Income and Expenditure.   Sess. 1819, (205.) vol. 2, p. 79. [44.]

39.—Second Report from the same Committee.   Sess. 1819, (206.) vol. 2, p. 111. [44.]
SUBJECT.—On the Army.——and see Nos. 28. 33; and under Head XXIV.

40.—Third Report from the same Committee.   Sess. 1819, (257.) vol. 2, p. 159. [44.]
SUBJECT.—On the Navy.——and see Nos. 32. 34; and under Head XXIV.

41.—Fourth Report from the same Committee.   Sess. 1819, (289.) vol. 2, p. 181. [44.]
SUBJECT.—On the Ordnance.——and see Nos. 29. 35. 45.

42.—Fifth Report from the same Committee.   Sess. 1819, (539.) vol. 2, p. 199. [44.]
SUBJECT.—On the Audit Office.——and see Nos. 13. 14. 19.

43.—Minutes of Evidence taken before the Select Committee on Public Income and Expenditure in 1819.   Sess. 1821, (284.) vol. 8, p. 125. [44.]
SUBJECT.—On the Audit Office.——*see*, as to *Army* and *Navy*, under Head XXIV.

In 1828:

44.—First Report from the Select Committee of Inquiry into the state of the Public Income and Expenditure.   Sess. 1828, (110.) vol. 5, p. 1.
SUBJECT.—Disadvantageous terms of life annuities granted by the Commissioners of National Debt,——and see under Head XIII.

45.—Second Report from the same Committee.   Sess. 1828, (420.) vol. 5, p. 3.
SUBJECT.—Ordnance Estimates.——and see Nos. 29. 35. 41.

46.—Third Report from the same Committee.   Sess. 1828, (480.) vol. 5, p. 479.
SUBJECT.—Superannuations.

47.—Fourth Report from the same Committee.   Sess. 1828, (519.) vol. 5, p. 543.
SUBJECT.—Revenue, Expenditure, and Debt.

Civil List, 1802 :

48.—Report from the Select Committee on Accounts relative to His Majesty's
Civil List. Sess. 1801–2, (28.) vol. 2, p. 13 ; and First Series, vol. xi. p. 195.

SUBJECTS.—Estimates of the charges of the Civil List Establishment, laid before Parliament.—Expenditure of the Civil List Establishment.—Excess of the expenditure above the estimate.—The assigned cause of this excess of expenditure.

From 1803—1820 :

49.—Report from the Select Committee appointed to consider of the Charge
upon His Majesty's Civil List Revenue. Sess. 1802–3, (147.) vol. 5, p. 335. [41.]

50.—Report from the Select Committee appointed to consider of the Charge
upon His Majesty's Civil List Revenue. Sess. 1803–4, (43.) vol. 5, p. 219. [41.]

51.—Report made by the Auditors of Public Accounts to the Lords Commissioners of the Treasury, on the subject of the Deductions of the Civil List.
Sess. 1808, (38.) vol. 3, p. 231. [41.]

52.—Report from the Select Committee upon the Civil List, &c.
Sess. 1812, (330.) vol. 2, p. 423. [41.]

53.—Report from the Select Committee upon the Civil List, &c.
Sess. 1812–13, (342.) vol. 4, p. 551. [41.]

54.—Report from the Select Committee upon the Civil List, &c.
Sess. 1814–15, (401.) vol. 3, p. 91. [41.]

55.—Report from the Select Committee on the Establishment of her late
Majesty, and the Estimate of the Expenses of the proposed Establishment
of His Majesty's future Household at Windsor. Sess. 1819, (56.) vol. 2, p. 47. [41.]

SUBJECTS.—Reductions capable of being made in consequence of the continued illness of the King.—Reduction in consequence of the Queen's death.—Propriety of allowing pensions to certain of her Majesty's servants.

56.—Resolutions respecting the Civil List. Sess. 1820, (8.) vol. 2, p. 227. [41.]

Civil List Accounts, 1831 :

57.—Report from the Select Committee on the Accounts relating to the Civil
List. Sess. 1830–31, (269.) vol. 3, p. 437.

SUBJECTS.—Expediency of confining the civil-list charges to expenses proper for the maintenance of their Majesties household.—Arrangement of expenses in classes.—Observations on the pension list.—Further inquiry into the expenses of His Majesty's household not considered necessary.—Statement of the estimated and proposed amount of each class.

Civil Government Charges, 1831 :

58.—Report from the Select Committee on Civil Government Charges.
Sess. 1831, (337.) vol. 4, p. 333.

SUBJECTS.—Arrangements for regulating the civil list in the reign of Geo. 4.—Proposed arrangements at the accession of His present Majesty Will. 4.—Reductions recommended.—In offices of state held by Members of Parliament.—In salaries of judges.—Expenses of the diplomatic service.—Small payments.—Charges on the four-and-half per cent. duties.—Civil-list charges of Ireland ; proposed abolitions and reductions.—Charges on the hereditary revenues of Scotland.

Civil List Charges, 1833 :

59.—Report from the Select Committee on the Charges borne on the Civil
List of his late Majesty, and remaining unprovided for.
Sess. 1833, (646.) vol. 7, p. 779.

SUBJECTS.—Arrangements for simplifying the charges, and ascertaining the legal origin of the claims made.—Payments to University professors.—Dean and chapter of Lichfield, and similar payments.—For the repairs of Lyme harbour, &c.—To the vicar of the Tower, and similar payments.—Governor of Hillsborough Fort.—Other antient grants of small payments.—Recommendation to charge such as were originally connected with the landed possessions of the Crown, on the land revenues.—Others to be discontinued or extinguished on compensation.

Public Accounts:

Mode of Constructing, 1822:

60.—Report from the Select Committee on the Public Accounts of the United Kingdom, annually laid before Parliament.   Sess. 1822, (618.) vol. 4, p. 293. [45.]

SUBJECTS.—*Mode of constructing the Public Accounts.*—Observations on the annual finance accounts.—Proposed improvements, with forms drawn up for that purpose.

Mode of Keeping, 1829:

61.—Report of the Commissioners on the mode of keeping the Official Accounts of Receipts and Expenditure in the Public Service.

Sess. 1829, (290.) vol. 6, p. 1.

SUBJECTS.—Form of account and method of entries.—In this Report, two of the commissioners concur in recommending the adoption of certain forms and system of account; but the third dissents, and makes the Report next following.

62.—Report on the same subject by the Third Commissioner.

Sess. 1829, (325.) vol. 6, p. 361.

SUBJECTS.—Proposed method of keeping the public accounts, and method of arrangement.—The principle recommended is the Italian mode by double entry.

63.—Letter from Mr. Abbott (the Third Commissioner), with Observations thereupon by Messrs. Brooksbank and Beltz, (the two Commissioners agreeing in the Report.)   Sess. 1830, (159.) vol. 29, p. 1.

64.—Papers relating to Public Accounts; being a Report of Messrs. Brooksbank and Beltz, on the progress made in carrying into effect the directions for a General System of Book-keeping, contained in a Minute of the Treasury, dated 14 July 1829.   Sess. 1831, (50.) vol. 14, p. 289.

SUBJECTS.—General observations on the system of book-keeping.—Difficulty of obtaining the concurrence of the officers of departments to the proposed alterations.—Success of the new arrangements.—Preferred to the plan of the public accountant.—Objections made by the Navy Board answered.—Difficulty of procuring complete concurrence on questions of accounts.—Plan proposed has borrowed from the commercial system where useful, and left it where inapplicable.—Approval of the Lords of the Treasury.

Receipt and Payment of Public Money, 1831:

65.—First Report of the Commissioners of Public Accounts.

Sess. 1831, (313.) vol. 10, p. 1.

SUBJECTS.—*On the Exchequer.*—On the manner in which the public money is received and paid, and on the system of keeping the accounts.—Antiquity and description of the forms and practices now existing.—Observations on the antient forms and terms used in the keeping exchequer accounts.—Changes and improvements proposed.—Forms of issuing money; proposed changes.—Simplified modes of keeping accounts recommended.—Superiority of the commercial system of accounts by double entry pointed out.

66.—Papers laid before the Select Committee on Public Accounts.

Sess. 1830–31, (40.) vol. 14, p. 1.

These are the same as those which form an Appendix to the preceding Report of the Commissioners on Public Accounts; 1831, Oct. 10, (313.) No. 65.

Receivers-General:

67.—Report from the Select Committee on the Duties of Receivers-General of Land and Assessed Taxes.   Sess. 1821, (630. 667.) vol. 8, pp. 5. 15. [45.]

SUBJECTS.—*Mode of remitting Taxes when collected.*—Present mode of collection.—Parish assessors and collectors.—Duties of receivers-general.—Emoluments.—Surveyors and inspectors.—District commissioners' clerks.—Commissioners.—Proposed to adopt the mode of remittance practised in the Excise, instead of lodging the money in the receiver-generals' hands.—Deputies not to be allowed.—Proposed to reduce their number.—Reduction of security proposed.—Audit of accounts to be simplified.—Compensation not to be allowed.

Irish Miscellaneous Estimates:

68.—Report from the Select Committee on the Irish Miscellaneous Estimates.

Sess. 1829, (342.) vol. 4, p. 127.

SUBJECTS.—Increase of their amount.—Support of public institutions in Dublin.—Principle on which Parliamentary aid has been granted.—On the propriety of continuing or withdrawing such aid.—Charges for stationery and printing.—Sir A. B. King's patent.—Printing statutes.—Record Commission.—Public works.——And see *Printing and Stationery,* under Head IV.; and *supra,* No. 18.

Public Accounts of France :

69.—First Report to the Lords of the Treasury.   By John Bowring.

Sess. 1831, (78.) vol. 14, p. 339.

SUBJECTS.—Character and workings of the system of financial accounts.—Confusion and expensiveness of the old method.—Uniformity and advantages of the present system.—Conducted on the double-entry system.—Renders investigation easy, and prevents any dishonesty.—Forms of accounts.

70.—Second Report to the Lords of the Treasury.   By John Bowring.

Sess. 1831, (289.) vol. 14, p. 501.

SUBJECTS.—Financial history of France.—Inefficiency of the fiscal system ; and consequent abuses.—Establishment of the present system of accounts.—At what period, and by whom, the commercial system of double entry was introduced.—Endeavours of successive finance ministers to enforce improvements grounded thereon.—Their difficulties, and disorder which prevailed in the accounts.—Remedied by the establishment of the present system.—Its operation described.—Security against fraud of agents, by actual money deposits by them.—Effect on the promptitude of all transactions in collecting, paying and accounting for the public revenue.—Uniformity of system enforced.—Benefit of central management.—Controlling authorities.—Forms of accounts.

71.—Third Report to the Lords of the Treasury.   By John Bowring.

Sess. 1831–32, (586.) vol. 28, p. 1.

SUBJECTS.—Military expenditure.—Their admirable order, derived from the present sound principle of book-keeping by double entry.—The system exemplified and explained.—Manner of forming the estimates for the yearly budget of military expenditure.—Accounts relating thereto.—Mode of bringing forward the budget.—Progress of the army expenditure traced through official documents.—Establishment of a controlling power.—Attentions and courtesy afforded to the inquiry by official persons in France.——— Appendix of instructions and formulas of accounts.

Public Accounts of the Netherlands :

72.—Report on the Public Accounts of the Netherlands.   By John Bowring.

Sess. 1832, (236.) vol. 28, p. 493.

SUBJECTS.—Difficulties attending the inquiry and in collecting information.—Manner in which the budget of expenses is formed.—Decennial budgets, by which the expenditure is provided for prospectively every tenth year.—Mode of keeping the accounts in the public departments.—Form of accounts.—Control over the receipts of the revenue.—Manner of keeping the accounts.—General statement of accounts.———State of Belgian accounts.

XI.

Banking—Coinage—Currency—Exchange.

Commercial Credit, 1793 :

1.—[Report from the Select Committee on the state of Commercial Credit.

Journals, vol. 48, p. 702.   Reprinted 1826, (23.) vol. 3, p. 123. [46.]

SUBJECTS.—1. Whether the existing difficulties require the interposition of the Legislature ?—2. If necessary, what is the most effectual plan of giving relief?—3. The prevention of similar inconveniences in future.——Failures of extensive mercantile houses.—
Run on houses that have issued paper, and embarrassments of houses of capital, and of
great respectability, from inability to get temporary accommodation.—Scarcity of money.
—Difficulty in getting advances on bills, or on large stocks.—Stoppage of manufactories,
and workmen thrown out of employ.—Commercial embarrassments in Scotland.—Nature of
relief proposed.—Rules to be observed.—Individual embarrassments not a ground for
relief.—Five millions in Exchequer bills recommended to be advanced.—Conditions.—
Commissioners to be appointed.—Details of the plan of management.

2.—Report from the Select Committee on the state of Commercial Credit.

Sess. 1810–11, (52.) vol. 2, p. 367. [46.]

SUBJECT.—On the embarrassments of trade, and the expediency of advances by
Parliament.

Bank of England, 1797 :

3.—[Reports from the Committee of Secrecy on the Outstanding Demands
of the Bank, and on the Restriction of Payments in Cash.

First Series, vol. XI. pp. 119. 120. 121. 192.   Reprinted 1826, (26.) vol. 3, p. 137. [46.]

SUBJECTS.—Amount of cash and bullion in the Bank, and of that exported for foreign
subsidies, and the cause of its diminution in this country.—Amount of Bank of England and of country bank notes, and the necessity of an increased paper currency.—
Causes which led to the restriction of the payments in cash ; as the alarm of invasion,
and the demands for cash for foreign subsidies.—Consequences of the limitation of discounts by the Bank.—High amount of the advances to Government.—Necessity of issuing
the Order in Council for restricting payments in cash, and the expediency of continuing it.
—State of the balance of trade, and of the course of exchange.

4.—Report of the Lords' Committee of Secrecy. Sess. 1810, (17.) vol 3, p. 233. [46.]

SUBJECTS.—Order of Council in 1797, relating to the Bank.

Bank ; Resumption of Cash Payments, 1819 :

5.—Reports and Minutes of Evidence from the Secret Committee on the expediency of resuming Cash Payments.   Sess. 1819, (202. 282.) vol. 3, p. 1. [47.]

6.—Reports from the Lords respecting the Bank resuming Cash Payments.

Sess. 1819, (291.) vol. 3, p. 363. [47.]

7.—Proposed Resolutions.   Sess. 1819, (326.) vol. 3, p. 357. [47.]

8.—Representation of the Directors of the Bank, 20 May 1819.

Sess. 1819, (338.) vol. 3, p. 359. [47.]

SUBJECTS.—State of the metallic and paper currency of the kingdom.—Cause of the
specie being withdrawn from circulation.—Prices of bullion.—Amount of the paper currency of the Bank.—Transactions of country bankers.—Reciprocal influence of commercial
transactions on each other, and the paper issues of the Bank.—Exchange with foreign
countries.—Efforts making by foreign states to diminish the amount of their paper money.—
Possibility of gradually withdrawing from circulation a considerable quantity of Bank
paper.—Probable effects of so doing on commerce.—Practicability of substituting specie.—
Plan for the gradual resumption of cash payments.
see likewise *Prevention of Forgery*, under Head XXII.

Bank Privileges, 1826 :

9.—Communications between the First Lord of the Treasury, &c. and the Bank of England, relating to an alteration in the exclusive Privileges of the Bank of England. Sess. 1826, (2.) vol. 19, p. 471. [47.]

> SUBJECTS.—*Effects of Country Banks.*—*Establishment of Branch Banks, for the Bank of England.*—Allowing country banking establishments without limitation of partners.—Allusion to the panic in the money market at the end of 1825.—Rash speculation fostered by the country banks.—Restraining the circulation of country notes, and recurring to gold circulation.—Bank of England not sufficient of itself to meet the demands of the present times.—Increase of country banks, arising from the new wants of the country—should be controlled.—Desirable to establish a sound system of country banks.—Proposed that the Bank should establish branch establishments, and waive their exclusive privilege as to the number of partners engaged.—System of Scotch banks on a good foundation.—Country banks keep the Bank of England notes out of circulation.—The Legislature not to be expected to accede to the continuation or renewal of Bank privileges—their acceding to the wishes of Government will greatly facilitate the perfection of the measures necessary to the support of public credit.—Observations of the Court of Directors.—Propositions of Government agreed to.

10.—Memorial from certain Merchants of the City of Dublin to the Treasury, respecting the exclusive Privileges of the Bank of Ireland. Sess. 1826, (51.) vol. 23, p. 277. [47.]

Bank Charter and Banking, 1832 :

11.—Report from the Committee of Secrecy on the expediency of renewing the Charter of the Bank of England, and on the system on which Banks of Issue in England and Wales are conducted. Sess. 1831-32, (722.) vol. 6.

> SUBJECTS.—Expediency of renewing the Bank charter.—Conduct of the Bank in the management of its affairs considered as a private concern, and in its monetary transactions with Government.—Expediency of establishing joint-stock banks.—On the general system of banking.——Management of the Bank of England.—Inquiry into the advantages and disadvantages of the exclusive privileges granted by its charter.—Confidence acquired by its management.—Utility of branch banks.—Principle by which the Bank regulates the amount of bullion in hand.—Effect of its exportation.—Amount of capital requisite to support the confidence of the public.—Bank transactions with Government.——Explanation of the accounts of the Bank.—Advantage of their publicity.——Advances by the Bank, their nature and extent.—Practice of London banks, and of country banks.—Deposits and discounts.—Exchequer bills held by the Bank on account of advances to Government.—— Credit attached to Bank-notes.—Principles by which the Bank regulates their issue and circulation.—Effect of enlarged issues, and contractions of circulation.—Important use in the issue of one-pound notes.—On the expediency of rendering Bank-notes legal tender. ——State of the currency.—Explanation of the "principle of currency".—Effect produced thereon by the operations of the Bank.—Coin and bullion in possession of the Bank.—On payments in gold.—In what way the influx of gold to the Bank, and its withdrawal, is regulated.—Demand for commercial and government transactions.—Hoarding.——State of foreign exchanges, and how regulated by the operations of the Bank.——History of the panics which have occasioned a sudden demand on the Bank, and private banking concerns.—Conduct of the Bank on those occasions.—Suspension of cash payments in 1797.— Commercial embarrassments in 1825.—Run on the Bank in 1832.——System of private banks—in London and in the country.—On establishing joint-stock banks, and their probable effect.—Issue and circulation of country bank-notes.—Assistance afforded by the issues of private banks to agricultural and manufacturing districts.—Mode of transacting business in London.—Business of the clearing-house.——System of Scotch banking explained.—Commission and interest accounts.——State of foreign national banks compared with the Bank of England.

Coinage, 1696-1797 :

12.—[Report from the Select Committee of Inquiry into the matter of Complaint touching the Coinage of Halfpence and Farthings. Journals, vol. 11, p. 545.

> SUBJECTS.—State of the coinage of the realm.—A kind of coin called tin-halfpence and farthings.—Inconvenience from this low condition of the currency so great, that the public willingly exchanged gold for the improved copper coin.—The duty of executing this coin confided to patentees, who were limited in their obligations as to the amount to be periodically exchanged.

13.—[Report from the Select Committee on the Miscarriages of the Officers of the Mint. Journals, vol. 11, p. 774.

> SUBJECTS.—The manner of conducting the business of the Mint is explained.—Country mints.—Dies surreptitiously carried away.—Insufficient control by the assay-master and melter.—Insufficient security for the trust reposed in them.—Allowance for coining.—The subjects of tin-money, the patent by which the privilege of coining copper-money is given to certain individuals, and the delay of changing the old for the new coin, are renewed in this Report from the preceding one of 1696.—Another subject is the connivance between Goldsmiths'-hall and the Tower assayers, so that plate marked as standard is defective in quality.

Bullion and Coinage, 1810—1816:

14.—Report, together with Minutes of Evidence and Accounts, from the Select Committee on the High Price of Gold Bullion.

Sess. 1810, (349.) vol. 3, p. 1. [48.]

Subjects.—State of the circulating medium.—Price of bullion —Foreign exchanges.

15.—Report of the Lords of the Committee of Council.

Sess. 1816, (411.) vol. 6, p. 403. [48.]

Subjects.—On the state of the coins of the kingdom, and the establishment and con-stitution of the Mint.

16.—Minutes of Evidence, taken in 1828, before the Committee for Coin, at the Board of Trade.   Sess. 1830, (31 .) vol. 17, p. 343.

17.—Report to the Treasury, dated 21 September 1717, from Sir Isaac Newton, on the state of the Gold and Silver Coin.

Sess. 1830, (110.) vol. 17, p. 359.

Exchange of Ireland, 1804:

18.—Report from the Select Committee on the Circulating Paper, the Specie and Current Coin of Ireland, and also of the Exchange between that part of the United Kingdom and Great Britain.

Sess. 1803-4, (86.) vol. 4, p. 1 ; and 1810, (28.) vol. 3, p. 385 ;
and 1826, (407.) vol. 5, p. 461. [48.]

Promissory Notes Circulation, 1826-27:

19.—Report from the Select Committee on the Circulation of Promissory Notes under the Value of £. 5. in Scotland and Ireland.

Sess. 1826, (402.) vol. 3, p. 257. [49.]

Subjects.—*State of Circulation in Scotland.*—*Manner of carrying on Banking Estab-lishments.*—Provisions in Scotland as to bankrupts' estates.—Partners unlimited.—Greater security of creditors, by partners being subject to more liability.—More facilities of obtaining information of the state of partners' property.—In three banks there are one hundred partners. —Interest allowed by Scotch bank on deposits.—Mode of conducting the business.— Affords the advantage of saving banks.—Amount of paper circulation in Scotland.— Consideration of the expediency of progressively establishing a metallic currency in Scotland. —Inquiry whether there is any ground for that country being allowed to issue small notes, through private bankers, when those of England are restrained from so doing.—Not advisable to interfere with that circulation, but to try, by further experience, whether it is or is not consistent with a metallic currency in England—but must be kept from inter-fering with the circulation in England.—Fears expressed that the crime of forgery may become more prevalent in Scotland.——Circulation of Ireland.—Metallic currency should be established in Ireland.—Issue of small notes to be restrained.

20.—Report from the Lords' Committee on the Circulation of Promissory Notes under the Value of £. 5. in Scotland and Ireland.

Sess. 1826-27, (245.) vol. 6, p. 377. [49.]

Subjects.—*Banking System of Scotland and Ireland.*—*Necessity of the Circulation of Small Notes.*—Uniformity of the system throughout Great Britain and Ireland desirable ; but diffi-culty of establishing it.——*Banking System of Scotland.*—Early existence of small notes in Scotland.—Stability of banking establishments there.—Custom of giving cash credit in advance, and charging or crediting interest on the balance daily.—Deposits received of small amount, and interest allowed.—Question as to how far the discontinuance of one-pound notes would affect the system.—Necessity of preventing the introduction of Scotch paper into England, and of establishing the metallic currency in England.——*Banking System of Ireland*—described.—Not of the stability of that of Scotland.—Any decided opinion deferred till the effect is seen of the change in the banking system of Ireland.——The Evidence is divided into three parts :—I. Ireland.—II. Scotland.—III. England.

XII.

Revenue from Duties—Land Revenue.

REVENUE FROM DUTIES.

Smuggling, 1745:

1.—[Report from the Select Committee appointed to inquire into the Practice of Smuggling.   Journals, vol. 25, p. 101.

> SUBJECTS.—Extent and systematic manner in which it is pursued.—Tea smuggled in great quantities.—Consumption of tea.—Account of the quantity on which duty is paid.—Number of persons and vessels employed in smuggling.—Great quantities of tea brought from Holland.—Want of vigilance in the Custom-house officers.—Desperation of the smuggler's character.—Means of prevention.

Frauds on the Revenue, 1783:

2.—[Reports from the Select Committee on the illicit Practices used in defrauding the Revenue, and on the most effectual methods of preventing the same.   First Series, vol. xi. pp. 228. 263. 282.

> SUBJECTS.—Articles fraudulently imported, without payment of duty.—Internal smuggling of foreign goods; and frauds on various articles of excise and customs.—Force, violence, and fraud of the smugglers; their connexion with persons on shore; and means suggested for checking their illicit proceedings.—Smuggling carried on to a great extent in Scotland; and how to be prevented.—Tea the principal article of illicit dealing; plan of a tax instead of the duties thereon.

Customs, 1733:

3.—[Report from the Select Committee appointed to inquire into the Frauds and Abuses of the Customs, to the prejudice of Trade, and diminution of the Revenue.   First Series, vol. i. p. 601.

> SUBJECTS.—Fraud in the Customs in taking drawback on exports.—In the linen, tea, tobacco and wine trades.—Abuses practised by revenue officers in connivance with dishonest merchants.—Smuggling carried on to a great extent, and with daring violence.—Injury sustained by the revenue.

Customs and Excise, 1820–1824:

4.—First to Sixth Reports of Commissioners of Inquiry into the Departments of the Customs and Excise, &c.   Sess. 1820, (46.) vol. 6, p. 559. [50.]

> SUBJECTS.—Explaining the routine of business; and stating proposed alterations and improvements.

5.—Seventh to Tenth Reports of the Commissioners of Inquiry.   Sess. 1821, (25.) vol. 10, p. 283. [50.]

> SUBJECTS.—*Warehousing System.*—East-country Docks.—Commercial Docks.—Surrey Canal and sufferance wharfs.—Appropriated to deposit of timber.—Mode of collecting that duty.—Proposed improvements.—Observation on the exclusive privileges of the Dock Companies.—Suggestions for creating competition among them.——*Solicitor's Department.*—Manner of remuneration—proposed to be altered from emoluments to salary. ——*Trade of Liverpool.*—Increase.—Regulations necessary to prevent abuses.—Proposed improvements.——*Customs in Ireland.*—Improvements in the management recommended.——*Buildings.*—Improvements of streets near the Custom-house.—St. Dunstan's church.——*Allowances to Surveyor.*—Charge for surveying new Custom-house, 13,670 *l.* —Recommends the method of procuring plans by open competition. ——*Superannuations.* —— *Uptown Warehouses.*—Memorial of proprietors, praying against any extension of privileged warehouse establishments.—Statement of merits compared with the docks.

Customs and Excise, 1820–1824 — continued.

6.—Eleventh and Twelfth Reports of the Commissioners of Inquiry into the Customs and Excise.   Sess. 1822, (87.) vol. 11, p. 29. [50.]

> SUBJECTS.—*Management in Scotland.—Outports.—Preventive Guard.—Coast Blockade. —Appointment of Officers.* —— *Eleventh Report.*—On the Report of the Commissioners of Customs, Scotland.—Manner of conducting the business of the departments.—Charges of management.—Expense of establishments.—High rate of expense of collection.— Reduction of the members of the Scotch Board.—Assignment of duties to each member. —Superintendence of the preventive guard.—Inspection of outports.—Appointment and promotion of officers.—Periodical reports, &c.—— *Twelfth Report.*—On the general system of the outports.—Practice of appointing officers who are natives and residents.—Officers not to be stationary.—On the prevention of smuggling.—Preventive water-guard.—Riding officers.—Coast blockade.

7.—Thirteenth and Fourteenth Reports of the Commissioners of Inquiry.
                    Sess. 1823, (425.) vol. 7, p. 175. [50.]

> SUBJECTS.—*Regulations at Outports.—Recapitulation of the subjects of the Reports.* – Bristol and Liverpool.—Officers to be interchanged.—Classification of ports, and rates of salaries.—Remittances of money.—Reductions proposed.

8.—Fifteenth Report of the Commissioners of Inquiry.
                    Sess. 1824, (141.) vol. 9, p. 183. [50.]

> SUBJECTS.—Import and Export Departments of the Excise.

9.—Sixteenth Report of the Commissioners of Inquiry.
> SUBJECTS.—Excise Department.—Seizures.   Sess. 1824, (429.) vol. 9, p. 195. [50.]

Revenue arising in Ireland and Great Britain, 1822–1829 :

10.—Four Reports of the Commissioners for inquiring into the Collection and Management of the Revenue arising in Ireland, and into certain Departments of Revenue arising in Great Britain.
                    Sess. 1822, (53. 563. 606. 634.) vols. 12 & 13. [51.]

> SUBJECTS.—*Collection and Management of the Revenue.*—Preliminary proceedings of the Commissioners.
>
> *Second Report.*—Incorporation of the several Revenue Boards in the United Kingdom.— An uniform system of revenue administration. — An improved collection of the public income in Ireland—and a reduction in the charges of management.—Assimilation of the respective modes of collection and management of the two countries with each other.— Removal of obstructions from duties and drawbacks.—Abolition of Union duties.—Defects of the Excise and Customs' departments.—Defective collection of assessed taxes alluded to.—Remission of taxation recommended in those, in preference to articles of consumption, as encouraging residence.—Appointment of officers improper, not being according to service—by promotion—compared with the superior practice in England.— Origin of the different Boards.—Details of the plan of incorporating them.—Judicial functions of the Revenue Boards.—— *The Appendix contains much information respecting the technical operations of the manufactures subject to the excise laws.*
>
> *Third Report.*—On the inconvenience of the countervailing duties, as affecting the commercial intercourse between the two countries.—Instanced as affecting the book-trade and printing.—Other instances, as leading to evasion of duty.—Proposals for repealing those duties, leaving the trade with Ireland in the same state as the trade with any other part of the kingdom coastwise.—— *See* under Head IV. and XXVI. *Printing and Stationery.*
>
> *Fourth Report.*—On the abolition of such of the Union duties as affect goods which are not manufactured in Ireland.—Injurious effects of those duties on Ireland.—Articles subject to them enumerated.—Observations on such articles as are manufactured in Ireland, or of which no manufacture exists there.—Vexations and losses occasioned by the process of assessing the duties.—Enumeration of such as are recommended to be repealed.

11.—Supplement to the Fourth Report of the Commissioners of Inquiry.
                    Sess. 1823, (270.) vol. 7, p. 237. [53.]

> SUBJECTS.—*Duties on Draperies.*—Respecting the manufacture of new draperies; and the expediency of continuing protecting duties in its favour.

12.—Fifth Report of the Commissioners of Inquiry.
                    Sess. 1823, (405.) vol. 7, p. 253. [53.]

> SUBJECTS.—*Distillation.—Distilleries.*—Amount of revenue, and number of gallons distilled.—Importance of the laws for collecting the revenue, as affecting the public morals.— Comparative state of England with Scotland and Ireland, as to the use of spirits.—Process of manufacture.—— *Irish system.*—Illicit distillation prevalent.—— *Scotch system.*—Rapidity

Revenue arising in Ireland and Great Britain—continued.

dity of discharging stills—formerly but once in twenty-four hours; now every three minutes.
—Use of the saccharometer.—Reason for the superiority of illicit spirits.—Malt and slow
distillation used; not unmalted grain and rapid distillation.—Landholders interested in the
illicit practice.———*English system.*—Small extent of illicit distillation, and confined to
London.——— *System recommended.*—Mode of charging duty.—Reduction of duty.—Malt
duty.—Malted oats, use of, to be permitted.—Size of stills.—Influence of landed proprietors.
—Warehousing.—Mashing.—Penal laws.—Effects of reducing the duty.—Beer.—Spirit
intercourse.———*See* likewise under Head VII. *Distillation, &c.*

13.—Supplement to the Fifth Report of the Commissioners of Inquiry on
Revenue arising in Ireland and Great Britain.

Sess. 1823, (498.) vol. 7, p. 661. [53.]

SUBJECTS. — Intercourse in spirits.— Acts relating to. — Drawbacks on exports from
each country.—Advantage derived by the Irish distiller from the facility of evasion.—
Powerful influence of distillers—shown in the case of Mr. Orme, servant to Mr. Langdale
—and in their monopolizing arrangements with each other.—Uniform distillery laws for
the United Kingdom recommended.———*See* likewise under Head VII. *Distillation, &c.*

14.—Sixth Report of the Commissioners of Inquiry.

Sess. 1823, (560.) vol. 7, p. 725. [54.]

SUBJECTS.—*Establishment and Appointment of Officers.*—Outports of Scotland.—Collection of revenue.—Establishments.—Reductions proposed.—Coast-guard.—Selection of
officers to be made from present ones.—Persons appointed unacquainted with their duties
—to be discontinued.—Removal of unnecessary restrictions on coasting-trade.

15.—Seventh Report of the Commissioners of Inquiry.

Sess. 1824, (100.) vol. 11, p. 1. [54.]

SUBJECTS.—Customs and Excise Establishments in Dublin.

16.—Eighth Report of the Commissioners of Inquiry.

Sess. 1824, (331.) vol. 11, p. 141. [54.]

SUBJECTS.—*Management and Collection of the Revenue.*— *Mode of conducting several
Trades.*—The collection of *quit-rents* ineffectual.———The tanning of *leather* badly conducted, from the levying the duty on the pits inducing a rapid process, by using vallonia
(quercus ægilops) and hot liquor.—Leather injured.—Hides kept in pits from eight months
to two years.—Charging on the pit to be discontinued.———*Paper*—inferior in Ireland,
from the duty being charged by the engine, which induces a rapid process, inconsistent
with good manufacture.—To be altered to the manner adopted in England, *i. e.* by weight.
—The obtaining an equality recommended as equitable to the book-trade of England.
———*Paper-Hangings.*— Duties to be levied as in England.———*Malt.*—Process of
charging the duty in England and Ireland described.—The practice to be assimilated to
the English method.———*See* likewise under Head VIII. *Leather, Tanning, Paper*; and
Head XVII. *Copyright*; and Heads IV. and VIII. *Printing and Stationery.*

17.—Ninth Report of the Commissioners of Inquiry.

Sess. 1824, (340.) vol. 11, p. 305. [54.]

SUBJECTS.—*Revenue Jurisprudence.*—Jurisdiction.—Objections to the existing system.
—Statutes creating judicial functions of the Customs and Excise.—Manner in which the
revenue jurisprudence is exercised in Ireland.—Objections to the character of the revenue
courts.—Proposed to transfer all causes to the decision of the Court of Exchequer.

18.—Tenth Report of the Commissioners of Inquiry.

Sess. 1824, (446.) vol. 11, p. 391. [54.]

SUBJECTS.—*Outports.*—Improved establishment and classification of ports.—Description
and duties of officers.—Warehouses and wet docks in Dublin, constructed at the cost of
the Crown; £. 573,284 having been already expended.—Contrasted with similar undertakings in England, formed at the cost of companies of individuals.—Trifling returns in
shape of storage-rents.—Warehouses to be let on lease.—Buildings to be abandoned at
Waterford.—Principle of erecting storehouses at the expense of the Crown objected to.—
Proposed harbour improvements at Belfast.—Objected to being done at the expense of
the Crown, but a loan recommended to be advanced to the merchants. — Amount of
reductions.—Allowance of two-and-a-half per cent. on payment of army and navy bills
to be discontinued.———*Preventive Coast-guard.*—Rendered necessary by the extent of
smuggling;—chiefly of tobacco.—Caves formed on the coast for secreting goods.—Eighty
of them broken up.—Other advantages of the guard, as aiding the police.—Reduction of
duty on tobacco recommended.——— *Quarantine.*—Proposed regulations.—Abolition of
pratique-master.———*Laws of Customs.*—Difference between the laws of England and
Ireland recommended to attention in the proposed " consolidation of those laws."———
Warehousing.—Removal of goods to be regulated.

Revenue arising in Ireland and Great Britain—continued.

19.—Eleventh Report of the Commissioners of Inquiry on Revenue arising in Ireland and Great Britain.   Sess. 1825, (389.) vol. 13, p. 1. [55.]

SUBJECTS.—*Customs in Scotland.—Edinburgh Establishments, &c.—Proposed Improvements.* — Effect of the alteration in the laws recommended by the Commissioners.— —Benefit of removing the restrictions by repealing the Uuion duties. — Manufacturing establishments in the north of Ireland.—Transfer of Mr. Hutchinson's cotton-factory, in consequence of riotous violence against him by the workmen.—Removal of inconveniences in mercantile transactions in Scotland.—Consolidation of establishments at Port Glasgow and Greenock.—Measures taken on the recommendation of the Sixth Report.—Officers' salaries.—Assistant collectors and comptrollers.—Duties of the comptroller.—Should keep a journal.—Re-weighing warehoused goods.—Warehousing at Grangemouth.—Hereditary revenue.—Amount.— New arrangement proposed. — Consolidation of accounts.—Coast-guard, and smuggling.— Edinburgh establishment.— Proposed reductions.—Comptroller-general and accountant-general. — Surveyor-general.— Jerquers and examiners offices.— Registrar of seizures.—Storekeeper and clerk of postages.— Inspector-general of imports and exports.— Receiver-general's office. — Supervisor of receiver-general's accounts.— Solicitors.—Proposed changes in that office.—Payment to be by salary, not by bills of costs. —Observations on the best mode of payment.—Solicitor for Scotch law not necessary.— Solicitor of Customs, Ireland.—Both of Scotland and Ireland not to transact private business—nor have in hand any balance of public money.—Agent at the Treasury to be abolished.—Housekeeper, officekeeper and messenger.—Extra allowances upon the establishment.—Meritorious exertions of Mr. Earl, President of the Board of Customs in Scotland.— Summary of the proposed reductions in the establishments of Edinburgh and Dublin.—Recommendation to resist the creation of new offices ; and to exact clear and simple accounts.———The Appendix contains many papers—a list of articles paying duty—examinations—forms of documents and accounts.

20.—Twelfth Report of the Commissioners of Inquiry.

Sess. 1825, (390.) vol. 14, p. 1. [56.]

SUBJECTS.—Excise, Scotland.—Receipts, Payments, and Accounts.—New Distillery Law. —Illicit Distillation.—Establishments.—Glass Duties.——*See* also No. 12, and under Head VII. *Distilleries.*

21.—Thirteenth Report of the Commissioners of Inquiry.

Sess. 1826, (435.) vol. 10, p. 1. [57.]

SUBJECTS.—*Board of Stamps, London.*—Constitution of the Board of Stamps.—Duties of the Commissioners.—Manner in which those duties have been performed.—Unfavourable impression as to the efficiency of the Board.—Establishment and salaries.—Allowance of residence to the Chairman objected to.—Habitual attendance of the Commissioners— very uncertain.—Warrants signed in blank.—Conduct of Mr. Sedgwick, as chairman, censured ;— Considered as having a superior responsibility,— Remissness, and want of knowledge of the Acts of Parliament relative to his department.—Constant disagreement between the chairman and another member ; and interruption to business in consequence. —Want of system in conducting the business of the Board.—Irregularity and delay.— Objections to members of the Board being engaged in private concerns.—The chairman a principal and directing proprietor of the British Press newspaper.—The chairman and other members directors of insurance companies.—Objection does not extend to the propriety of public functionaries holding capital in such concerns ; but to their being engaged so that their private interests come in collision with their public duties.— Necessity of constituting a Board on which reliance can be placed for their efficiency and cordial co-operation to carry into effect any improvement in the system of revenue collection.

22.—Fourteenth Report of the Commissioners of Inquiry.

Sess. 1826, (436.) vol. 10, p. 69. [57.]

SUBJECTS.—*Department of Stamps.*—Nature of the stamp revenue.—Course of proceeding at the office.—Supply to the country.—Amount of revenue in 1823 to 1825.—Establishment. — Secretary's office. — Scale of salaries.———Solicitor's department. — Mr. Sykes's appointment—approved of as preferable to a solicitor who was allowed to pursue his private practice.—Scale of salary for the establishment of the office.———Receiver-general's department.—Insufficiency of security.—Receipts of money.—Manner of conducting the office business.—Improved arrangements recommended.———Accountant and comptroller-general.—Establishment of the office.—Duties.—Inconsistency of the private and official duties of the present officer, being a private solicitor.—Mode of keeping the accounts of the several duties.—Revenue arising in the country.—Defective control.—No security required of the accountant and comptroller-general.—Imperfect audit ;—particularly of cancelled stamps.—Establishment proposed.———Registrar of warrants.—Detail of business.———Stamping-room.—Possibility of frauds.—Instances of their being practised.—Proposed regulation of their office.—Rolling-press or newspaper stamps, &c.— Course of business.—Proposed regulations.—Country bank notes.—Sir Wm. Congreve's plans ;—inapplicability ;—dilatory and expensive. ——— Sale-warehouse—proposed to be established for supplying the public, instead of furnishing their own paper.——— Warehouse of unstamped goods.———Warehouse of stamped goods for supplying country distributors. —Stamps on law proceedings.—Allowance for spoiled stamps.—Paper and parchment becomes the perquisite of the Board messenger.—Defects in the system.—Improved regulations proposed.—Attornies' certificates and bankers' licences.—Medicine labels.—Newspaper and Pamphlet office.—Duty should be graduated proportionate to the length of the advertisement.—Pamphlet duty—to be more strictly enforced.—Proprietor of the British

Press

Revenue arising in Ireland and Great Britain—continued.

> Press is Mr. Sedgwick, chairman of the Board.—Other persons registered as such, for the purpose of concealment.—Objections to any officer holding such engagements.——Sea policies.—Office to be abolished.——Cards and dice.—Evasion of duty.——Stage-coach department;—Mile duty.—Licences.—Manner of collecting them.—False returns of journies performed.—Proposed regulations.——Distributors.—Unequal apportionment of districts.—Securities.—Stocks in the hands of the distributors—disproportionately large in some districts.—Rate of poundage to distributors.—Proposed regulations for supplying the country with stamps.—Arrears and balances.—Irrecoverable debt to be expunged from the accounts.—— Inspectors.—Reports insufficient. — Sufficiency of securities to be reported on.—Annual inspections recommended.——*Fire Insurances.*—Insufficiency of the present mode of ascertaining the correctness of the accounts.—County Fire-office.—Irregular claim of allowances for stamps.—Mr. Sedgwick, the chairman, a director.—Mr. Barber Beaumont alleges that it arose from a conspiracy of clerks, now discarded, to injure the character of the office.—Prosecution recommended.——*Post-horse Duty.*—The mode of collecting it by farmers objectionable.—Management proposed to be transferred to the Tax-office.——*Race-horse Duty.*— Recommended to be discontinued. —— *Plate.*— Imperfect mode of collection.—Frauds and evasions.—Proposed remedies.—Assay to be entrusted to the Mint.—(*See* likewise under the Head XI.)——Discounts, &c.—— Penalty on stamping deeds after execution.——*Consolidation of stamp laws.*——*Classification* and *simplification* of duties.

23.—Fifteenth Report of the Commissioners of Inquiry on Revenue arising in Ireland and Great Britain.   Sess. 1828, (6.) vol. **13**, p. 1.
> SUBJECT.—Stamps, Scotland.

24.—Sixteenth Report of the Commissioners of Inquiry.
> SUBJECT.—Stamp Revenue, Ireland.   Sess. 1828, (7.) vol. **14**, p. 1.

25.—Seventeenth Report of the Commissioners of Inquiry.
> SUBJECT.—Stamp Revenue, Ireland.   Sess. 1828, (8.) vol. **15**, p. 1.

26.—Eighteenth Report of the Commissioners of Inquiry.
          Sess. 1829, (161.) vol. **11**, p. 1.
> SUBJECT.—Post-office Revenue of the United Kingdom.

27.—Nineteenth Report of the Commissioners of Inquiry.
> SUBJECT.—Post-office Revenue of Ireland.   Sess. 1829, (353.) vol. **12**, p 1.

28.—Twentieth Report of the Commissioners of Inquiry.
> SUBJECT.—Post-office Revenue of Scotland.   Sess. 1830, (63.) vol. **13**, p. 1.

29.—Twenty-first Report of the Commissioners of Inquiry.
          Sess. 1830, (94.) vol. **13**, p. 367.
> SUBJECT.—Post-office Revenue of England.—Twopenny-post.

30.—Twenty-second Report of the Commissioners of Inquiry.
          Sess. 1830, (647.) vol. **14**, p. 1.
> SUBJECT.—Post-office Revenue of the United Kingdom.—Packet Establishment.

Excise Establishment and Revenue :

31.—First Report of the Commissioners of Inquiry into the Excise Establishments, and management and collection of the Excise Revenue throughout the United Kingdom.   Sess. 1833, (T.) vol **21**, p. 417.
> SUBJECT.—Tea Permits and Surveys.

32.—Second Report of the same Commissioners.   Sess. 1834, (T.) vol. **24**, p. 1.
> SUBJECT.—Wine Permits and Surveys.

33.—Third Report of the same Commissioners.   Sess. 1834, (T.) vol. **24**, p. 87.
> SUBJECT.—Summary Jurisdiction.

34.—Fourth Report of the same Commissioners.   Sess. 1834, (T.) vol. **24**, p. 159
> SUBJECT.--Survey of Breweries.——*See* likewise under Head VII.

35.—Fifth Report of the same Commissioners.   Sess. 1834, (T.) vol. **24**, p. 205.
> SUBJECT.—Stone Bottles and Sweets.

Excise Establishment and Revenue—continued.

36.—Sixth Report of the Commissioners of Inquiry into the Excise Establishments, and management and collection of the Excise Revenue throughout the United Kingdom.　　　　Sess. 1834, (т.) vol. 24, p. 237.

    SUBJECT.—Tobacco and Spirits.

37.—Seventh Report of the same Commissioners.　　Sess. 1834, (т.) vol. 25, p. 1.

    SUBJECT.—British Spirits, Part 1.

38.—Eighth Report of the same Commissioners.　　Sess. 1834, (т.) vol. 25, p. 459.

    SUBJECT.—Starch.

39.—Ninth Report of the same Commissioners.　　Sess. 1834, (т.) vol. 25, p. 541.

    SUBJECT.—Vinegar.

40.—Tenth Report of the same Commissioners.　　Sess. 1834, (т.) vol. 25, p. 585.

    SUBJECT.—Malt Duties, Ireland.——*See* likewise under Head VII.

Salt Duties, 1801 :

41.—[Reports from the Select Committee on the Laws relative to the Salt Duties, and on the means of remedying the inconveniences arising therefrom.　　First Series, vol. x. pp. 506, 507 ; and 1st Report, Sess. 1805, (35.) vol. 3, p. 69.—2d Report, Sess. 1818, (115.) vol. 5, p. 299.

    SUBJECTS.—Intricacies and perplexities of the salt laws, and their bad effects on the fisheries, &c.—A relaxation or revision of the present salt duties necessary, and the best method to be adopted.—Frauds committed on the revenue by the evasion of the duties on salt.

Salt Duties, 1817 :

42.—Report from the Select Committee on the use of Rock Salt in the Fisheries ; Regulations on the use of and storing of Refined Salt ; Allowance of Salt duty free ; Duties on Foreign Salt imported, and state of the Duty upon Mineral and other Alkali.　　Sess. 1817, (247.) vol. 3, p. 121.

    SUBJECTS.—Disadvantage to the fisheries if prevented from using foreign salt.—Use of crushed rock salt.—Experiments to be made to ascertain its relative quality.—No additional duty should be imposed on foreign salt.—Preference of British salt for curing herrings.—Manufacture of alkali and kelp to be encouraged.

43.—Report from the Select Committee on the Laws relating to the Salt Duties.　　Sess. 1818, (393.) vol. 5, p. 339. [135.]

    SUBJECTS.—Effect of the duty in discouraging the use of salt in manufactures and other beneficial purposes.—Use of salt in agriculture :—by grazing farmers in feeding cattle.—Different qualities of salt.—Proportion used in curing bacon and pork.—Prices of those meats.—Domestic consumption.—Kelp.—Curing fish.——*See* likewise *Agriculture,* under Head VI.

Tea Duties :

44.—Report from the Select Committee on the expediency of establishing a fixed Rate of Duty on all descriptions of Tea imported into the United Kingdom.　　Sess. 1834, (518.) vol. 17, p. 1.

    SUBJECTS.—History of the manufacture of Canton bohea.—Great quantity of tea exported from China by the Americans.—Description of the manufacture of tea.—Quality of tea depends very much on the season.—No difficulty in distinguishing hyson and its dependent manufactures.—Lower classes of the people will not be benefited by the change in the proposed alteration of tea duties.—Greater profit to be made by importing bohea than congou.—A uniform rate of duty the best mode of preventing teas being smuggled.—Observations as to the working of the scale of rated duties with reference to its effect in a financial point of view.—Price of tea regulated by the supply and demand.—Amount of duty on teas in America.—Custom-house regulations in America with regard to the collection of duties.—Statement showing the decreased consumption of congou, and the increased consumption of bohea, at two different periods.—Probable operation of one duty on all teas.—Operation of the present scale of British duties.—Operation of the scale of duties adopted in the United States—and in Holland.

LAND REVENUE.

Derwentwater Estate, 1732 :

45.—[Report from the Select Committee relating to the Sale of the forfeited Estate of James late Earl of Derwentwater, and invested in His Majesty for the use of the Public.   First Series, vol. 1. p. 351.

>   SUBJECTS.—Fraudulent sale of estates, &c.—Suspicious circumstances attending the sale of an annuity charged on the Derwentwater estate.—Destruction, obliteration or suppression of records.—Misconduct of the Commissioners in transacting their duties.—Suspected to have concerted the irregular sales, and to have connived at the destroying or suppression of records.———See *Highland Roads and Bridges*, under Head XIX.

Woods, Forests, and Land Revenue :

>   1787–1793:

46.—[Seventeen Reports of the Commissioners appointed to inquire into the State and Condition of the Woods, Forests and Land Revenues of the Crown. —Dated from 25 January 1787, to 28 March 1793.

>   Journals, vol. 42, p. 310; vol. 43, pp. 145, 559; vol. 44, pp. 126, 552; vol. 45, p. 120; vol 46, p. 97; vol. 47, pp. 141, 883, 1031 ; vol. 48, p. 267.—[IV. V.]

>   SUBJECTS.—History of the Royal Forests, and other estates of the Crown.—Claims on them in virtue of grants, or by custom or prescription.—Supply of timber for the navy. — Observations on the growth of oak.———Considerable information on the tenure of estates enjoyed under the Crown, and situated in, or reclaimed from, the King's Forests.

>   1797–1809:

47.—Four Reports of the Surveyor-General of His Majesty's Land Revenue, in pursuance of Act 34 Geo. 3.   Sess. 1812, (274.) vol. 12, p. 513. [VI.]

>   1812–1834:

Reports of the Commissioners of His Majesty's Woods, Forests and Land Revenues ; in obedience to the Acts 34 and 50 Geo. 3.

48.—First Report.   Sess. 1812, (357.) vol. 12, p. 347. [VII.]

>   SUBJECTS.—New system of management established by 34 Geo. 3, c. 75.—Recommendations in Mr. Fordyce's Reports in consequence.—Department of Land Revenue.— Leases granted.—Sales and purchases of estates.—Enfranchisements.—Improvement of Marylebone Park, on its reverting to the Crown.—Design by Messrs. Leverton & Chawner, and Mr. Nash.—Regent's Canal.—Improvement at Whitehall-place.—Near the Opera House.—In the line of Titchborne-street and Swallow-street—Drury-lane end of Holborn—At the Savoy.———Department of Woods and Forests.—Consumption of oak timber.—Necessity of setting apart land for its cultivation, and progressive growth.—State of Royal Forests.

49.—Second Triennial Report.   Sess. 1816, (147.) vol. 15. [VII.]

>   SUBJECTS.—Leases granted.—Fee-farm rents sold.—Enfranchisements.—Sales and purchases.—Improvement of Whitehall-place—Opera House.—Sale of palace at Newmarket.— Inclosures.—Approbation of Mr. Nash's Plan for improving Marylebone Park—which is carrying into execution.—Plan for a new street from Portland-place to Pall-mall, opposite Carlton-house.———State of the Royal Forests.—Plantations in Dean and New Forests, manner of managing them.—Nurseries established in the forests for raising plants.—Maintenance and repair of lodges and buildings in parks and forests.

50.—Third Triennial Report.   Sess. 1819, (474.) vol. 19. [VII.]

>   SUBJECTS.—Transactions since the last Triennial Report.—Purchase of the Claremont estate.—Grants of sites for churches.—Whitehall-place.—Sale of Newmarket palace.— Progress in improvements of Marylebone Park.—Purchase of St. Marylebone Rectory. —New street from the " northern parts of the Metropolis to Charing-cross."—Money raised by loan and otherwise.—Purchase of property wanted for the new street.—Difficulty of adjusting claims for good-will.—Continuation of Pall-mall to St. Martin's Church.—Appropriation of land for the growth of timber.———Management of the Royal Forests.— Waltham or Hainault and Epping Forests. — Proposition for disafforesting and inclosing, for preserving the growth of timber.———Progressive growth of oak trees, ascertained by comparison at different periods.

51.—Fourth Triennial Report.   Sess. 1823, (110.) vol. 11. [VII.]

>   SUBJECTS.—*State of Crown Property.*—Proceedings of Commissioners since the last Report.—New leases granted.—Progress of the New Street,—and of Regent's Park.—Plantations in royal parks and forests.—Oak plantations.—In what cases reduction of rents has been granted.

Woods, Forests and Land Revenue—continued.

52.—Fifth Triennial Report of the Commissioners of His Majesty's Woods, Forests and Land Revenues.   Sess. 1826, (368.) vol. 14. [VII.]

>   SUBJECTS.—*Improvements in the Parks.—Proposed New Streets.—Public Buildings.*—Progress in the management of the Crown estates.—Leases granted.—Sale of lands.—Improvements in the plan of building in Regent's Park.—Grant to St. Catherine's Hospital.—Progress of the New Street.—Improvements at Pall-mall and Charing-cross—British Museum and Holborn—Lincoln's-inn-fields—Oxford-street.—Improvements postponed.—Downing-street and the Strand.—Improvement of the Parks for the gratification of the public by the King's desire.—Forests and timber.—General account of income.———See *Public Works*, under Head XIX.

53.—Sixth Triennial Report.   Sess. 1829, (317.) vol. 14. [VII.]

>   SUBJECTS.—Leases granted and sales made.—Fee-farm rents and enfranchisements.—Grants and purchases.—Lighthouse.—Derelict lands in Lincolnshire, and waste lands at Hastings.—Property in the Island of Alderney, and annuity to Duke of Atholl on duties in the Isle of Man.—Westminster-mews.—Buckingham Palace.—York-house.—Carlton-buildings on the site of Carlton-house and Gardens.—St. James's and Hyde Park improvements—At Charing-cross.—Land revenue in Ireland.———Whittlewood, Salcey, New and Parkhurst Forests.

54.—Seventh, or First Annual Report, under 10 Geo. 4, c. 50.
                Sess. 1830, (508.) vol 16.

>   SUBJECTS.—No inquiries concerning the estates of the Crown from the time of Queen Anne to 1786.—Proceedings since then to the present time.———Leases granted and sales made, and other dispositions of the land revenue.—Exchanges and grants.—Derelict lands at Hastings.—New street at Charing-cross.———Land revenue in Ireland.—General receipts and expenditure.

55.—Eighth, or Second Annual Report.   Sess. 1831, (179,) folio vol.

>   SUBJECTS.—Leases granted.—Sales—Of Apsley-house to the Duke of Wellington.—Other sales and enfranchisements.—Progress of Charing-cross and Strand improvements.—Accounts of general receipts and expenditure.

56.—Ninth, or Third Annual Report.   Sess. 1831–32, (718.) folio vol.

>   SUBJECTS.—Leases, sales, and enfranchisements.—Charing cross and Strand improvements.—New street from opposite Waterloo-bridge to Covent-garden.—Windsor Castle and Buckingham Palace.

57.—Tenth, or Fourth Annual Report.   Sess. 1833, (738.) folio vol.

>   SUBJECTS.—Appointment under Act 2 Will. 4, c. 1, of Three Commissioners to perform the duties of the former Commissioners and Surveyor-general.—Leases made.—Sales and enfranchisements.—Proceedings in improvements at Charing-cross and the Strand.—General statement of receipts and disbursements.

58.—Eleventh, or Fifth Annual Report.   Sess. 1834, (607.) folio vol.

>   SUBJECTS.—Leases granted and sales made.—Enfranchisements made, and fee-farm rents sold.—Purchaser.—Progress of Charing-cross improvements.—Grants of land for vicarage-house and national school in St. Martin's parish.—Holyhead roads and bridges placed under the direction of the Board.—Debts due from the Board, and progress of liquidation.

Land-Tax Redemption :

59.—Statement of the Proceedings of the Lords Commissioners respecting Sales, &c. of Estates for the Redemption of the Land-Tax.

>   SUBJECT.—Proceedings of the Commissioners.   Sess. 1806, (214.) vol. 6, p. 517. [99.]

60.—Report of the Commissioners for the Sale and Redemption of the Land-Tax on Church and Corporation Estates.   Sess. 1810, (325.) vol. 9, p. 119. [99.]

>   SUBJECT.—Proceedings of the Commissioners.

61.—Report of the Commissioners for the Sale and Redemption of the Land-Tax on Church and Corporation Estates.   Sess. 1812-13, (71.) vol. 5, p. 527. [99.]

>   SUBJECT.—Further proceedings ; and suggestions for promoting the object of the Commission.

Windsor Forest :

62.—First, Second and Third Reports of the Commissioners on the State of Windsor Forest ; and Appendix to Second and Third Reports.

Sess. 1809, (132. 133. 134.) vol. 4, pp. 263. 271. 343. [72.]

SUBJECTS.—Boundaries.—Manerial rights.—Claims of pasturage.—Forest courts and laws.—Encroachments.—Cultivation of timber.—Evil habits encouraged by scattered residences on forests.

63.—Fourth Report of the Commissioners.   Sess. 1810, (115.) vol. 9, p. 173. [72.]

SUBJECTS.—Mode of allotting the forest, and principle of making compensation for rights extinguished.—Claims of the Crown.

Crown Leases :

64.—Report from the Select Committee on the conduct of Mr. Nash, so far as regards the granting of Leases of, or Sale of, Crown Lands in Suffolk-street, Pall-mall-street, Regent-street, and adjoining the Regent's Canal.

Sess. 1829, (343.) vol. 3, p. 37.

SUBJECTS.—On the proceedings of the Office of Woods in granting leases.—Imputed irregularity in respect of leases granted to Mr. Nash, one of the architects and surveyors employed by the Board.—Resolutions approving his integrity ; but recommending the discontinuance of the practice of allowing an officer to become a lessee of the Crown in cases where it becomes his duty to report on his own buildings.

65.—Report from the Select Committee on the management of the Woods, Forests and Land Revenues of the Crown.   Sess. 1833, (677.) vol. 14, p. 235.

SUBJECTS.—Amount of revenue of Crown lands in Middlesex collection.—Arrears of Crown rents, and portion that is irrecoverable.—Freehold estates subject to a life interest do not sell so advantageously as if sold in fee.—Great depreciation in the value of villa and house property.—Suggestions for improvement in the mode of keeping accounts.—Arrears in entries of accounts.—Manner the expense of building Carlton-terrace was defrayed.—Particulars as to Chancery suits connected with York-house.—Collectors of Crown rents in Ireland very diligent.—Crown rents.—Fees on granting leases.—Crown lands usually let on leases without fines.—Management of the Scotch and Irish land revenue transferred to the Office of Woods and Forests.—Complaints of the depredations made by the deer in the New Forest.—Particulars respecting the sale of Ort's estate.—Nature of the expenditure on the different Parks by the Office of Woods and Forests and Board of Works.—Proceeds of quit-rents invested in the funds.—Receivers of Crown rents.—Expense of paving Regent-street.—Value of the tolls arising from Romford market.—Surveyors of Crown estates.—Opposition of Commissioners of the Thames Navigation to suggestions of Messrs. Driver.—Valuation of Crown property.—Duties and management of the Office of Woods and Forests ; its establishment, and reductions therein, and control of the Treasury over it.

66.—Report from the Select Committee on the management of the Woods, Forests and Land Revenues of the Crown.   Sess. 1834, (579.) vol. 15, p. 457.

SUBJECTS.—Amount of Crown rents and expense of collection.—Crown lands generally sold by public auction.—Sums expended on the improvements at Ort's estate near Reading.—Expenditure for inclosing forests for planting and protecting timber very considerable.—Reduction in the disbursements connected with Windsor parks.—Arrears of Crown rents in Wales.—Difficulties in defining boundaries of Crown and private property.—Ferries belonging to the Crown should not be granted on lease to private individuals.—Particulars respecting improvements made since the Crown obtained possession of the lands at Pobble O'Keefe.—(and see *Public Works*, under Head XIX.)—Value of Crown property in Orkney, and expense of management.—Land revenue of Ireland ; mode of selling quit-rents there.—The rights of the Crown in Ireland are not barred by fine and recovery.——See likewise under Head XIX.

XIII.

Annuities.—Usury.—Friendly Societies.

Annuities :

1.— Report from the Select Committee on the Petition of Cadogan Williams, recommending the purchase of Life Annuities under the authority of Government.   Sess. 1829, (284.) vol. 3, p. 247.

> SUBJECTS.—Proposition of Cadogan Williams for establishing, under the authority and management of Government, a plan for allowing the purchase of deferred annuities.—Advantage to the industrious classes.—Mr. Higham's plan for making Savings Banks sub-servient to this purpose by converting deposits into annuities.—Mr. Finlaison's tables of the value of such annuities, and explanation of the principles on which they are constructed, and on the practicability of calculating tables for granting annuities under any conditions required.—Plan proposed in 1773.—Existing power of Commissioners of National Debt to grant deferred annuities explained.

2.—Report of John Finlaison, Actuary of the National Debt, on the Evidence and Elementary Facts on which the Tables of Life Annuities are founded.
                                  Sess. 1829, (122.) vol. 3, p. 287.

> SUBJECTS.—Explanation of the principles of calculation ; with many tables.—Statement of facts and arithmetical conclusions deduced from observations on the mortality of the nominees in the various tontines, and sets of life annuities granted by Government.— Twenty-two observations, with the facts or data, and arithmetical consequences resulting, arranged in tables for easily conveying information.—Two tables : 1. showing the value of an annuity of 1,000 *l.*, deduced from various observations : 2. a comparison of the law of mortality deduced from certain observations.

Usury and Annuities, 1777 :

3.— [Report from the Select Committee on the Laws against Usury, and on the present practice of granting Annuities.   Journals, vol. 36, p. 489.

> SUBJECTS.—Laws for settling the rate of interest.—Year's purchase of annuities.—Cal-culations of the real value of annuities.—Mr. Mavor's tables ;—Mr. Morgan's.—Opinion that the rate of interest should be graduated according to the age of the person on whose life the annuity is granted;—resolution thereupon.

Usury Laws, 1818 :

4.—Report from the Select Committee on the Usury Laws.
                                  Sess. 1818, (376.) vol. 6, p. 139. [22.]

> SUBJECTS.—*Expediency of their Repeal.*—Laws ineffectual.—Evaded, and higher rates of interest obtained than five per cent.— Money difficult to be raised on mortgage at that rate.—Granted by way of annuity.—Laws disadvantageous to landed property.—No restric-tion in Holland, Hambro', &c.—Fears as to the effects on tradesmen's bills drawn from the country.—Mode of transacting loans by way of annuities.—Mode of conducting sales of goods by brokerage, where money is advanced.— Opinion of several eminent conveyancers and solicitors on the subject of the rate of interest as affecting landed property, from the difficulty of raising money at five per cent. on mortgage.

Friendly Societies :

5.—Report from the Select Committee on the Laws respecting Friendly Societies.   Sess. 1825, (522.) vol. 4, p. 321. [134.]

> SUBJECTS.—*Mode in which they are constituted.—Management.— Utility.—Defects in the principle of Management in many instances, from Miscalculations.*—Progress and present state of the law —Principles that should guide the interference of the Legislature in societies for lawful purposes —Advantages of Mr. Rose's Act.—Number of friendly societies, and members.—No power given to judge of the adequacy of the means of creating funds.— Defect in provisions to prevent dissolution.—Inadequacy of funds from defective calcula-tions of the rate of contributions.— Evils of assembling in public-house.—Some evils as
> tending

Friendly Societies—continued.

tending to facilitate combinations of trades.—Other objections to friendly societies answered.
—Greater good effected by the contributions of many to a common fund, than by individual savings.— Comparison of Saving Banks with friendly societies.—Necessity of
sanctioning justices having reference to the proportion of the contributions to the payments.
—Allowances wrongfully admitted, for contingencies not natural, as confinement for debt.
—Number of persons supposed to be necessary to ensure the expected advantage.—Large
county societies most advantageous; but the people prefer small clubs.—Difficulty of
applying the power of the law, in requiring the sanction of *actuaries* to the rates of deposit
and allowance.—Necessity of procuring accurate tables.— No data ascertained till lately.
—Dr. Price's hypothesis—near approach to practical results.—Mr. Morgan's and Mr.
Frend's concurrence.—Mr. Finlaison's opinion on the law of sickness. – " The Scots Tables"
on the same subject ;—important information contained in them.— " Royal Union Association."— " Mutual Insurance Benefit Institution,"—objects and management.— Insurance of
old age annuities.—Importance of securing a sufficient contribution for superannuation allowances.—On regulations respecting the obtaining of the sanction of actuaries.—Production
and rearing of children.—On the construction of Dr. Price's tables.— Recommendations on
certifying the rules of friendly societies, depositing funds, &c., and making returns.—On
extending the objects of these societies to the endowment of children.—Difficulty of procuring trustees in small societies under Act of 1819.— Provisions to prevent fraudulent
dissolutions of societies.—On investing money of societies in Savings Banks, or other securities.—On secret articles of some societies not included in their printed rules.— Apprehended perversion of benefit societies to purposes of combination not true to any extent.—
Guarantee of debenture interest to be confined only to such societies as draw their deben-
tures direct from the Bank of England, not to those depositing in Savings Banks.— Acts to
be consolidated — Progress of similar societies in France.—Subject too important to have
been fully discussed—but useful materials furnished by the Committee.——Tables of
average duration of life ;—of liability to sickness and accident ;—of proportionate contributions and allowance for sickness, accidents and old age ;— of the purchase of annuities ; of
endowments for children ;—and of other deferred annuities, payments or benefits.

6.—Report on the Laws respecting Friendly Societies.

Sess. 1826-27, (558.) vol. 3, p 869. [134.]

SUBJECTS.—*Continuation of the preceding Subject.*—*Doctrine of Life Annuities as applied
to Friendly Societies.*—Society at Southwell under the direction of the Rev. J. B. Becher
established on good principles.—Their tables of duration of life approved.—Comparative
merits of several tables.—The Carlisle tables applicable to general purposes.—Comparative value of male and female life.—Societies should be on as large a scale as possible to
insure success.—Expediency of forming an Act embodying the improvements suggested
by the Committee.——On the principle of constructing the Southwell and Northampton
tables :—the Carlisle tables.—On calculating annuities for old age.—Longevity of the
Swedes.—Duration of life in England increased.—Utility of the Enumeration Returns.—
Singular fact resulting from registers in France, that there are a greater proportion of
female illegitimate children than of female legitimate children born.— Number of persons
necessary to form an advantageous society, and capital necessary.——Life of married
women better than that of single women.—Comparative production of early and late marriages,—and mortality of infants.— Influence of the mother's occupation and the father's
health on the child produced.—Practice of different assurance societies.—On the methods
of calculating deferred annuities.—Tables constructed by Mr. Finlaison under the direction
of the Lords of the Treasury, for the contributions of benefit societies.—Various tables,
showing the law of mortality ; of contributions for insuring deferred annuities, and for the
endowment of children.

And further respecting Annuities, see *Finance*, Head X.

XIV.

East India Affairs.

State of the Company, 1698 :

1.—⎡Report from the Select Committee appointed to inspect the Books of the
Company.   Journals, vol. 12, p. 311.

> Subjects.—State of the affairs of the then existing Company, and extent of their
> ability to carry on a beneficial trade.—Expediency of incorporating other individuals, who
> offer to Government an advance of a considerable loan.

Trade, Possessions and Government, 1756–1770 :

2.—⎡Five Reports from the Select Committee on the Affairs of the East India
Company.   First Series, vol. III.

> Subjects.—1. Charters, &c.—Company's trade, possessions and government.—Seizure
> of Calcutta, and confinement of the English in the Black-hole.—Murder of Ramnarrain.—
> Elevation and deposition of Meer Jaffier.—Expulsion of Cossim Ali Khan.———2. Con-
> duct of the Company's servants.—Cojamaul's petition.—American merchants.—Country
> trade.———3. War with Cossim Ali Khan.—Presents to Europeans.———4. Trade in
> salt, betel-nut, &c.———5. Conduct of Lord Clive.—Receipt by him of five lacs of
> rupees.

Debts, Credits, Government and Judicature, 1772–1773 :

3.—⎡Nine Reports from the Select Committee on the Affairs of the East India
Company.   First Series, vol. IV.

> Subjects.—Appointment of commissioner for superintending and regulating the affairs
> of the Company in the East.—Debts and revenues of the Company.—Territorial manage-
> ment, particularly in Bengal and Bahar.—Civil and military establishments.—Lord Clive.
> —Hindoos.—Freight and demurrage.—Drawing and accepting bills. — Salt trade.—
> Society trade.—Betel-nut.—Former and present state of the judicature in Bengal.

Carnatic War, 1774–1781 :

4.—⎡Six Reports from the Committee of Secrecy on the causes of the War in
the Carnatic ; and the condition of the British Possessions in those Parts.
                                                 First Series, vols. VII & VIII.

> Subjects.—Military transactions.—Civil and political transactions.—Financial affairs.—
> Trade and commerce.—Religion, manners and customs.

Administration of Justice, 1775–1783 :

5.—⎡Report from the Select Committee relative to the Administration of
Justice, &c. in India.   First Series, vol. V.

6.—⎡Eleven Reports from the Select Committee on the State of the Administration of Justice in Bengal, Bahar and Orissa.   First Series, vols. V. & VI.

7.—⎡Two Reports on the Petitions of the East India Company, relating to
Financial Affairs.   First Series, vol. VI.

> Subjects.—Administration of justice in India.—Political transactions.—Civil transac-
> tions.—Military arrangements.—Trade and commerce.—Financial affairs of the Company.
> —Religion, manners and customs.

Financial, Commercial and Political Affairs, 1805–1813 :

8.—Report from the Committee on the Account between the Public and the
East India Company.   Sess. 1805, (197.) vol. 6, p. 789. [58.]

9.—First Report from the Select Committee on the Affairs of the Company.
                                      Sess. 1808, (261.) vol. 3, p. 159. [58.]

> Subjects.—Revenue and charges, and commercial concerns of the Company.

Financial, Commercial and Political Affairs—continued.

10.—Second Report from the Select Committee on the Affairs of the Company.

SUBJECT.—Revenue and charges.   Sess. 1810, (363.) vol. 5, p. 13. [59.]

11.—Third Report from the Select Committee on the Affairs of the Company.   Sess. 1810–11, (250.) vol. 7, p. 1. [59.]

SUBJECT.—Extraordinary receipts and disbursements.

12.—Fourth Report from the Select Committee on the Affairs of the Company.   Sess. 1812, (148.) vol. 6, p. 1. [59.]

SUBJECT.—Trade.

13.—Supplement to the Fourth Report of the Committee.

SUBJECT.—Private Trade.   Sess. 1812, (151 & 182.) vol. 6, p. 117. [59.]

Indian Debt:

14.—Report of the Select Committee on the Company's Petition.

Sess. 1812, (280.) vol. 6, p. 429.

Internal Government, and Territorial Revenue:

15.—Fifth Report from the Select Committee on the Affairs of the Company.

Sess. 1812, (377.) vol. 7, p. 1. [60.]

SUBJECT.—General management, history and government of India.

16.—Glossary to the Fifth Report.   Sess. 1813, (148.) vol. 10, p. 431.

SUBJECT.—The vernacular names and terms occurring in the Reports on East India Affairs are explained, and their derivation shown from the Oriental languages, representing them in the Arabic, Persian, Sanskrit and Hindustany characters, and conveying their pronunciation by the English in the European type.—This work was compiled by *Dr. Wilkins*, librarian of the East India Company.

Raising Capital:

17.—Report from the Select Committee on the Affairs of the East India Company.   Sess. 1810, (255.) vol. 5, p. 1. [61.]

SUBJECT.—On the injurious effects of raising money by increasing their capital stock.

Renewal of the Charter:

18.—Minutes of Evidence taken before the Committee of the whole House, and the Select Committee, on the Affairs of the East India Company.

SUBJECT.—Renewal of their Charter.   Sess. 1813–14, (122.) vol. 7, p. 1. [61.]

19.—Report from the Committee of Correspondence to the Court of Directors on the subject of the Trade with the East Indies and China.

Sess. 1812–13, (78.) vol. 8, p. 3. [59.]

China Trade, and General Affairs, 1830:

20.—First Report from the Select Committee on the Affairs of the East India Company.   Sess. 1830, (644, comprising 99. 155. 236. 246. 396. 514.) vol. 5.

SUBJECT.—China Trade.

21.— Second Report from the same Committee.   Sess. 1830, (655.) vol. 5, p. 675.

SUBJECTS.—Effects of abolishing the East India Company's Charter, and allowing the British a free trade.—On the trade of America.—Effects on the consumption of manufactures.———Manner of conducting trade between the Company and the Hong.—Mode of contracting for manufactures and tea.—Cotton trade as carried on by the Company.——— Factory at Canton.—Its influence in managing transactions with the Chinese government. —Method of conducting business.—Protection and advantage to trade —Shopmen-traders or out-side dealers at Canton.—Chinese-trade carried on by European and other States. ———Territorial revenue and charges.—Manner of keeping the accounts.—Revenue of India and China.—Derived from tea.———Opium trade.—Great extent and increase.——— Tea trade.—Growth.—Cost.—Supply.—Manner of conducting the trade.———Exports between England and China, and the East Indies.—Freights.—Shipping, British, India, East India Company and Foreign.—Woollen trade.———Character and disposition of the Chinese,—their capacity, and manner of conducting trade.—Disposition of the government towards foreigners and foreign trade.———Character, conduct and capacity of East Indians, *i. e.* Anglo-Indians, Indo-Britains, or Half-Castes.—Education.—Civil distinctions.—Employments.—Numbers and Importance.

China Trade, and General Affairs, 1830 – continued.

22.—Report from the Select Committee of the House of Lords on the present state of the Affairs of the East India Company.   Sess. 1830, (646.) vol. 6.

SUBJECTS.—East India Company's commercial capital.—Manner of conducting their affairs.—Influence and power at Canton.—Advantage of the tea trade.—Management of their shipping.—State of their trade.—Private and privilege trade.—Territorial and Commercial revenues.—Of Indigo.—British manufactures; extent of demand for, in India and China.———Interior trade of India.—Articles of trade.—Cultivation of cotton; its quality and manufacture.—Cultivation, manufacture, and trade of tobacco.—Of indigo.—Of opium; extent and management of that trade.—Manufacture of and revenue from salt.—Cultivation and manufacture of silk.———China trade.—Manner of conducting.—Probable effects of throwing it open.—Character and use of the Hong merchants.—Cultivation of the tea plant.—Management of the tea-trade—consumption, prices and revenue.———American trade with China.———Character and condition of the Hindoos; their language, manners and customs.—State of education; and effect of their religious principles.—Of Mahomedans.—General state of society in India.———Character and condition of half-castes; their education, religion and morality; their capacity for business, and the expediency of allowing them to take a part in public duties and employments.———Prevalence of suttees, and practicability of their suppression.—(and see *infra,* Nos. 50–56.)———Extent of slavery, and condition of slaves.———Extent and state of education in India.—Progress of the English language and literature. ———Europeans resident in India.—Influence of their character.—Advantage of their capital and skill.—Effect of unrestrained residence.—Population of India.———Administration of justice.—Applicability and introduction of English law.—Jurisdiction of Supreme Court.—Introduction of juries.—Law of inheritance.—Tenure and cultivation of land.—Revenue from land.—Ryotwar and zemindary systems.—Effective state of the police.—Provincial courts.

Government, Trade and Judicature, 1831 :

23.—Report from the Select Committee on the present state of the Affairs of the East India Company; and on the state of the Trade between Great Britain, the East Indies, and China; with Appendix I. of Accounts and Papers.—Appendix II. China Papers.—Appendix III. External and Internal Commerce of Bengal, Madras and Bombay.—Appendix IV. Opium and Salt Monopolies.—Appendix V. Legislative Councils and Courts of Justice in British India.   Sess. 1831, (65. 320 A, 320 B, 320 C, 320 D, 320 E.) vols. 5 & 6.

SUBJECTS.—1.—On the constitution and administration of the government of India.—The policy and impolicy of investing the Company with the government, combining a commercial and sovereign character.—Inquiry into the advantages and disadvantages of the trading affairs of the Company.—Effect of the monopoly on individual capitalists, and the trading interests of the country.———Territorial and commercial revenue.—Statements and explanations of its amount and fluctuations.—Accounts and statements of the Company's transactions in trade.—Extent and effect of free trade.—Imports and exports; nature, amount, value and duties.—Shipping and freight.———Financial state of the Company; explanation of accounts.—Debt and interest.—Land revenue and land-tax; management and collection.—Evils of the farming system.—Management of the revenue of the Ceded Provinces.———State of coinage and currency.—Exchange and remittances.—Antiquity of Indian gold and silver coinage.—Authorized coinage by the East India Company.—Value and denomination of the circulating medium.———Banking system in India.—Connexion of the Company with such establishments.—Management of the chartered bank at Calcutta.—Native banks, and nature of their transactions.———Manufactures.—Wages.—Rude description of the native machinery used in India.—Value of British manufactures imported.—Duty.—Great extent of consumption.———Products of India.—Particularly indigo; extent and importance of the trade.—Establishment of factories, and mode of carrying on the business.—Character of the planters.—Iron; extent of the mines.—Produce of ore, and quality, and of manufactured iron.—Silk; production, quality and manufacture.—Management of the trade.—Sugar; increasing cultivation.—Capability of its production.—Extent and importance of the production of cotton.—Cultivation and quality.—Defect of machinery for cleansing cotton.—Native manufacture of cotton.—In what degree interfered with by the importation of English manufacture.—Silk monopoly; investigation of its advantages and disadvantages.—Effect on trade.—How manufactured.—Revenue derived therefrom.———China trade.—Difficulties in altering the present system.—On the practicability of increasing its extent.—Management of the factory at Canton.—Disputes with the Chinese government and interruptions of trade; in consequence of the loss of life in affrays with the natives; from disputes concerning restrictions on trade; from objections to the residence of females at the Factory.—Administration of justice in China, as regards affrays between Europeans and natives.—Character of the Hong merchants, and the manner of conducting their trade.———Administration of justice in India.—Estimation of the King's courts.—Number, appointment and salaries of judges.—Judicial system adapted to the country.—Confidence of the natives.—Its defects and remedies.—Nature and character of native courts.—Character and utility of native pleaders.—Construction of juries.—Exclusion of natives.—Zillah judges.—Police.—Justices of peace; fitness of natives to hold commissions.———Tenure of land.—Zemindar and ryotwar tenure.—Zemindar, ryotwar and village systems explained.—Connexion between zemindars and ryots.—Extent of zemindary influence as a landed interest.—Condition of ryots.—Investigation of their rights.—State of cultivation of lands.—Irrigation; its importance, and the magnitude of ancient works for that purpose.———Education and civilization.—Probable effect of education on the

power

Government, Trade and Judicature, 1831—continued.

power of England in India.—Of the unlimited permission of emigration.—Increased knowledge of the English language and literature.—Travelling; vexatious regulations as to passports.—Evils of the present system of purveyance.—State of Christianity.—State of Indo-Britons; their character, capacity and employments.—Privileges and deprivations.—Licences and security-bonds for European residence.—Inconvenience.—To what extent enforced.—Policy.—Character of the Company's native commercial servants. – Moral and physical character of the natives.—Condition of the agricultural classes. – Hindoos.—Mussulmen.—Progressive improvement by education.——Their feelings towards the English Government.—Their condition in the interior.—Population.—Subsistence and habitation.——Roads and public works.—Trigonometrical surveys.—Superior state of the roads in Java. – Steam boats and engines introduced into India.—Supplies of coal found in India from extensive mines.

II.—Conduct and policy of the Chinese government.—Particular customs and prejudices of the Chinese.—Chinese law of homicide.—Detention of ships and suspension of trade in consequence of discussions respecting the death of Chinese in affrays with the English; and arising from infringement of privilege of trade.—Lord Amherst's embassy in 1816.—Firing on the Chinese forts by His Majesty's ship Alceste.—Alleged breach of the laws of China by the residence of females at Canton, and the use of sedan chairs by Europeans.—Death of Mr. Mackenzie at Canton.—Employment of an armed force for the protection of the Company's Factory.—Bankrupt merchants.—Embarrassment of Hong merchants.—Attempt to establish a co-hong.—Combination of tea merchants.—Frauds in tea contracts. – Burthens and extortions on trade, and contraband practices.

III.—Reports and statements of the articles of importation and exportation.—Account of value.—Comparison of Company's and Private trade.—Observations on the fluctuations of demand in particular branches of trade.—And on the prospects of trade with particular places.

IV.—Opium.— 1. Culture and manufacture.—Generally.—In particular places.—Illicit.—Restraining regulations.——2. Trade.—Exclusive rights of the Company.– General trade.——3. Revenue; duties, and regulations.——4. Consumption and sale; restraining regulations, internal and external.——5. Qualities and prices.——6. General regulations.——Salt.—Manufacture.—Quality.—Duty and revenue.—Export.—Profit.—Regulations.—Illicit trade.

V.— Legislative Councils.—Administration of justice.—New code of laws.——Origin and power of the King's courts.—Authority of local courts.—Interference in the collection of the public revenue.—Establishment of Supreme Court in Bengal.—Dissentions between the King's courts and local governments.—Authority of King's courts over landed and moveable property.—In questions of public revenue.—Authority of Supreme Court in criminal cases.—Proposed establishment of judicial districts and circuits.——Anomalies arising from various laws, regulations and institutions in India.—Difficulties arising from two systems of laws.—Practicability of framing a code applicable to all persons.——Insufficiency of legislative powers invested in the Indian government.—Necessity of local legislation.—Practicability of forming a legislative council.—How to be constituted.—Powers to be entrusted to it.

Renewal of the Charter:

24.—Report from the Select Committee on the Affairs of the East India Company.   Sess. 1831-32, (734. 735.) vols. 9, 10, 11, 12, 13, 14.

Report and General Appendix.——The subjects discussed in this General Report and Appendix are inquired into in detail in the Evidence taken before the Committee, and which are arranged under the following heads:

I. *Public.* Evidence and Appendix.——II. *Finance and Accounts.—Trade.* Part 1. Finance; Evidence and Appendix.—Part 2. Commercial; Appendix.——III. *Revenue.* Evidence and Appendix.——IV. *Judicial.* Evidence and Appendix.——V. *Military.* Evidence and Appendix.——VI. *Political and Foreign.* Evidence and Appendix.

SUBJECTS.—General review of the affairs of the East India Company.—Origin of their Charter.— Amount of capital.—Commercial profit.—Constitution of the Court of Directors, and their functions.—Management by committees and boards.—Duties and powers.—Patronage of directors.—Functions of the Court of Proprietors.—Constitution and powers of the Board of Control.—Trading concerns of the Company.—Export and import trade.—Financial affairs.—Debt and revenue.—State of Indian revenue.—Sources and management.—Territorial finances.—Banking transactions in India.—History of the acquisition of the Company's power in India——Articles of Indian manufacture and produce, and objects of commerce. — Indigo cultivation. — State of planters. —Disputes, and organized gangs of fighters.—Importance of the trade and manufacture.—Opium cultivation, trade and revenue.—Salt, manufacture and revenue.—Silk manufacture.—Tobacco.—Rate of wages, and extreme cheapness of labour.——Government of India.—Necessity of a supreme power.—Constitution of local governments.—Proposed improvements.—Legislation in India.—Proposed formation of a legislative council.—On the native governments.—Their evil effect on the Asiatic people.—Character of Mahomedan rulers.——Political state of Hindostan.—Probabilities and nature of charges.—Effects of Christianity.—Notions of political rights.—Indian settlements compared with the United States.—Subsidiary states; opinion on the nature of the subsidiary system.—Treaties with Asiatic states.——Administration of justice.—Company's courts and supreme courts.—Judicial officers and servants.—Hindoo and Mahomedan codes.—Specimens showing their character and tendency.——Hindoo civil and criminal law.—Severity of punishments.—Character of native judges.——Military government of India.—Appointment and powers of the Governor-general.—Duties and responsibilities.——

Condition

Renewal of the Charter—continued.

> Condition and expense of the army.—The King's—Native—Military establishments. – Disbursements.—Expense of the King's naval force.—Of the Company's Indian navy.—Relative importance.——State of civil establishments.—Number and regulations of servants.——
> Ceded and conquered provinces.—Revenue and management.—Tenure of land.—Ryots and ryotwar system.—Zemindary system.——State of education.—Haileybury College——Its success.—College at Calcutta.—Inquiry into its utility.—Progress of education among the native Indians—and efforts made for its diffusion.—Desire of the natives to acquire the English language.—Control of the press.—Hindoo colleges.—Native schools.——Public works and fortifications.—Improvements in Calcutta.—Construction of tanks.—Formation of squares and streets—Quays, bridges and canals.—Importance of steam-navigation between Europe and India by the Red Sea ports.——Colonization of India.—Question of the expediency of permitting the ingress and residence of Europeans.—Advantages and disadvantages of the settlement of Europeans in India, and permitting them to hold lands.—Extent and character of Anglo-Indian population.—Abilities.—State of education.——Hindoo compared with the Mahomedan population.—Character.—State of society.—Great degeneracy.—High character of Rajpoot princes.—Manners, customs, and superstitions of the natives.—Origin and effects of castes.—Immoral tendency of the ceremonies of the Hindoo religion.——State of Christianity.—Means by which its spread might be promoted.—State of the church establishment.—State of natives as to their civil rights on a change of reliigon.—State of the Syrian Christians.

Company's Patronage :

25.—Report of the Select Committee appointed to inquire into the existence of any Abuses in the Disposal of the Patronage of the East India Company.
Sess. 1809, (91.) vol. 2, p. 483. [58.]

> SUBJECTS.—Sale of the patronage of G. W. Thellusson, Esq.—Prices given for writerships—for cadetships.—Inquiry by the Court of Directors.—List of appointments sold.—Difficulty of detection.—Evil effects of these practices in invalidating the appointments of offices abroad.—Practice of agents engaged in the traffic of patronage.

Shipping and Trade :

26.—Report from the Select Committee on Petitions relating to East India Shipping.
Sess. 1817, (301.) vol. 3, p. 175. [62.]

> SUBJECTS.—Inadequacy of the freights contracted to be paid, in consequence of the high price of outfitting continuing after the conclusion of the war.—Equity of authorizing compensation, and altering the terms of the contracts.

27.—Minutes of Evidence taken before the Select Committee on Petitions relating to East India-built Shipping.
Sess. 1813–14, (115.) vol. 8, p. 1. [62.]

Lacam's Harbour in Bengal :

28.—Report from the Select Committee to whom was referred the Petition of Benjamin Lacam, Esq. Grantee of the New Harbour in Bengal.
Sess. 1806, (289.) vol. 3, p. 1043.

> SUBJECTS.—Mr. Lacam, twenty or thirty years past, explored a new passage, and proposed its being formed and marked out for navigation.—A Committee of the House of Commons recommended its adoption; but the East India Company, on a false representation of their surveyors, decided against it. Recent navigators make use of the channel, and conduct large ships through it; thus proving the truth and practicability of the original proposition. Mr. Lacam now again applies for assistance and compensation from Government.

Lascar Seamen :

29.—Report from the Select Committee respecting Lascars, and other Asiatic Seamen.
Sess. 1814–15, (471.) vol. 3, p. 217. [134.]

> SUBJECTS.—Mode of procuring crews in the East Indies.—Regulations as to the manner of providing for them when in England; and for their return.

30.—Correspondence relative to the Care and Maintenance of Lascar Seamen.
Sess. 1816, (279.) vol. 10, p. 349. [134.]

Calcutta Bankers :

31.—Report from the Select Committee on the Claims of Calcutta Bankers.
Sess. 1822, (603.) vol. 5, p. 815.

Registrar of the Supreme Court:

32.—Report from the Select Committee on the Claims of Sufferers by the Insolvency of the late Registrar at Madras.   Sess. 1829, (258.) vol. 3, p. 409.

Military Transactions, 1803—1825 :

Marhatta War, 1803 :

33.—Bengal, also Fort Saint George, and Bombay Papers, presented to the House of Commons from the East India Company, relative to the Mahratta War in 1803.   Sess. 1804, (116.) vol. III. folio.

> SUBJECTS.—An historical detail of the campaigns in India during the year 1803.—The military transactions were under the command of General Gerard Lake and Major-General the honourable Arthur Wellesley. The principal events are, the battles of Delhi, Assye, Laswaree, and Argaum.—With plans of the battles.

Nepaul War, 1817, 1818 :

34.—Papers relating to the Origin, Continuation and Termination of the late War in that State.   Sess. 1817, (2.) vol. 11, p. 389. [65.]

35.—Papers relating to Hostilities with the Peishwah.
     Sess. 1818, (369.) vol. 11, p. 183. [65.]

36.—Papers relating to Aggressions with the Pindarries.
     Sess. 1818, (370.) vol. 11, p. 239. [65.]

37.—Treaties with Native Princes and States.
     Sess. 1818, (371.) vol. 11, p. 287. [65.]

Killedar of Talneir, 1819, 1820:

38.—Papers relating to the Execution of the Killedar of Fort Talneir.
     Sess. 1819, (54.) vol. 13, p. 827. [65.]

39.—Further Correspondence.   Sess. 1820, (61.) vol. 6, p. 391. [65.]

> SUBJECTS.—*Political Transactions.—Military Punishment.*—He had refused to deliver up a fort in his command, in obedience to the orders of his sovereign ; which made it necessary to take the place by assault. He was hanged, as being guilty of rebellion.

Burmese War, 1825 :

40.—Papers respecting Discussions with the Burmese Government.
     Sess. 1825, (360.) vol. 24, p. 91. [65.]

Religion, Manners and Customs :

Christianity in India—Papers respecting :

41.—Answers of the Judges of Circuit respecting the Moral Character of the Natives of India.   Sess. 1813, (166.) vol. 8, p. 409. [63.]

42.—Papers respecting the Mutiny at Vellore ; Christians in Malabar ; Roman-catholic Chapel ; Temple of Jaggernaut ; Missionaries ; &c. &c.
     Sess. 1813, (194.) vol. 8, p. 489. [63.]

43.—Papers relating to the Missionaries.—Nos. 6, 7, 8, and 9, of Paper No. 142.
     Sess. 1813, (142.) vol. 8, p. 275. [63.]

44.—Mr. C. Buller's Letter respecting the Temple of Jaggernaut.
     Sess. 1813, (224.) vol. 8, p. 597. [63.]

45.—Letters of Dr. Buchanan in Reply.
     Sess. 1813, (262. 331.) vol. 9, p. 465 ; vol. 10, p. 309. [63.]

46.—Answers of the Judges respecting the new system of Revenue, and Judicial Administration ; Police ; Missionaries ; Religion of the Hindoos ; Infanticide ; first introduction of Christianity into India.
     Sess. 1813, (264.) vol. 9, p. 1. [63.]

47.—Papers relating to the College of Fort William.
     Sess. 1813, (276.) vol. 10, p. 1. [63.]

Religion, Manners and Customs—continued.

48.—Letters from John Bebb, Esq. respecting the $\frac{11}{12}$ and 13th Propositions on a Church Establishment in India.

Sess. 1812–13, (294. 305.) vol. 10, p. 147. [63.]

49.—Mr. Grant's Observations on the State of Society among the Asiatic Subjects of Great Britain in 1792.   Sess. 1813, (282.) vol. 10, p. 31. [63.]

> These Papers were produced to illustrate the subject of legalizing the Church establishment in India, as connected with endeavours to improve the religious, moral, and intellectual state of the natives.

Religious Observances of the Natives:

Hindoo Widows:

50.—Papers relating to Hindoo Widows and voluntary Immolations.

Sess. 1821, (749.) vol. 18, p. 295. [64.]

> SUBJECTS.—*Religious Observances of the Hindoos as to Immolations.—Endeavours to restrain the practice.*—These Papers contain many very interesting accounts of the prejudices and superstitious practices of the natives of India.—1. As to women burning themselves with their husbands.—2. Suicides as a kind of sacrifice on personal affronts received.—3. Burying persons alive afflicted with loathsome diseases.—4. Suicides on attempts to enforce payment of taxes —5. Burning of young persons of very tender age. —6. Burying widows alive with their husbands of a particular caste.—7. Regulations to restrain suttees; and interference of magistrates preventing or absolutely forbidding.— 8. Texts of the Shasters, and opinions of learned Hindoos, respecting the obligations of widows to burn on the funeral pile.—9. The annual number of suttees.—10. On the policy of prohibiting the practice.—11. As to influence used to induce women to become suttees; and of force being used to compel them.

51.—Papers relative to the Burning of Females on the Funeral Piles of their Husbands.   Sess. 1833, (466.) vol. 17, p. 167. [64.]

> SUBJECTS.—The same as the Papers of 1821.—Remarkable instance of force being used.—Instance of extreme youth, only 11 years ;—of a women setting fire to a shed in which she resided, and burning with it, because prevented from burning on the funeral pile.

52.—Copies or Extracts of all Communications and Correspondence relative to the Burning of Hindoo Widows on the Funeral Piles of their Husbands, since 23 March 1823.   Sess. 1824, (443.) vol. 23, p. 311. [64.]

> SUBJECT.—A continuation of the Papers of 1821.

53.—Further Papers on the same subject.

Sess. 1825, (508. 518.) vol. 24, pp. 225. 231. [64.]

54.—Further Papers on the same subject.   Sess. 1826–27, (354.) vol. 20, p. 305.

55.—Further Papers on the same subject.   Sess. 1828, (547.) vol. 13, p. 149.

56.—Despatches from Bengal, Madras and Bombay, relating to the practice of Suttee.   Sess. 1830, (550.) vol. 28, p. 1059.

> And see *supra*, No. 22.

Infanticide:

57.—Copies of all Correspondence which has taken place on the subject of Hindoo Infanticide, and of all Proceedings of the Indian Government with regard to that practice.—1789—1820.   Sess. 1824, (426.) vol. 23, p. 167. [64.]

> SUBJECTS.—*Origin of the Custom.--Endeavours for its Suppression.— Historical Account of Human Sacrifices.*—Rajkoomars deduce their origin from the princes of Delhi.—Put to death their female children, that disgrace may not be incurred by their marriage in inferior ranks.—Endeavours to suppress the practice in 1789.—Government laws for its punishment. —Crime committed by starvation, strangulation, and poison.—Only certain tribes will receive rajkoomar females as wives, and demand so high a dower, as to induce the practice of infanticide to prevent ruin.———Practice of the rajpoots of Kutch.—Drowning in milk.—Affect that Divine incarnation has taken place in their families, and therefore that no man is worthy to be matched with his daughter ; so she is killed.— Purchase wives of another tribe ;—these, when mothers, adopt the practice of the tribe to which they become allied.—Rajpoots will not allow their offspring to obey any one, even a husband.— Prejudice that misfortune attends those instances where females are preserved ; and when given in marriage no male offspring is produced. — In the Kutch district all the chieftains
> are

Infanticide—continued.

are jahrejahs and relations ; and as marriages between relations are disallowed, no husbands could be found for the females, therefore they are destroyed. — No equals on which they can be bestowed in marriage.—Daughters by women of inferior rank may be preserved or killed at option ; but not daughters by rannees, or consorts of rajpoot rank.———— Appointment of Major Walker to the command of an expedition into the Guicowar state, with instructions to obtain from the chiefs the renunciation of the practice of child-murder.—His procedings.—Inquiries into the subject.—Various modes of destroying the infant ;—by opium, strangulation, or exhaustion.—The supposed superiority of their caste causes a belief that it should be supported, in the marriage of their daughters, by giving large portions ; which being unable to do, and celibacy being a great disgrace, gives rise to the custom of female murder.—Instances of jahrejahs preserving their daughters. — Do not destroy their illegitimate daughters, considering them inferior.—Major Walker's proceedings in suppressing the practice.—Apathy of the women to the subject, though of tribes where the practice does not exist.—Success in obtaining the abolition of infanticide with the Guicowar governments in Guzerat.————Another account of the origin of the custom is, that the Mahomedan conquerors having demanded the rajah's daughters in marriage, the daughters were killed to avoid the disgrace ; and female infanticide became customary.————Vacillating results of the endeavours to suppress infanticide in Kutch.—Evasion by the chiefs of the promises for its suppression.—Proposal to insure detection by rewards to informers.————Colonel Walker's representations to the Court of Directors, respecting the unfavourable results of the endeavours to suppress the practice, and offering suggestions for giving them more success.————Practice of infanticide at Sangor by drowning.—Case of drowning a child afflicted with disease.—Sacrifice of aged persons, and the fifth child, on the full moon. — Thirty-nine sacrificed at one time. — Successful interference of the police to prevent the practice. — Regulation published by the Bengal government, declaring the practice to be a capital offence.—Suppression of human sacrifices at the annual fair of Sangor.

58.—Further Papers relating to the practice of Infanticide in India.

Sess. 1828, (548.) vol. 23, p. 183.

59.—Correspondence relative to Hindoo Infanticide.

Sess. 1830, (178.) vol. 28, p. 783.

Ceylon :

60.—Report of Colonel Colebrooke on the Government of ; Revenues and Judicial Establishments.　　Sess. 1831–32, (274.) vol. 32, p. 65.

For Papers and Accounts relating to Ceylon, *see* the *General Index to Parliamentary Papers.*

XV.

Colonies and Slavery.

COLONIES.

African Forts:

1.—Report from the Select Committee on Papers relative to the African Forts.
Sess. 1816, (506.) vol. 7 B, p. 1. [66.]

SUBJECT.—Management of the colony, and manners of the natives.

2.—Report from the Select Committee on African Forts.
Sess. 1817, (431.) vol. 6, p. 401. [66.]

SUBJECTS.—On the affairs of the Company, and on the policy proper to be pursued towards them, and in the government of the African settlements.

African Settlements:

3.—Reports from Commodore Sir George Collier, concerning the Settlements on the Gold and Windward Coasts of Africa.   Sess. 1820,(90.) vol. 12, p. 317. [66.]

SUBJECTS.—On the state of the settlement; productions, soil, and inhabitants.

Berbice:

4.—Report of the Commissioners appointed to inquire into the Management of the Crown Estates in Berbice.   Sess. 1816, (509. 528.) vol. 8, pp. 409. 457. [67.]

5.—Proceedings of the Court of Criminal Justice of the Colony of Berbice, on the Trial of two Slaves for the Murder of the Negress Madalon.
Sess. 1823, (348.) vol. 18, p. 505. [67.]

SUBJECTS.—*Customs and Superstitions of Negro Slaves,—and Practice of Obeah.*—These Papers are interesting, as showing the influence of superstitious practices over the minds of the negroes; and the dangerous power exerted by the pretenders to supernatural agency.

Canada:

6.—Minutes of the intended Arrangements between Earl Bathurst, His Majesty's Secretary of State, and the proposed Canada Company.
Sess. 1825, (303.) vol. 19, p. 461. [67.]

SUBJECT.—Disposing of certain portions of clergy reserve lands, and carrying on improvements, and making settlements.

7.—Report from the Select Committee on the Civil Government of Canada.
Sess. 1828, (569.) vol. 7, p. 375.

SUBJECTS.—Causes of existing dissatisfaction, and of the impediments to the improvement of the province.—Defective state of the representative system—that of Lower and Upper Canada considered.—Disproportionate size of counties.—Disagreements between the Government and the House of Assembly as to the control of the public revenues.—Constitution of the legislative council.—Complaints of the conduct of the Government in the arbitrary dismissal of official servants, officers of militia, and vacating commissions of peace.—Retarded progress in the settling and cultivation of lands.—Evils from large grants of lands remaining neglected. — Difficulty of forming roads, by reason of the neglected grants, and the uncultivated state of the clergy and Crown reserves.—Law of real property.—Nature of the tenure of lands according to the English law ;—according to the French law.—Their comparative advantages and disadvantages.—Seigneurial rights.—French law of dower, and claim of children and wife's relations on her death, during the husband's life.—Rights of distribution by will.—Distribution of intestate property.—Establishment of courts of law for determining questions relating to real property.—Administration of law in the French language.—Insecurity in transferring property and advancing money, from the
defectiveness

Canada—continued.

defectiveness of notarial instruments, and the want of registration of deeds.———State of religious feelings, and instruction.—Condition of Protestant congregations.—Provision for the clergy by reserved lands.—Evils from their remaining uncultivated, and intervening between other lands.—Their produce inadequate to support the clergy.—Question whether applicable exclusively to the established church ?———State of institutions for education. —Appropriation of jesuits' lands.—Establishment of the King's College at York.

Rideau Canal :

8.—Report from the Select Committee respecting the Rideau Canal.

Sess. 1830–31, (395.) vol. 3, p. 529.

SUBJECTS.—Importance of an uninterrupted water communication between Montreal and Kingston.—Proposed to be effected by the Rideau Canal.—Proceedings of Government in 1819.—First estimate greatly exceeded by subsequent ones.—Inadequate manner of forming the estimates, and observations.—Great exceedings of the supposed expense.—Suspension of works of fortification.—Purchase of land.—State and expense of the works on the Ottawa. —Reasonableness of calling upon the Canadian legislatures to bear a portion of the expense, according to their original proposition.—Observations and resolutions respecting the undertaking extensive public works.

9.—Report from the Select Committee on the Accounts and Papers relating to the Canada Canal Communications.   Sess. 1831–32, (570.) vol. 5, p. 25.

SUBJECTS.—Additional sum required for completing the Rideau Canal.—Sums expended on the canals on the Ottawa.—Extent of canal communications in Canada.—Considerable traffic expected on the Rideau Canal.—State of canals in Canada.—Manner in which money issued to officers conducting works there.——*Papers laid before the Committee :* being Extracts of correspondence, between the Board of Ordnance and Officers under their orders in Canada, respecting the progress of the canal communication in that country ; and other correspondence, in 1831 and 1832, respecting the expenditure and management of the funds appropriated to that work.—Estimate for increasing the width of Grenville Canal for steam-boat navigation.—Statement of the expenditure on the Ottawa Canals to 31 December 1831, with amount required to complete from that date ; also the amount of approved estimates for those works, and the probable saving or excess on each, made up from the latest reports received from Canada.—Note in explanation of the contracts for works carrying on at the Rideau Canal.—Memorandums relative to water communication between Montreal and Kingston, and map of the Rideau and Ottawa.

10.—Report from the Select Committee of Inquiry how far the grievances complained of in 1828 by certain inhabitants of Lower Canada have been redressed ; and to inquire into certain other grievances now set forth in Resolutions of the House of Assembly of Lower Canada in the present session.

Sess. 1834, (449.) vol. 18, p. 227.

SUBJECTS.—The endeavours made by Government to carry into effect the suggestions of the Committee of 1828, on the grievances complained of by certain inhabitants of Lower Canada, have in several important particulars been completely successful.—The differences at present existing between the branches of the Colonial Legislature, and between the House of Assembly and His Majesty's Government, are calculated to check the progress of improvement there, and to affect most injuriously the general interests of the British Empire.

Cape of Good Hope :

Treatment of Slaves :

11.—Memorial of Mr. Launcelot Coke respecting the state of Prize Slaves at the Cape of Good Hope.   Sess. 1826–27, (42.) vol. 21, p. 1.

12.—Correspondence relating to the condition and treatment of Slaves and Hottentots ; Grants of Lands ; Bushmen ; and Population.

Sess. 1826–27, (202.) vol. 21, p. 175.

State of the Colony :

13.—Reports of the Commissioners of Inquiry.   Sess. 1826–27, (282.) vol. 21, p. 203.

14.—Documents referred to in the preceding Reports.

Sess. 1826–27, (406.) vol. 21, p. 287.

SUBJECTS.—I. Administration of Government.—II. Finances.

15.—Further Papers relating to the Government of the Cape of Good Hope.

Sess. 1826–27, (371.) vol. 21, p. 647.

16.—Communications between the Colonial Department and Lieutenant-general Sir Rufane Donkin.

Sess. 1826–27, (444.) vol. 21, p. 755.

17.—Correspondence between Lord Charles Somerset, Mr. Brink, and the Colonial Department.

Sess. 1826–27, (454.) vol. 21, p. 769.

Cape of Good Hope—continued.

18.—Papers relating to the South African Commercial Advertiser, and its Editor, Mr. George Greig.   Sess. 1826-27, (470.) vol. 21, p. 775.

       Trade and Navigation :

19.—Report of the Commissioners of Inquiry into the Trade, Navigation and Improvements of the Harbours of the Colony.   Sess. 1829, (300.) vol. 5, p. 249.

       Subjects.— External and internal trade.—Productions.—Harbours.—Imports and exports.

20.—Reports of Commissioners of Inquiry into the condition of the Native Tribes of South Africa.   Sess. 1830, (584.) vol. 21, p. 139.

       Subject.—State of the Hottentot population of the Cape of Good Hope, and of missionary institutions.

Demerara :

21.—Papers respecting the trial of John Smith, a Missionary at Demerara.

             Sess. 1824, (158. 333. 338.) vol. 23, pp. 373. 465. 565. [66.]

       Subjects.—*Conduct of Missionaries.*—Insurrection of negroes.—Charges against Mr. Smith, a missionary, alleging that he made use of the influence obtained over the negroes by religious persuasion, to promote disobedience.—Papers in defence of his conduct, refuting those charges.

Honduras :

22.—Correspondence relative to the Condition and Treatment of Slaves at Honduras, 1820–1823.   Sess. 1823, (457.) vol. 18, p. 351. [66.]

       Subjects.—Defection of some negroes.—Harsh treatment given as their ground of complaint—chiefly by the lower class of settlers.—Ineffectual trial of a person for cruelty towards a slave who had been chained to a bed-post for six weeks, and severely beaten.—Punishments irregularly inflicted by the magistrates.—A female slave tied down on her belly, each arm and leg to a stake, exposed naked, and flogged.—Inflicted by Bowen, a magistrate, on his own slave.—Bowen tried and acquitted, though the facts clearly proved.—Native Indians illegally held in slavery.—Eighteen persons liberated on a trial, who had been held in slavery many years.—Other proceedings to establish their freedom.—Bowen employs a disbanded drummer to flog a slave that he lately had a quarrel with.—Proceedings of a commission to ascertain the rights of the enslaved natives.—Award in their favour.—The inhabitants refuse to obey it, and to liberate them.—Origin of the Mosquito Indians, and of the English settlements.

23.—Number of Negro Population at Honduras.   Sess. 1824, (439.) vol. 24, p. 83. [66.]

Hudson's Bay, 1749 :

24.—[Report from the Select Committee respecting that Settlement.

             First Series, vol. ii., p. 213.

       Subjects.—State of the countries adjoining Hudson's Bay.—North-west passage.—Their products, cultivation and climate.—Inhabitants.—Manners and character.—Animals.—Hudson's Bay Company.—Particulars respecting its origin, &c.—Trade carried on.

Isle of St. Vincent :

25.—Report from the Select Committee of Persons interested in Estates in that Island.   Sess. 1812–13, (182.) vol. 3, p. 375, [66.]

       Subjects.—Effects of the volcanic eruption of the Souffrier mountain.—Petition for compensation for losses.—Statement of losses and sufferings.—The whole is interesting, as giving a very pictorial description of a tremendous phenomenon of nature.

Newfoundland Trade, 1793 :

26.—[Three Reports from the Select Committee on the state of the Trade to Newfoundland.   First Series, vol. x. pp. 392. 409. 433.

       Subjects —Legislative provisions respecting Newfoundland, considered as to their effects on the trade, and the general welfare of the island.—Some account of the country, its inhabitants, and population.—Treatment of the native Indians by the residents.—Manner of conducting the fishery.—Account of the trade ; and to what cause its decrease is to be attributed, and how it may be revived.—The government best adapted to Newfoundland.—Administration of justice, and internal police.—Utility of restraining the number of residents, and the expediency of providing for the return of servants of fishermen.

Newfoundland Trade, and Settlement :

27.—Report from the Select Committee on the Newfoundland Trade.

Sess. 1817, (436.) vol. 6, p. 465. [66.]

SUBJECT.—On the distressed state of the colony, and state of the fishery.

New South Wales :

28.—Report of the Commissioner of Inquiry into the state of the Colony of New South Wales.

Sess. 1822, (448.) vol. 20, p. 539. [67.]

SUBJECTS.—*Government and Police of the Colony.—Management of the Convicts.— Character and Habits.—State of Society. – Agriculture and Trade.*———I. Condition and treatment of convicts during the passage to New South Wales.—Clothing.— Plunder among themselves.—Management of female convicts.—Difficulty of preventing licentiousness.— Discipline.—Average length of voyages.—Trading by officers.———II. Debarkation and muster of convicts, male and female.—Inquiry into complaints.—Assignment and distribution of convicts.———III. Nature of the employment of convicts when retained in the service of Government.—In constructing buildings.—In care of horses and carts used in public works.—Public agricultural establishments.—Use of the eucalyptus bark.—Cultivating wood, and sawyers' work.—Public roads.—Dockyards.—Quarrying stone.—Grass cutting.—Employment in barracks.—Discipline.—Religious instruction.—Description of convicts employed as clerks.———IV. Superintendence of convicts in the service of Government.—William Hutchinson principal superintendent.—Overseers.—Difficulty of finding men of integrity.———V. Subsistence and clothing of convicts retained by Government; and employment of female convicts.—Description.—Proportions issued.—Scarcity of clothing.—Rations of subsistence, and quality.—Manner of disposing of the female convicts.—Defective mode of employment.—Immoral habits.—Character of those in Van Diemen's Land.———VI. Nature of the labour of convicts in the service of settlers.— Regulations.—Wages.—Hours of labour.—Their condition in the different classes of settlers.—Description of food.—Useful qualities of maize.—Irregularity of habits, and uncleanliness of appearance.—Attempts to improve their religious habits.—Jurisdiction of magistrates.—Appointment of persons, formerly convicts, to the magistracy.—Misconduct and dismissal of some.—Admitting convict attornies to practise in the courts.——— VII. Control of convicts in the service of settlers.—Offences.—Punishments.—Convict population of Sydney and its districts.—Effect of the punishment of transportation to the Coal River.—Evil from the colonial period of transportation terminating with the original period.—Evils of allowing emancipated convicts to have convict servants assigned to them. —State of convicts for forgery.—Marriages of convicts.—Character of native-born youth. —Disproportion of females to male convicts.—Pastoral employment in Van Diemen's Land.—Bushrangers.—Coal-mines.———VIII. Nature and extent of remissions of punishments, and their effects upon the convicts.—Number of pardons and remissions granted.— Method of procuring them.—Abuses of the grants of pardons.—Tickets of leave.—Difficulty of disposing of those who have been in situations above the common class of society. —Conduct of Halloran.—In his and similar cases, not worse than in England.—Effects of pardon granted by the governor—compared with the effects of the completion of sentences. —Land held by convict settlers.—Characters of several convicts holding land.—Few instances of sincere reformation.—Still worse in Van Diemen's Land.—Observations on the introduction of certain free convicts into the governor's society,—and in bestowing favours and employments upon them.—Introduction to military society—Repugnant to the military character.—Endeavours to introduce them into other societies, as the Bank, Agricultural Society, &c.—Exception in favour of Mr. Gatehouse, by Lieutenant-governor Sorrel, of Van Diemen's Land.—Permission to practise as solicitors.—Feelings of hostility between the free settlers and emancipated convicts.—General mild character of Governor Macquarrie's government.———IX. Nature of the future establishments for convicts in New South Wales.—Evils from the accumulation of convicts in towns.—Number exceeds the demand for labour.—Proposed improvements in their management.— Formation of new settlements in the interior recommended.—Rules to be observed in granting pardons.— Plan of future management.

29.—Report of the Commissioner of Inquiry on the Judicial Establishments of New South Wales and Van Diemen's Land.

Sess. 1823, (33.) vol. 10, p. 515. [67.]

SUBJECTS.—*Judicial and Police Establishments.—State of the Civil and Criminal Jurisprudence.*—Authority by which established.—Description of courts.—Civil courts.—Fees.— Persons practising as solicitors.—Effect of legal disabilities in the remitted convict suitors, witnesses, &c.—Character of the judicial determinations.—Expensiveness of law charges. —Mode of proceeding in the criminal courts.—Extent of operation of certain statutes against criminal offences, in the applicability to New South Wales.—Punishment of solitary confinement not successful.—Objections to the constitution of the criminal courts.—Proceedings in cases of libel.—Incongruity of characters held by Mr. Judge-advocate Wylde. —Defects in the structure of the criminal court.—Eligibility of establishing trial by jury— not thought practicable.—Judicial establishments in Van Diemen's Land.—Property of intestates.—Extension of equity jurisdiction.—Regulations proposed in the supreme and criminal courts.—Want of professional assistance.—A colonial agent recommended to be appointed.———State of the police in New South Wales and Van Diemen's Land.— Insufficiency of magistrates.—Establishment of constables; their duties—and allowances. Licensing spirit-dealers.—Consumption of spirits.—Observance of Sunday.—Severity of Government police orders,—instanced in those for preventing trespasses on the Government park.—Port regulations.—Proposed improvements.

New South Wales—continued.

30.—Report of the Commissioner of Inquiry on the state of Agriculture and Trade in the Colony of New South Wales. Sess. 1823, (136.) vol. 10, p. 607. [67.]

SUBJECTS.—*Agriculture.*—*Trade.*—*Ecclesiastical Establishment.*—*Population.*—*Revenue. Medical Appointments.*——State of Agriculture.—Description of soil, rivers, rocks, &c.—State of cultivation. — Crops of maize and wheat. — Imported seed of artificial grasses preserve the European seasons of flowering till after the second crop.—Depasturage of cattle.—Kinds.—Successful breeding of sheep.—Capability of producing profitable growth of wool.—Breed of horses.—Causes prejudicial to crops.—Rate of mechanics' labour.—Prices of grain.—Soil and cultivation of Van Diemen's Land.—Growth of hops.—Brewing of beer successful.——Regulations respecting the grants of land.— Amount. — Conditions of grants.—Reservations of timber.—Building regulations in Sydney.—Proportions of lands granted to settlers.—— State of trade. — Manufactures.—Timber.—Vessels. — Importations from Europe. — Trade with New Zealand,— its nature ; — difficulty of carrying it on. — Trade with China and Bengal. — Exports to Batavia, the Cape, and Calcutta. — Establishment of a bank. — Notes in circulation. —— Ecclesiastical and charitable establishments. — Chaplains. — Churches. — Catholics.—Wesleyans.— Clerical residences.— Attendance at divine service.—Establishments of instruction—and of charity. — School for native black children ;—their natural capacity good.—Not favoured by the native parents.—Bible and benevolent societies.—*Invidious distinctions between free and convict classes has given way in these societies.*—Associations for relief of the poor.—Proposed improvements.——State and character of the population.—Consist of, 1. Settlers ; 2. Children of free persons or of convicts ; 3. Convicts whose terms of sentences have expired ; 4. Convicts now under sentence.—Manner of taking the musters.—In 1820 the total population was 23,939.—Classification of the population.—Total population of Van Diemen's Land in 1820, 5,460.—Transported to the colony since its settlement, 25,878.—State of the climate favourable to health. —Superiority in character of the native-born inhabitants contrasted with their parents.—Gradual diminution of the native black population.——State of the Revenue.—Duties levied.—Police account.—Duties on spirits.—Various other duties.——Expenditure.—Salaries.—Victualling convicts.—Public works.—— Medical establishment. — Establishment of surgeons, &c. at Sydney hospital. — Public hospitals.—Application of medicine to private use of medical officers.—Gratuitous allowance of medicine to inhabitants.—Proposed improvements.

31.—Report and Letter from the late Major-General Macquarrie to Earl Bathurst. Sess. 1822-23, (477.) vol. 21, p. 531.

SUBJECTS.—General view of Major-general Macquarrie's administration ; and respecting Mr. Commissioner Bigge's Report on the state of the Colony.

32.—Correspondence between the Secretary of State for the Colonial Department and the Governor of the Australian Provinces ; and between the Secretary of State for the Home and Colonial Departments.

A Chart is inserted. Sess. 1834, (82.) vol. 47, p. 121.

33.—Further Correspondence. Sess. 1834, (614.) vol. 47, p. 295.

Parga :

34.—Papers relating thereto. Sess. 1820, (263.) vol. 12, p. 447. [66.]

SUBJECTS.—*Political Transactions with the Greeks.*—Oppressions apprehended by the inhabitants on the cession of the town to the Turks.—That event unavoidable on the conclusion of the general peace.—Measures taken to secure the inhabitants from injury.—Allowed to emigrate, and an indemnity stipulated for them from the Ottoman Porte.—Alleged inadequacy of the indemnity.—Defence of the English authorities.

Sierra Leone Company, 1802 :

35.—Reports from the Select Committee on the Progress, State and Prospects of the Colony of Sierra Leone, and on the Affairs of the Company.

Sess. 1801-2, (100.) vol. 2, p. 339 ; and First Series, vol. x. p. 736.

SUBJECTS.—State of the funds granted for the support of the colony.—Prospect of the ultimate utility of the settlement.—Maroon and Nova Scotia settlers require the assistance of Government.—Some account of the country and its productions.

36.—Report on the Petition of the Court of Directors of the Sierra Leone Company. Sess. 1803-4, (24.) vol. 5, p. 81. [66.]

SUBJECTS.—State of the colony.—Habits of the settlers.—Probable utility.——*Appendix* A. *is the Report of the Committee of* 1801-2.

37.—Same Title and Subject as the preceding. Sess. 1806-7, (55.) vol. 2, p. 61. [66.]

38.—Papers respecting the Trade and Population of the Colony. Sess. 1825, (520.) vol. 25, p. 919. [66.]

Sierra Leone :

39.—Report of the Commissioners of Inquiry into the state of the Colony.

Sess. 1826–27, (312. 552.) vol. 7, pp. 267. 379.

SUBJECTS. –*First Part :* I. Extent and boundary of the colony.——II. Population.——III. Liberated Africans, and engineer department.——IV. Religious institutions and education of youth.——V. Agriculture.——VI. Trade. – —VII.—Revenue and expenditure.——VIII. Judicial and civil establishments. – IX. Climate.———*Second Part :* I. Dependencies in the Gambia.——II. On the Gold Coast.

Sierra Leone and Fernando Po :

40.—Report from the Select Committee on the present state of those Settlements.

Sess. 1830, (661.) vol. 10, p. 405.

SUBJECTS.—Unhealthiness of the climate. – Objects of the settlement not obtained.—Improvement of liberated Africans retarded by the influx of captured slaves.—Unsuitableness of the settlement for the mixed commission court, and preference given to Fernando Po.—Better calculated for the settlement of liberated Africans than Sierra Leone.—State of the country contiguous to Sierra Leone.—Slow progress of Christianity.—Articles of African trade.—Collecting of gold dust.———Description of the climate by naval officers who have been on duty on that station.—Condition of the maroons and other settlers.—Description of the island of Fernando Po.—Habits and character of the inhabitants.—Suitableness for locating liberated Africans.—Condition and treatment of slaves when captured.—Productions.

Tobago :

41.—Correspondence with the Colonial Department, and the Governor, &c. of Tobago, relating to certain Charges laid before that Department by His Majesty's late Attorney-general for that Island.

Sess. 1820, (293.) vol. 12, p. 401. [66.]

SUBJECT.—*Colonial Judicature.*—Touching the conduct of the public authorities in the administration of justice.

Trinidad :

42.—Report of Commissioners of Inquiry on the subject of Titles to Lands in the Island of Trinidad. Sess. 1826–27, (478.) vol. 23, p. 63.

43.—Report of Commissioners of Legal Inquiry.

Sess. 1826–27, (551.) vol. 23, p. 285.

West Indies :

44.—Report from the Select Committee on the Commercial State of the West India Colonies. Sess. 1807, (65.) vol. 3, p. 1. [66.]

SUBJECTS.—Situation of the planters now and since 1799.—Progressive deterioration. – Causes —High price of production and low price of sale.—Depreciation in the price of rum.—Disadvantages of the British colonist, compared with the hostile colonies, who trade under neutral flags.—Enforcement of restrictions of neutral trade recommended. – Effect of the interruption of trade with the United States, not equal to the disadvantage of the neutral-trading.

45.—Report from the Select Committee appointed to consider of the practicability and expediency of supplying our West India Colonies with Free Labourers from the East. Sess. 1810–11, (225.) vol. 2, p. 409. [66.]

SUBJECTS.—Inclination of Chinese to emigrate, and their good conduct as emigrants. —Forbidden by the laws of China.—Expectation that the Chinese might be induced to emigrate to the West Indies.—Difficulties in procuring a proportionate female population.—Difficulties from the jealousies of the Chinese Government.—Advantages from the introduction of a new class of free people into the West Indies.—No plan recommended.

46.—Report of the Commissioners of Revenue Inquiry.

Sess. 1812, (356.) vol. 10, p. 327.

SUBJECT.— New Table of Fees for Customs revenue officers in the ports of the West India Colonies.

Administration of Justice :

47.—First Report of the Commissioners of Inquiry into the Administration of Civil and Criminal Justice in the West Indies.

Sess. 1825, (517.) vol. 15, p. 233. [67.]

SUBJECTS.—State of justice in Barbadoes, Tobago, and Grenada.—Laws of England in force. Local Laws.—Account of the printed and manuscript laws.—Necessity of their consolidation and amendment.——— Slave laws.—Courts of judicature, civil and criminal.———General complaints of irregularity, delay, uncertainty and expense.——— Character and capacity of Judges and Law Officers. – Justices of Peace, Coroners, &c —Defects of jurisdiction, and existence of wrongs without redress.—Cases of individual complaints.

West Indies—Administration of Justice – *continued.*

48.—Second Report of the Commissioners of Inquiry into the Administration of Civil and Criminal Justice in the West Indies.   Sess. 1826, (276.) vol. 26, p. 37.

> SUBJECTS.—A continuation of the subjects of the First Report, as to *St. Vincent* and *Dominica.*

49.—Third Report of the Commissioners of Inquiry into the Administration of Civil and Criminal Justice.   Sess. 1826-27, (36.) vol. 24, p. 1.

> SUBJECTS.—State of Antigua.—Montserrat.—Nevis.—St. Christopher and the Virgin Islands.

50.—First Report of the Commissioners of Inquiry [Second Series].

> Sess. 1826-27, (559.) vol. 24, p. 285.
>
> SUBJECT.—State of Jamaica.

51.—Second Report of the Commissioners of Inquiry.

> Sess. 1828, (577.) vol. 23, p. 507.
>
> SUBJECTS.—State of Demerara, Essequibo and Berbice.——Constitution of courts in Demerara and Essequibo.—Officers, and their duties.—Form of proceedings and practice. —Proposed reforms.

52.—Third Report of the Commissioners of Inquiry.

> SUBJECTS.—Honduras and the Bahama Islands.   Sess. 1829, (334.) vol. 24, p. 187.

Commercial State of the West India Colonies, 1832:

53.—Report from the Select Committee on the Commercial state of the West India Colonies.   Sess. 1831–32, (381.) vol. 20, p. 657.

> SUBJECTS.—Distress in the Colonies.—Causes from which it has arisen.—Condition of the general body of planters.—Condition of estates, and depreciation in their value.— State of cultivation.—Position of estates as regards mortgages ; and difficulty of procuring advances.—General state of the slave population.—Amelioration laws.—Value of slave-labour.—Mortality. — Treatment.—Effect of the partial abolition of the slave-trade.— Commercial transactions with England.—Rate of freight from the Colonies.—Insurance.— Imports by the Colonies.—Trade between the Colonies and America.—Connexion and charges between merchants and planters.—Shipping employed in the West India trade.— Manner in which shipping is found, and contracts made for conveyance of produce to England.—Benefit that would result by increasing the consumption of West India produce, by allowing the use of molasses in breweries and distilleries.—By allowing the refining of sugar to be done in the Colonies.—Effect of duty on rum.—Cultivation of sugar.—Deno-minations of manufactured sugar.—Consumption.—Duties.—Depreciated value of estates. —Growth and manufacture.—Quantity produced.—Price.—Produce of sales.—Coffee pro-duced in the West Indies.—State of the plantations.—Inquiry whether an advantageous production.—Government of the Colonies, and commercial policy in respect to them.— Opinions of the Four-and-a-half per cent. Duties.

Colonial Military Expenditure :

54.—Report from the Select Committee on the state of the Military Esta-blishments and Expenditure in the Colonies and Dependencies of the Crown.

> Sess. 1834, (570.) vol. 6, p. 1.
>
> SUBJECTS.—Economy in military expenditure recommended.——*Cape of Good Hope.* —Reduction in the amount of force recommended.—Savings proposed in the barrack department.——*Ceylon.*—Reductions suggested in the amount of the garrison.—In the adjutant-general s department.—In the quartermaster-general's department, by transferring a proportion of the duties of the office to the civil engineer.—Reduction in the number of stations, and in salaries of officers employed.——*Gibraltar.*—Garrison not to be reduced. —Medical staff.—Necessity of keeping so large a store of salt provisions for the garrison to be obviated.——*Ionian Islands.*—When military defences of Corfu completed, one bat-talion of force to be diminished.—Office of lord high commissioner and commander of the forces to be united, except under special circumstances.—Proposed constitution of the military staff. — Commissariat establishment. — Formation of the annual estimates of the expenditure for the Ionian Islands.——*Malta.*—Garrison not to be reduced.—Mal-tese Fencibles to be increased.—Resolutions as to salt provisions and baking.——*Sierra Leone.*—Reduction to be made in the ordnance, store and barrack departments.—Conso-lidation of the naval, victualling and commissariat departments.——*Western Africa.*— Amount of force not to be reduced.

Colonial Revenue :

55.—Reports of the Commissioners appointed by His Majesty's Warrant to inquire into the Receipt and Expenditure of the Colonies and Foreign Possessions.   Sess. 1830–31, (64.) vol. 4, p. 1.

> SUBJECT.—Malta.—Gibraltar.—Australia.

56.—Report of the same Commissioners.   Sess. 1830–31, (194.) vol. 4, p. 121.

> SUBJECT.—State of Mauritius.

SLAVERY.

Slave Trade in the Mauritius :

57.—Report from the Select Committee appointed to inquire whether the Slave Trade has prevailed in the Mauritius, and to what extent.

Sess. 1826, (430.) vol. 3, p. 87. [66.]

SUBJECTS.—*On the Extent of the Trade in that Colony.*—The investigation commenced. —Minutes of Evidence reported, but the printing of them postponed, as being premature. —Offered facility of Government to further the prosecution of the inquiry.

58.—Minutes of Evidence taken before the Select Committee of 1826.

Sess. 1826–27, (90.) vol. 6, p. 287. [66.]

SUBJECTS.—*Manner of carrying on the Slave Trade.*—*Difficulty of suppressing it.*— Connivance of the public authorities at the debarkation of captives for slavery.—Slave-dealing clandestinely carried on.—Difficulty of prosecuting offences against slave-dealing. —Population.—Manner of keeping the slave registries.—Slaves brought from Madagascar. —Necessity of preserving the treaty with Radama for suppressing the slave-trade.—Efforts made by the naval force to prevent the landing of slaves.—The inhabitants generally implicated in the trade.—Peculiarity and great pains in the manner of dressing the hair of the Madagascar people of rank.—Extensive trade carried on at the Seychelles.—Description of the slave-trade from the eastern coast of Africa to Zanzebar.

Abolition of Slavery :

59.—Report from the Select Committee on the extinction of Slavery throughout the British Dominions. Sess. 1831–32, (721.) vol. 20, p. 1.

SUBJECTS.—Policy, justice and practicability of abolishing slavery.———Plan for gradual emancipation; and justice of compensation to slave propriecors.———State of West India property.—Probable effect of emancipation.—Practicability of cultivation by free-labour.—Expected difficulty of cultivating sugar by emancipated negroes.———Precautionary measures necessary on the abolition taking effect.—Establishment of a magistracy and police.———General condition of slave population.—Treatment.—Cruelties subjected to, from managers of estates having the power of flogging.—Periods allowed of cessation from labour.—Habits of life, and comforts and property possessed by slaves.—Manner in which they are maintained.—Food and clothing.—Inquiry into their capacity to maintain themselves when emancipated.———Increase of intelligence.—Beneficial effects and capability of receiving instruction and religious knowledge.—Excited expectations of emancipation.—Conduct of the clergy.—Difference of opinion as to the extent of proportioning instruction.—General character and habits of negroes.—Attachment to their masters.———State of society.—Moral character of the slave population.—Marriage not encouraged, being incompatible with slavery.—Women of colour prefer concubinage with white men, to marriage with men of colour.—Prevailing immorality.—Inquiry how far attributable to the condition of slavery.—Compared with other countries.———Provisions raised by negroes.—Inquiry into the probable difficulty in continuing the cultivation when left to voluntary labour.———Nature of slave labour.—Nature of cane-hole digging, and the cultivation of the sugar-cane.—Compared with agricultural work in England.—Necessity of corporal punishment in enforcing labour in a state of slavery.—Difficulty of inducing voluntary labour of such kind in a tropical climate.—Night-work during crop-time. ———Probable effect of emancipation on the moral character and habits of industry.— Opinions on the capacity of the negroes to benefit by emancipation.—Inquiry as to the probability of emancipated negroes working for wages.———Conduct of free-blacks.— Manner in which they employ themselves.—Dislike of working in the field.—Opinions of their habits of industry and moral improvement.———Condition of Hayti and Spanish Colonies where cultivation is carried on by free-labour.———Causes of the late insurrection.—Opinions of the conduct of the missionaries.—Extent of the conspiracy.—Disappointed expectation of emancipation.—Subsequent exasperation against the missionaries.— Good conduct of many slaves.—Atrocities committed.—Punishments.———Conduct of religious missionaries.—Tumultuary acts against them, and destruction of their places of religious worship.———Particulars relating to the cultivation and manufacture of sugar. —Necessity of enforcing uninterrupted labour during that process.

Aboriginal Tribes :

60.—Papers relative to the state of the Aboriginal Tribes in British Possessions.

Sess. 1834, (617.) vol. 44, p. 339.

XVI.

—

Emigration.

EMIGRATION.

1.—Report from the Select Committee on Emigration from the United Kingdom.   Sess. 1826, (404.) vol. 4, p. 1. [68.]

SUBJECTS.—*Excess of Population.—Encouragement of Emigration.*—Redundancy of population in several parts of Ireland, England and Scotland.—Consequent depression of wages, from there being more labourers than employment.—Extensive unoccupied tracts of land in the British colonies, Cape of Good Hope, New South Wales, and Van Diemen's Land. —Advantages to the mother-country in removing the excess of population, and to the colonies in receiving it.—Emigration should be voluntary,—and expense incurred by the public repaid.—Manner in which the system of emigration might be conducted.—Expense.—Propriety of making the poor-rates applicable to that purpose.

2.—Reports from the Select Committee on Emigration from the United Kingdom.   Sess. 1826–27, (88. 237. 550.) vol. 5, pp. 1. 2. 223. [68.]

SUBJECTS.—*State of Population in the United Kingdom.—Condition of the Poor, and Administration of the Poor Laws.—Inadequate Pay for Labour.—Emigration.——* 1st Report.—Resolution that private and local contributions ought to form the basis of any system of emigration.——2d Report.—Superabundant population in cotton manufacturing districts unemployed, in consequence of the introduction of power looms.—The event lamented, but the cause not to be restrained.—Extensive districts relieved in part by voluntary contribution.—Pressure on the poor-rates.—Same kind of relief cannot be continued long.—Emigration proposed as a remedy.—Expense of removing families.—Class of persons fittest for emigration.—Grant of 50,000 *l.* recommended.—Importance of applying the principle to Ireland.

> ☞ *From p. 9 to the end is reprinted in the Third Report, for the purpose of having the whole subject together, and that the references from the Third Report, which embraces all the evidence, and the references of the Index, might be complete. It need not, therefore, be attached to this Report, when both are placed in a volume.*

3d Report.—Effect of redundant population in reducing the wages of labour.—Evil from the redundant population of Ireland pouring itself into England and Scotland.—— I.—*Ireland.*—State of population.—Low rate of wages.—Disquiet state prevents the introduction of capital.—Emigration a proper remedy.—Evil if not diverted from England — Endeavours of proprietors to diminish the population on their estates.—Evil of ejecting tenantry without some provision for them.—Opinions of Mr. Malthus as to the effect on the comfort of the English labourers from the migrations from Ireland to England.—— II.—*England.*—Population of Sussex.—Cultivation of land, and undertaking public works, *merely* for employing the poor, not beneficial.—On charging the poor's-rate with the expense of emigration.—On relief from poor's-rate to able-bodied paupers.——III.—*Scotland.*— No evil of much extent from over population.—When so, owing to the influx of Irish labourers.——IV.—*Application of a system of emigration.*—High and low wages compared to the variation in price of marketable commodities.—Impossibility of regulating them.—Depression of labour not advantageous to the capitalist.—Opinion condemned that redundancy of labour will correct itself by mortality.—Emigration the remedy. —— V.—*Pecuniary Advance; and probability of repayment.* —Grant recommended. —Calculations of the effect.—Emigrants would be able to repay the advance.—Advantages accruing to the colonies.—Argument, from the success of the experiments in 1823 and 1825, of emigration from Ireland.——VI.—*Board of Emigration.*—Expediency. —Duties.—Rule of accepting emigrants.—Classes of persons to be preferred.——VII.—*Distinction between Emigration and Colonization.*—1st, Without capital ;—2d, With capital.—Description of colonization hitherto practised.—All legal impediments to emigration should be removed, but unaided will not succeed.—Injustice of allowing pauper emigration without provision for their necessities.—Want of labourers in New South Wales and Van Diemen's Land, and the Cape of Good Hope.——VIII —*Concluding Observations upon the Advantage of a regulated Emigration.*

EVIDENCE.

Emigration—SUBJECTS of the Reports from Committee of 1826-27—*continued.*

EVIDENCE.—State of cotton weaving trade in Glasgow.—Association for emigration.—Desire of many weavers to emigrate, and to repay expenses.—Probability of repayment.—Distress for want of work in Renfrewshire.—Inequality of the operation of the poor laws in respect to England, Scotland and Ireland.—Law of Scotland as to settlement and maintaining able-bodied paupers.—Endeavour in Stirlingshire to assist emigration.—Condition of the working people at Manchester in 1823—Effect of machinery.—Rate of earnings.—Evil of desultory emigration to the United States.—On parochial contribution in aid of emigration.—On payments out of poor-rates for rent and deficiency of wages.—State of the parish of Shipley, and several parishes in Sussex.—The rental and poor-rate nearly equal.—Expense of passage to America.—Sum necessary to locate a settler.—Charitable contributions for destitute emigrants arriving at Quebec.—Manner of settling in Canada, particularly in 1825.—Desire of the landed proprietors in Ireland to promote and contribute to emigration.—Extent of artificial employment found for the poor.—State of colonization at the Cape of Good Hope.—Demand for labourers.—Rate of wages.—Produce of the Cape.—Healthiness of the colony.—Requisite supplies for an emigrant on first settling, and calculated returns.—Produce of settlements on the Fish River, in Africa.—Crops likely to succeed.—Account of eighty persons sent from Headcorn, near Maidstone.—Influx of Irish labourers counteract the benefit of emigration.—Distressed state of the working class at Bolton, near Manchester—yet population increases, particularly in illegitimate children.—Regulation of passage-vessels.—Description of emigrants taking passage from Liverpool.—Manner of settling in Nova Scotia.—State of Irish peasantry, and the advantage of diminishing their number by emigration.—State of workmen in the cotton trade at Carlisle.—Account of an emigration from the western islands of Scotland, particularly the island of Rum.—Detail of plan for conducting the emigration to the Cape, and to Van Diemen's Land.—Opinions that the numbers drawn by recruiting the army from Ireland, favoured the increase of the population;—and that notwithstanding the destruction by war, and revolution in France, the population is increased.—Disturbances in Ireland mostly agrarian not political.—Mr. Malthus's opinions on the state of the population in Ireland.—Great tendency to increase.—Capabilities of the bogs in Ireland of cultivation.—Principles on which marsh lands in England, in the reigns of Henry the Eighth and James the First, were drained;—applicable to Ireland.—Success of Lord Palmerston in draining bog.—Obstacles to the improvement of bog land, arising from the uncertainty of the boundary lines.—Estimate of waste lands in Great Britain.—Ill success of the attempt to promote emigration from Nottinghamshire.—Improvement of Mr. Marshall's estate at Kerry, in Ireland.—Statement of the improvements by settlers from Ireland in Newcastle and Bathurst in Canada.—Growth of timber in American forests, and annual proportion necessary for fuel.—Quantity of land best suited for allotting to settlers.—Extent of the practice of clearing estates in Ireland of superfluous tenants.—Instances of over-tenanted farms.—Operation of the Act against subletting.—Proprietors deterred from residing on their estates in Ireland by the distress of the surrounding redundant population.—Ruinous effects of the migrations to England, by lowering the wages of labour.—Scheme of expense of conveyance to the Cape.—Account of the settlement in Colombia.—Abstract of the applications for emigrating.—Plan of the system of surveying by the United States; with maps.—— See *Highlands of Scotland,* under Head XIX.

3.—Report of Lieut.-Col. Cockburn on the subject of Emigration.

Sess. 1828, (109.) vol. **21**, p. 359.

4.—Appendix to the last-mentioned Report.   Sess. 1828, (148.) vol. **21**, p. 379.

SUBJECTS.—Instructions to Lieut.-Col. Cockburn for surveying land in Nova Scotia for settlers, and making arrangements for provisions and implements.—Report of proceedings.—Observations on the state of cultivation of the countries through which he passed, and on the districts suited for settling emigrants.—Accounts of the condition of several settlements, and instances of success of individual emigrants.

5.—Reports from the Commissioners for Emigration to the Colonial Secretary.

Sess. 1831-32, (724.) vol. **32**, p. 209.

6.—Account of the number of Persons who have Emigrated from the United Kingdom to any of the Colonies of Great Britain, in 1820 to 1830.

Sess. 1830, (650.) vol. **29**, p. 435.

7.—Extracts of Correspondence respecting Emigration, and as to the disposal of Crown Lands; the Consumption of Rum in Van Diemen's Land; and the difficulties experienced by the Masters of assigned Servants.

Sess. 1834, (616.) vol. **44**, p. 291.

XVII.

Literary and Scientific.

Cottonian Library, 1732:

1.—[Report from the Select Committee appointed to view the Cottonian Library, and such of the public Records of this Kingdom as they think proper.

First Series, vol. 1. p. 443.

> SUBJECTS.—Fire at Ashburnham-house, and the injury occasioned to the Cottonian Library thereby.—History of the Cottonian Library : 1. Its foundation, and other particulars ; 2. Legislative or other measures formerly taken for its preservation ; 3. Proposed measures for its future preservation.—State of the public records of this kingdom. and of their repositories.

British Museum, 1774—1825 :

2.—[Report from the Select Committee respecting the mode of Admission of Visitors.   Journals, vol. 34, p. 738.

> SUBJECTS.—Importance of the Museum.—Existing regulations for the admission of visitors.—Foreign Museums.—Resolutions of the Committee ; one of which is to allow the Trustees to receive money for admissions, in certain cases.

3.—Report from the Select Committee on the Petition of the Trustees of the British Museum, respecting the late Mr. Townley's Collection of ancient Sculptured Marbles.   Sess. 1805, (172.) vol. 3, p. 319. [78.]

4.—Report from the Select Committee relative to the Lansdowne Manuscripts.

Sess. 1807, (22.) vol. 2, p. 19. [78.]

5.—Report from the Select Committee on the Petition of the Trustees of the British Museum respecting the Greville Collection of Minerals.

Sess. 1810, (258.) vol. 2, p. 239. [78.]

6.—Report from the Select Committee on the Petition of Diana Hargrave, Wife of Francis Hargrave, Esq. relating to his Collection of Books and Manuscripts.

Sess. 1812–13, (316.) vol. 4, p. 415. [78.]

7.—Report from the Select Committee on the Petition of the Trustees of the British Museum, respecting a Collection of Medals and Coins.

Sess. 1813–14, (255.) vol. 3, p. 109. [78.]

> SUBJECTS of the preceding Reports.—The value of the collections, and the expediency of purchasing them for the benefit of the public.

8.—Report from the Select Committee on the Earl of Elgin's Collection of Sculptured Marbles, &c.   Sess. 1816, (161.) vol. 3, p. 49. [78.]

> SUBJECTS.—Nature of the collection.—Antiquity. — High sculptural merit.— Great utility as studies for artists, and as forming standards of taste in sculpture, and for the school of design.—Estimate of its pecuniary value.

9.—Report from the Select Committee on the Petition of the Trustees of the British Museum, relating to the Collection of the late Dr. Burney.

Sess. 1818, (205.) vol. 3, p. 355. [78]

> SUBJECTS.—Nature of the collection, its importance to literature, and its value.

British Museum— continued.

10.—Report from the Select Committee on the Petition of the Trustees respecting Mr. Rich's Collection of Manuscripts, Antiquities and Coins.
Sess. 1825, (152.) vol. 5, p. 107. [78.]
SUBJECTS.—*Nature and Merits of the Collection*—Contents of the collection:—Manuscripts in Arabic, Persian, Turkish and Syriac languages;—Gems and various antiquities;—and Roman coins.—Value of the manuscripts.—Value of the coins;—of the antiquities.—Recommendation of the Committee to purchase the collection for 7,500 *l.*

Royal Library :

11.—Report from the Select Committee on Papers relating to the Royal Library which His Majesty has been graciously pleased to present to the British Nation.
Sess. 1823, (271.) vol. 4, p. 41. [78.]

12.—Papers relating thereto. Sess. 1823, (134.) vol. 4, p. *56. [78.]
SUBJECTS.—*Nature and Extent of the Collection.*—Dr. Johnson's letter on the means of forming it.—Made under Mr. Barnard's direction.—65,250 volumes.—Library in a complete state.—Accompanied with coins and medals.—Money annually appropriated for purchases.—Modes proposed for disposing of it.—Reasons for connecting it with the British Museum.—A new building contiguous to the British Museum necessary.—Decaying state of that building.—Sums granted to the trustees.—Bequests of individuals.—Acknowledgment of His Majesty's munificence.

Herculaneum Manuscripts :

13.—Papers relating to Dr. Sickler's Experiments in unrolling and decyphering the Herculaneum Manuscripts. Sess. 1818, (144.) vol. 15, p. 23. [78.]

Dramatic Literature :

14.—Report from the Select Committee on the Laws affecting Dramatic Literature; and on Dramatic Entertainments. Sess. 1831–32, (679.) vol. 7, p. 1.
SUBJECTS.—State of the law affecting the drama.—Decline of dramatic literature, and of the public taste for theatrical performances—Power and practice of licensing theatres.—Power of licensing plays; and fees paid.—Protection of dramatic authorship.—Conditions of the patents of Covent-garden and Drury-lane.——Origin and history of the censorship.—Manner in which his power is exercised.—Causes of the change in public taste.—Nature of objections made by the licencer.—Attraction of actors.—Eligibility of the size of theatres, both as to the power of the actor and comfort of the audience.—Remuneration of authors.—Anecdotes of dramatic authorship, and their productions.—Restrictions on minor theatres narrows the means of advancement of rising actors.—Power of magistrates over minor theatres.—Copies of patents,—Licences of theatres, appointments of examiners of plays, and other documents.——Comparative plans of theatres, drawn to the same scale.

Copyright of Books, 1734–1774 :

15.—[Report from the Select Committee respecting Copyright of Books.
1734: Journals, vol. 22, p. 411.
SUBJECTS.—Intentions of the Act of 8th Anne.—This Act gives the property to the purchaser of the copyright for 14 years, and to return back to the author at the end of that term, if living, and to continue his right for 14 years longer.—Surreptitious editions.—Examination of several eminent men connected with literature.—Inefficacy of the law to prevent impressions printed in Ireland and in foreign countries from being imported into England.

16.—[Another Report on the same subject. 1774: Journals, vol. 34, p. 588.
SUBJECTS.—Construction of the Act of 8th Anne, by which the right to the property of books *already printed*, was given for 20 years after the 10th April 1710.—Reference made to the determination of the Lords respecting copyright by common law.—The booksellers, till then, considered themselves as having a perpetual right in purchases by common law.—Honorary copyright.—Nature of copyrights, and grounds of title.—Trade sales—A particular account of the manner of conducting partnership works.—Much information on the manner of conducting the bookselling business.

1813—1818 :

17.—Report from the Select Committee on Acts of Anne for the Encouragement of Learning, &c. Sess. 1812–13, (292.) vol. 4, p. 999. [78.]
SUBJECTS.—*Delivery of Copies of Books to Public Libraries.*—The Report recommends enforcing the law for delivery of copies to the public libraries, with some modification as to delivering the finest copies of the impression.

18.—Minutes of Evidence taken before the Select Committee.
Sess. 1812–13, (341.) vol. 4, p. 1003. [78.]
SUBJECTS.—*Effect of the Law on Literary Property.*—Operation of the law on the interest of authors and proprietors of books.—Considerable information on the subject of literary property.—Some bibliographical information.

Copyright of Books—continued.

19.—Report from the Select Committee on the Copyright Acts.

Sess. 1818, (402.) vol. 9, p. 249. [78.]

20.—Minutes of Evidence taken before the Select Committee on Copyrights.

Sess. 1818, (280.) vol. 9, p. 257. [78.]

SUBJECT.—Continuation or renewal of the subject of the preceding Report.

Public Records, 1772 :

21. — [Report from the Select Committee on their condition, and on the state of the Repositories wherein they are kept.   Journals, vol. 33, p. 791.

SUBJECT.—The decayed state of the records deposited at *The Rolls.*
See likewise under Head XIX.

1800 :

22.—[Two Reports from the Select Committee appointed to inquire into the state of the Public Records of the Kingdom.   First Series, vol. xv.

SUBJECTS.—1. Nature of the public records.—2. Buildings appropriated to their custody; with engraved plans.—3. Duties of the keepers; their fees and emoluments.—4. Analysis of the contents of the returns transmitted.—5. Means of reference to the public records.—6. State of preservation.—7. Constitutional information contained.—8. Historical information.—9. Local or topographical information.—10. Information connected with antiquities.—11. Information connected with heraldry.—12. Information concerning the modes of writing, the materials most proper for records, and the best mode of preserving the records and papers of the realm.—13. Fac-simile exemplars of public records.—14. Table of public records systematically classed.—15. Table of public records alphabetically arranged.—16. Records recommended for publication.

1800–1819 :

23.—Reports from the Commissioners appointed to execute the Measures recommended by the Committee of the House of Commons, respecting the Public Records of the Kingdom; with an Account of their Proceedings.

Sess. 1819, (545.) vol. 20. [X.]

PLATES - - - - - - - - - - - - - - [XI.]

1810–1825 :

24.—First to Fifteenth Report from the Commissioners appointed to execute the Measures recommended respecting the Public Records of Ireland.

Sess. 1812–13, (337.); Sess. 1814–15, (342.); Sess. 1819, (582.) vol. 21; Sess. 1824, (44.) vol. 12, p. 451 ; Sess. 1825, (428.) vol. 16, p. 1. - - [XII. XIII. XIV.]

25.— Reports of the Proceedings of Commissioners, as far as relate to Scotland, from 1806 to 1808.   Sess. 1808, (148) vol. 15.

26.—Further Proceedings of the Commissioners.   Sess. 1809, (70.) vol. 4, p. 392.

27.— Report from the Select Committee on Public Records of the Kingdom.

Sess. 1822, (134.) vol. 4, p. 61. [13.]

SUBJECT.—On the distribution of the Works printed under the Record Commission.

28.—Sixteenth and Seventeenth Reports from the Commissioners of Public Records, Ireland.   Sess. 1828, (50.) vol. 12, p. 455.

SUBJECTS.—Proceedings of the Commissioners in 1826 and 1827.—Report on the Annesley MS.—Security of Record depository at the Four Courts.—Formation of a new Crown Rent-roll.

29.— Eighteenth and Nineteenth Reports from the Commissioners.

Sess. 1830, (174.) vol. 16, p. 129.

Longitude :

Harrison's Claims, 1763–1767 :

30.—[Reports from the Select Committee on the Petition of John Harrison, respecting the Construction of a Time-keeper.

Journals, vol 29, p. 546. 566 ; vol. 30, p. 280.

SUBJECTS.—Acts for encouraging the discovery of the longitude.—Mr. Harrison's watch.—Examinations as to its merits.—Experiments of its going.—An account of the invention, with observations on similar ones.—Difficulties in perfecting such instruments from heat, cold and agitation.—Various statements and calculations.—Memorial stating his claims.—70 years of age.

Longitude—Harrison's Claims, 1763–1770—*continued.*

31.—[Another Report on the Petition of John Harrison respecting his Time-keeper. Journals, vol. 31, p. 270; vol. 32, pp. 838. 864.

SUBJECTS.—Further evidence in support of Mr. Harrison's claims to reward.—States his having received 10,000*l.*—Mr. Mudge's evidence.—The state of mechanism represented to be bad in England.—Endeavours by French watchmakers to construct time-keepers, which are incited by the reward obtained by Mr. Harrison.— Resolution, that unless two or more watches are produced similar to the first, in five years, Mr. Harrison is not to be entitled to receive the other 10,000 *l.*

Account of money paid by the Board of Longitude. - - - Journals, vol. 34, p. 662.

Mudge and Arnold, 1793:

32.—[Report of the Select Committee on Mr. Mudge's Petition respecting his Claims for Reward for constructing Time-keepers. Journals, vol. 48, p. 700.

SUBJECTS.—Evidence of the trial of the time-keepers.—Their accuracy commended. Comparative excellency of Mr. Arnold's.—Price of Mr. Mudge's, and time required to make one.

33.—[Another Report on the same subject. Journals, vol. 48, p. 877.

SUBJECTS.—Appointment of persons to receive, confidentially, Mr. Mudge's explanations.—Trial of the watches for three months by a gentleman of science.—Registers of their going.—Observations on the mode of trial, and on the rates of going, taken as criterions.— Diversity of opinion thereon.—Results of trial of Mr. Mudge's watches;—of Mr. Emery's;—of Mr. Arnold's.—Great accuracy of many of the latter artist's.—Superiority of Mr. Mudge's over Mr. Arnold's in a voyage to Newfoundland.—The Committee " incline to say that Mr. Arnold's had gone with a greater degree of accuracy than Mr. Mudge's."— Accidental circumstances influencing the going of watches.———— Examination into what are the particular parts of Mr. Mudge's improvements.—Report of the Bishop of St. David's, G. Atwood, J. Ramsden, E. Troughton, J. Holmes, C. Haley, W. Howells and J. A. De Luc, in favour of these particular improvements.—Merit of Mr. Mudge as an artist; his devotion to the pursuit of making discoveries;—injury resulting to his fortune;—advanced age.—Recommended to be rewarded for these particular improvements.—N.B. 2,500 *l.* was afterwards voted to him.————The evidence inquires into the different construction of watches; and as to those peculiar contrivances introduced to produce the accuracy aimed at in time-keepers;—as escapements—balance-springs,—thermometer compensation pieces, for adjustment to heat and cold, &c.———— Mr. Ludlam's testimony in favour of Mr. Arnold.—Remonstrance of the Board of Longitude against rewarding Mr. Mudge.—Registers of the rates of going of several watches.

Arctic Seas, 1834:

34.—Report from the Select Committee on the circumstances of the Expedition to the Arctic Seas, commanded by Captain John Ross, R.N., with a view to ascertain what reward may be due for the Services rendered on that occasion.

Sess. 1834, (250.) vol. 18, p. 43.

SUBJECTS.—The merits or extent of the discoveries by Captain Ross not discussed by the Committee, but whether any reward is due to him on the general facts.—Proposition made by Captain Ross to the Government to undertake the expedition;—declined.—Undertaken by Mr. Felix Booth, who defrays the expense.—Accompanied by Commander James Clark Ross (Capt. Ross's nephew), who, with Mr. Thom as purser, serve without pay.— Account of proceedings.—Reaches the Magnetic Pole.—Importance of this to magnetic science.—Merits of such enterprizes.—Promotions granted by the Admiralty.—Recommendation of a grant of 5,000*l.* to Captain Ross.———Acknowledgment of the public spirit of Mr. Booth.—Early services of Captain Ross.—His losses.—Effect of the Magnetic Pole on the needle described.—Extremity of cold.—The want of spirits contributed to the health of the crew.—Manner of sleeping in woollen or skin bags, and lying in trenches of snow.—Scantiness of provisions.—Danger of the navigation in Prince Regent's Inlet and in Baffin's Bay.—Commercial advantages of the expedition.—Capt. Ross's opinion as to future attempts to discover the Northwest Passage.—Inquiry whether Commander Ross expects any portion of the solicited reward.—Ascertainment of the exact position of the Magnetic Pole.—No observations are made by Captain Ross on magnetic electricity.— Voluntary offer of Captain Hoppner and Captain Back, without pay and in any capacity.— Captain Beaufort's opinion of the scientific and commercial advantages of the expedition.— Part taken by Commander James Clark Ross in the expedition.—His observations for determining the Magnetic Pole.—On geology, natural history and botany.—Inquiry as to what were his expectations of pecuniary reward.—His services in similar expeditions.— Losses.—Opinion that the observations made on the expedition show the existence of the Northwest Passage.— Coincidence of Professor Barlow's inferences from former calculations, and Captain Ross's experiments determining the position of the Magnetic Pole.—Opinion of the accuracy of Commander Ross's observations on natural history.—Reasons and motives of Mr. Booth for promoting the expedition.—Amount of expenses incurred by him in fitting out the ships.

Medical :

Health of Prisoners of War at Winchester, 1780 :

35.—[Report from the Select Committee on the Health of the Prisoners of War confined at the King's House at Winchester.   First Series, vol. x. p. 766.

> SUBJECTS.—Nature of the distemper prevailing among the prisoners.—Alarming appearance and rapid increase.—Regulations and measures adopted for repressing the disease, particularly by means of fumigation, &c. as recommended and practised by Dr. James Carmichael Smyth.

Nitrous Fumigation, 1802 :

36.—[Report from the Select Committee on the Petition of Dr. James Carmichael Smyth.   First Series, vol. XIV. p. 189 ; and Sess. 1802, (114.) vol. 2, p. 381.

> SUBJECTS.—Efficacy of the nitrous fumigation in destroying contagion.—Ingredients, and mode of using them.—Instances of its successful application.—Claims of Dr. Smyth to the discovery.—Great expense incurred by him.

Vaccine Inoculation, 1802 :

37.—[Report from the Select Committee respecting the discovery of Vaccine Inoculation.   First Series, vol. XIV. p. 172 ; and Sess. 1801–2, (75.) vol. 2, p. 267.

> SUBJECTS.—Inquiry into its efficacy.—Dr. Jenner's claim to the merit of the discovery. —His exertions in ascertaining its efficacy and promoting the practice.—Great sacrifice of emolument.

Vaccine Board :

38.—Report from the Select Committee on the Expediency of continuing the Vaccine Board.   Sess. 1833, (753.) vol. 16, p. 149.

Contagion and Contagious Fever :

39.—Report from the Select Committee on Contagious Fever in London.
        Sess. 1818, (332.) vol. 7, p. 1. [78.]

> SUBJECTS.—On the prevalence of contagious fever in London.—Means adopted for its prevention.—Institutions for that purpose.

40.—Reports from the Select Committee on Contagious Fever in Ireland.
        SUBJECTS.—The same.   Sess. 1818, (285. 359.) vol. 7, pp. 53. 59. 75. [78.]

Plague :

41.—Report from the Select Committee appointed to consider the validity of the Doctrine of Contagion in the Plague.   Sess. 1819, (449.) vol. 2, p. 537. [78.]

> SUBJECTS.—Account of the nature of the disease of the plague.—Various opinions whether it be contagious or not.—Explanation of the doctrine of contagious diseases.— Reference to the plague of London in 1665 ; and question whether it was the Levant plague ?—Consideration of the expediency of enforcing the quarantine laws in their existing severity.—Quarantine regulations.—No persons employed in the lazarettos known to have been affected.—Examination of many eminent professors of physic.—Considerable medical information.
> *see likewise* Second Report on *Foreign Trade*, under Head IX. ; and *Fever Institution, infra.*

Lunatics, and Lunatic Asylums :

42.—Report on the state of Criminal and Pauper Lunatics.
        Sess. 1807, (39.) vol. 2, p. 69.

> SUBJECTS.—The necessity of providing a place of custody for criminal lunatics, and of providing for pauper lunatics.

43.—Reports from the Select Committee on Madhouses in England.
        Sess. 1814, (296.) vol. 4, p. 801. [88.]

> SUBJECTS.—Regulations and superintendence.—Mode of treatment.—Accommodation. —Plans of improved buildings.

44.—Three Reports from the Select Committee in continuation of the subject.
        Sess. 1816, (227. 398. 451.) vol. 6, pp. 249. 349. 353. [88.]

45.—Report from the Select Committee on the Lunatic Poor in Ireland.
        Sess. 1817, (430.) vol. 8, p. 33. [88.]

> SUBJECTS.—State of the lunatic poor ; and as to the receptacles provided for their safe keeping.

Medical—Lunatics and Lunatic Asylums —*continued.*

46.—Report from the Select Committee on the state of Pauper Lunatic Asylums in the County of Middlesex. Sess. 1826-27, (557.) vol. 6, p. 75. [88.]

SUBJECTS.—*Defective Management.—Want of Curative Plan.— Inefficient Visitations.— Expediency of County Establishments.*—Treatment of pauper lunatics at Mr. Warburton's, Bethnal-green.—From the examination of that establishment, conclusion that the erection of county asylums would be beneficial.—Abuses existing, as reported on in 1815, not diminished.—Recommendation of that Committee concurred in.—Propositions for future legislation.———Description of a visit to Mr. Warburton's house by the guardians of the Marylebone poor.— State of the infirmary.— Idiotic patients confined in a room from Saturday night to Monday ; and cleaned on Monday morning by *mopping.*—Paupers sent more for custody than for mental treatment.—Great want of classification of patients.—Mode of restraint.—The infirmary a mere place for dying.—On appointing resident and visiting medical attendants. — Insufficiency of keepers. — Description of food supplied. —Description of the cribs where *wet* patients are kept; and manner of chaining them down.—Improper confinement of persons.— Account of the confinement of Solomon.—The coming of parish visitors prepared for.— Manner in which the Commissioners proceed in the execution of their duties.—Deficiency in their powers.—Inefficiency of their mode of visiting.—Neglect of curative attention.—Superior management of Bedlam.—St. Luke's.— Estimated expense of patients at Bedlam per head.—Diet there.—Rate paid by parishes for pauper lunatics. — Full description of the management of Warburton's establishment. — Medical attendance.—Medical treatment generally applicable to insanity.—Defect of the law as to signing certificates.—Persons retained in madhouses after restored to sanity.— Frequently neglected by their relatives.—Paupers better visited than others.—Extracts from Commissioners' Report on the state of different asylums. — No publicity given to the Commissioners' Reports.

Lunatic Asylums, Ireland :

47.—Copies of all Correspondence and Communications between the Home Office and the Irish Government, during the year 1827, on the subject of Public Lunatic Asylums in Ireland. Sess. 1828, (234.) vol. 22, p. 223.

SUBJECTS.—Inquiry into the effect of Acts passed in Ireland.—Asylum erected.— Management and expenditure.—Description of the arrangement of the buildings.—Admission and discharge of patients.—Account of Cork Asylum; miserable state of the idiot and maniac before a receptacle was provided for them —Singular illusion of some patients.— Dreadful effects of intoxication.—Instances of remarkable cures.———Plans of several buildings are inserted.

Fever Institution :

48.—Report from the Select Committee on the Petition of the Society for bettering the Condition of the Poor. Sess. 1803-4, (154.) vol. 5, p. 907. [134.]

SUBJECTS.—Parliamentary aid is petitioned for, and recommended to promote the establishment of an institution for the prevention of fever, called "the London Fever Hospital in Gray's-Inn-lane."———See *Contagion, supra.*

Surgeons, 1774 :

49.—[Report from the Select Committee respecting their separate incorporation. Journals, vol. 24. pp. 729. 738. 773.

SUBJECTS.—Incorporation of Barbers as Surgeons, 1 Edward IV.—Joint incorporation of barbers and surgeons, 32 Henry VIII.—Examination before the joint company.—Inconvenience of the junction.—Proportion of expenses borne by each body.—Considerable portion of the funds designed for the sole encouragement of surgery.—Upon the recommendation of the Committee propositions are made for the division of the joint property.— A separation declared expedient.

Hunterian Collection, 1796 :

50.—[Report from the Select Committee on the Petition of the Trustees of Mr. John Hunter's Will, respecting the Purchase thereof by the Public. Journals, vol. 51, p 512.

SUBJECTS.—The nature of the collection.—Its utility to the study of surgery.—Its value. —Dr. Matthew Bailie examined. —Reasons for offering the collection to Parliament.—Its nature and utility.—Probability of the duration of the preparations.—Difficulty of making such a collection.—Mr. Everard Home examined.—Utility of the collection in the study of comparative anatomy.—Employed 30 years labour.—Valued at 15,000*l.*———Mr. Henry Cline examined.—Differs from other collections, because it illustrates the structure of the human body by a view of similar parts taken from animals generally.—Valued at 20,000 *l.*—Mr. William Cruikshank, Mr. William Blizard, Mr. John Abernethie, Sir Charles Blagden, Dr. G. Fordyce, Dr. David Pitcairn, examined to the same points.——— Sir George Baker recommends lectures on the objects of the collection :—that it should be accessible to students ;—a descriptive catalogue should be made.—Sir Joseph Banks states its utility in illustrating general natural history.—Mr. Joseph Planta thinks no foreign collection equal. —Dr. Edward Gray and Dr. George Shaw consider it of use in general natural history and anatomy.

Medical—continued.

Anatomy :

51.—Report from the Select Committee on the manner of obtaining Subjects for Dissection in the Schools of Anatomy, and into the Laws affecting Persons employed in obtaining or dissecting Bodies.   Sess. 1829, (568.) vol. 7, p. 1.

SUBJECTS.—Difficulties anatomists have had to contend with.—Protection given by Government to the science in the time of Henry 8.—Reformation of the system by Dr. William Hunter.—Number of anatomical students previous to 1798 to 1828.—Subjects dissected in London per year.—Means taken to obtain subjects.—Prices given.—State of the law against non-interment and disinterment.—Resort of students to France for dissection.—Number and bad character of exhumators.—Providing subjects in the schools of anatomy in Paris.—Suggestions for providing subjects for the schools in Great Britain.—Legislative measures that are desired.—Repealing clause of Act of George 2, as to bodies of murderers.—Great necessity of dissection.—Difficulty of obtaining bodies.—Number of schools of anatomy in London.—Indulgence shown by the Home Secretary to anatomical teachers.—Number of unclaimed bodies in the London hospitals.—Importation of bodies.—Unclaimed bodies in workhouses.—Director of anatomy proposed.—Bodies in France ; in Ireland.—Expense of medical education.—French anatomists.—Irish students of anatomy.—Representation to Government by members of the Anatomical Society.—English students studying anatomy abroad.—Certificates granted by the Apothecaries' Company.—Dissection not insisted on.—Anatomy in Holland.—Obstacles thrown in the way of importation of bodies.—Feeling of the Irish respecting their dead, and against dissecting-rooms —Suppression of Mr. Bennett's School of Anatomy in Paris.—Inscription tickets in Paris.—Degree of officier de santé.—Comparative medical and surgical education in England and France.—Medical science and anatomy in Portugal.—Ecole Pratique and La Pitié in Paris.—Anatomy and medical science in Germany and Hanover.—At Vienna ; at Parma and Bologna ; at Philadelphia and Baltimore.—Manner of obtaining bodies in Glasgow.—Process used by exhumators to obtain bodies.—Study of anatomy at Pavia and Berlin.—Persons dying on board the Grampus hospital ship, whose bodies are not claimed.—Laws that should be repealed.—Burial service.—Post mortem examinations not so much objected to among the poor as formerly.—Public lectures do away with the prejudice against dissection.—Order stopping post mortem examinations at Guy's Hospital.—Dissection and lectures there.—Coroners' inquests in hospitals.—Judicial duties of magistrates with regard to exhumers and lecturers.—Seizure of bodies on board Irish steam-boats.—Necessity for the qualifications of teachers being ascertained.—Bye-laws of the College of Surgeons in 1823 and 1824.—Actions against surgeons for injudicious treatment.

Ophthalmic Hospital :

52.—Report from the Select Committee on the Ophthalmic Hospital.
        Sess. 1821, (732.) vol. 4, p. 335. [134.]

SUBJECTS.—*Improvements in the Medical Treatment of Ophthalmia.*—Claim of Sir William Adams to a remuneration for his services in introducing a new mode of operation and cure in ophthalmic diseases.———The Evidence taken before the Committee was not printed.

Canine Madness :

53.—Report from the Select Committee on the Bill to prevent the spreading of Canine Madness.   Sess. 1830, (651.) vol. 10, p. 685.

SUBJECTS.—Increase of the disease.—Symptoms described.—What dogs most liable and most dangerous.—Experiments to ascertain the causes of disease.—Instances of the disease being communicated by the licking of the dog.—Success of applying caustic and excision to the parts bitten.—Inquiry how the disease is generated.—Incurable in the dog.—Seat of the disease in men.—Increase of the disease.—Increase of useless dogs.—Suggestions for preventing the spreading of the disease.—History of a recent case.—Less prevalent in foreign countries.———See *Cruelty to Animals,* under Head XXVI.

Medical Education :

54.—Report from the Select Committee on the Laws, Regulations and Usages regarding the Education and Practice of the Medical Profession in the United Kingdom.   Sess. 1834, (602.) vol. 13.

Part I.—Royal College of Physicians, London.———*Part* II.—Royal College of Surgeons, London.———*Part* III.—Apothecaries.———*Part* IV.—Miscellaneous, England.———*Part* V.—Scotland.———*Part* VI.—Ireland.

Botanical Collectors :

55.—Extract of a Letter from Sir Joseph Banks to George Harrison, Esq. recommending the appointment of Botanical Collectors for the Royal Gardens at Kew.   Sess. 1821, (374.) vol. 21, p. 37. [78.]

SUBJECTS.—*Advantage of employing Persons in Foreign Countries.*—High character of the botanical gardens at Kew.—Plan on which collectors have been appointed :—their salaries.—Proposed arrangements.—Applications of foreign personages of distinction to His Majesty, &c. for plants.—Commerce to foreign countries in plants.—Domestic trade therein.

Babbage's Calculator :

56.—Copies of Correspondence between the Lords Commissioners of His Majesty's Treasury and the President and Council of the Royal Society, relative to an invention of Mr. Babbage. Sess. 1823, (370) vol. 15, p. 9. [78.]

SUBJECTS.—*Mechanical Calculation.*—Nature of the invention :—for calculating and printing mathematical tables.—Suggestion of the idea.—Capability of the machine invented. —Applicability to *composing* the tables for printing.—Errors of the press in the present mode of printing.—Experiment with the engine.—Mode of correcting errors.—Prony's tables.—Applicable to the production of similar ones.—Capable of doing the work of the compositor,—and the necessity of correcting the press avoided.—Apology ;—the scheme not Utopian nor Laputan.—Reference from the Lords of the Treasury to the Royal Society : —their approbation.

Survey and Valuation of Ireland :

57.—Report from the Select Committee, and Resolutions, on the Survey and Valuation of Ireland. Sess. 1824, (445. 360.) vol. 8, pp. 77: 79. [82.]

SUBJECTS.—*Statistical Valuation for the purpose of Local Assessment.*—Necesssity of a new survey and valuation.—Measures formerly taken.—Inquiry into the proceedings on British and Foreign territorial surveys.—*Doomsday book.*—Lord *Strafford's* survey of forfeited lands.—Sir *W. Petty's* or *Down* Survey.— William the third's survey of forfeited lands : In *France*—*Bavaria*—*Savoy* and *Piedmont.*—*Neapolitan.*— *United States.*——In the survey of Ireland, the divisions of town lands to be traced.—To be executed by the Ordnance Board.—Plan of execution.—Difficulty of settling the principle of valuation.—Importance of the measure, and recommendation for its being carried on with energy.—— Manner of proceeding in the Ordnance survey of Great Britain, and proposed in the intended Irish survey.—Bog survey.—Maritime survey of Ireland contemplated by the Admiralty.— Original of the Down survey preserved in France :—carried there at the abdication of James the second.—Character of the modern county surveys, done by directions of grand juries.—Mines of coal, stone and metal described.—Usefulness of modelling.— Enumeration of the various existing ancient as well as modern maps of Ireland.—Modes of measuring bases of triangles.—Account of foreign maps.—Extracts from Reports of former Committees.——The Appendix to the Evidence contains statistical returns :—likewise a table for registering information on that subject ; and a list of characters and abbreviations proposed to be used in the intended survey.

58.—Report of Mr. Griffith, Engineer, of Progress made in 1823, on the Southern District, comprehending the Counties of Limerick, Cork and Kerry. Sess. 1824, (352.) vol. 21, p. 715. [82.]

59.—Papers relative to the Valuation of the County of Cork. Sess. 1825, (87.) vol. 22, p. 289. [82.]

60.—Account of the Progress made in the Statistical Returns of Ireland : Barony of Rathvilly, County of Carlow. Sess. 1825, (214.) vol 22, p. 309. [82.]

Weights and Measures, 1758–1759 :

61.—[Two Reports from the Select Committee on the Laws relating to Weights and Measures. First Series, vol. II. pp. 411. 453.

SUBJECTS.—Original standards of weights and measures.—Ancient laws for enforcing uniformity.—Present standards used.—Scientific experiments.—Diversity of existing weights and measures.—Proposition for establishing a standard consistent with the intention of the laws, and reducible to practice.

62.—Report from the Select Committee appointed to inquire into the original Standard of Weights and Measures, &c. Sess. 1813–14, (290.) vol. 3, p. 131. [82.]

SUBJECTS.—The Reports of 1758 and 1759 (inserted in the second volume of the First Series of Reports) are referred to.—This Report recommends the fixing the standard from some natural object, and contains resolutions to that effect ; viz. the length of the pendulum vibrating seconds, and the weight of a given quantity of water at a certain temperature.

63.—Report from the Select Committee on Weights and Measures. Sess. 1821, (571.) vol. 4, p. 289. [82.]

SUBJECTS.—*Ascertaining a Natural Standard on Philosophical Principles.*—Concurrence expressed with the Commissioners' opinion, as to the inexpediency of any change in standard.—Preference of the present subdivision to the decimal scale.—Existing standard recognised.—Standard of capacity proposed to be made uniform.—Imperial gallon ; its contents.—Great assistance from Captain Kater acknowledged.

64.—Papers relating to Experiments for ascertaining the Length of the Pendulum vibrating Seconds, in the Latitude of London. Sess. 1818, (361.) vol 15, p. 31. [82.]

These experiments are connected with the subject of the "Standard of Weights and Measures."

Weights and Measures—continued.

65.—First Report of the Commissioners appointed to consider the subject of Weights and Measures.   Sess. 1819, (565.) vol. 11, p. 307. [83.]

> Subjects.—*Ascertaining a Natural Standard on Philosophical Principles.*—Does not recommend any alteration of the standard.—No great advantage in having a standard equal to any quantity originally existing in nature.—Advantages of the present subdivisions equal to that of decimal subdivisions.—Standard yard.—Pendulum.—Standard weight;—and of measure.—Revision of the laws on this subject recommended.—Abstract of the statutes relating to weights and measures.

66.—Second Report of the Commissioners.   Sess. 1820, (314.) vol. 7, p. 473. [83.]

> Subjects.—*Ascertaining a Natural Standard on Philosophical Principles.*—Comparison of existing standard with the instruments employed in making certain trigonometrical experiments.—Declaration of the length of the pendulum vibrating seconds.———An Index of terms relating to weights and measures is contained in the Appendix.

67.—Third Report of the Commissioners.   Sess. 1821, (383.) vol. 4, p. 297. [83.]

> Subjects.—*Ascertaining a Natural Standard on Philosophical Principles.*—Proposed data for determining the standard yard—pound weight—and gallon measure, which is proposed to be called the *Imperial Gallon.*

68.—Report (brought from the Lords) on the Petition of the Directors of the Chamber of Commerce, &c. at Glasgow.   Sess. 1824, (94.) vol. 7, p 431. [83.]

> Subjects.—Ascertaining a natural standard on philosophical principles.

69.—Letter from the Commissioners of Weights and Measures, dated 14 January 1825, transmitting a Report of Progress made in the preparation of the Models of the new Weights and Measures.   Sess. 1825, (3.) vol. 15, p. 147. [83.]

> Subjects.—Difficulties attending the endeavours to procure a correct casting of a bushel in metal.—Intention of determining the capacity of the bushel by measurement relinquished, and the method adopted of doing it by the weight of distilled water.—Model weights successfully made.—In consequence of these delays, a prolongation of the time of commencing the use of the new standards recommended to be obtained by an Act of Parliament.

70.—Evidence taken before the Select Committee on the Bill to amend two Acts of the 5th & 6th Geo. 4, relating to Weights and Measures.
     Sess. 1834, (464.) vol. 18, p. 231.

> Subjects.—Verification of all weights and measures are superintended in the Tally Office department.—Complaints very general as to the form of weights.—Process of plugging weights very difficult of detection.—Mode adopted with respect to adjusting the weights and measures belonging to the county of Surrey.—Benefits derived from Mr. Frankland Lewis's Act for regulating the sale of coals.—Use of the imperial measure should be made compulsory throughout the three kingdoms.—Penalties for light weights should not be at the discretion of magistrates.—Expense of stamping weights and measures at the Exchequer.—Founders'-hall and Guildhall.—Troy weight might be abolished, except for jewellers and apothecaries.—Measures for fruit vary much.—Account of the different weights in use in Scotland, with the names they are generally known by.

XVIII.

Arts connected with Trade.

Bramah's Locks. See No. 6, *infra.*

Cartwright's Weaving Machine :

1.— Report from the Select Committee on Dr. Cartwright's Petition respecting his Weaving Machine.   Sess. 1808, (179.) vol 2, p. 135. [134.]

   SUBJECTS.—Opposition to the introduction of machinery.—Factory where used burnt down.—Loss of Dr. Cartwright by the suspension of the use of his looms ; manufacturers being terrified from adopting them.

Drugs :

2.—[Report from the Select Committee on the Apothecaries' Petition respecting the Examination of Drugs, to prevent Adulteration. 1747 : Journals, vol. 25, p. 592.

   SUBJECTS.—Incorporation of Apothecaries and Grocers into one joint company.—Abuses in compounding medicines. — Separation.—Act James 1.— Regulations —Examination to ascertain competency in the practisers ; and to discover the quality of drugs.—Saving as to right of surgeons to administer outward applications.—Charter extends to London, and seven miles round.—Insufficiency of the powers given by the Charter to authorize the destruction of adulterated drugs.—Sale of bad or spurious drugs.—Irregular practices.— Acts of Parliament relating to the subject.

Dyeing :

3.—[Report from the Select Committee on John Berkenhout's Petition, respecting his discovery of a Scarlet Dye.   1779 : Journals, vol. 37, p. 392.

4.—[Report from the Select Committee on Louis Borell's Petition for a Reward for discovering his method of Dyeing the colour of Turkey Red upon Cotton Hanks and in the Piece.   1786 : Journals, vol. 41, p. 467.

   SUBJECTS.—The Report states the importance of the discovery, and the evidence of the effect of the method.———*See* Madder, No. 7, *infra.*

Elm Bark :

5.—[Report from the Select Committee on Edward Sealy's Petition.

           1798 : Journals, vol. 53, p. 543.

   SUBJECTS.—Experiments to show that elm bark could be used as a fit substitute for oak bark.—Leather so tanned equally fit for shoes.—Value of oak and elm bark.—Salt used with elm bark.—Annual quantity of oak bark consumed.—Opinion in favour of the utility of the discovery.———*And see* under Head VIII. *Leather Trade, Tanners.*

Foden's Chrystalline Size. See No. 14, *infra.*

Locks, Bramah's :

6.—[Report of the Select Committee on the Petition of Joseph Bramah for prolonging his Patent.   1798 : Journals, vol. 53, p. 371.

   SUBJECTS.—Observations on locks generally.— Superiority of his locks from their being constructed on scientific principles.—Endless diversification can be obtained in the structure, so that strange keys cannot fit.—Perfection of his work.—Complete and extensive machinery for this manufacture.

Madder :

7.—[Report from the Select Committee respecting the Importation and Growth of Madder.   1758 : Journals, vol. 28, p. 108.

> Subjects.—Quantity imported.—Mr. Miller's evidence in favour of the growth of madder in this country, of a better quality than that grown in Holland.—Instance of a favourable crop.—Scarlet dyers prefer it to the Dutch.—Use of madder to calico printers. —— see *Dyeing*, No. 4, *ante.*

Marine Acid and Alkali :

8.—[Report from the Select Committee on Mr. Alexander Fordyce's Petition.
                                        1780 : Journals, vol. 37, p. 893.

> Subjects.—Quality of marine acid and alkali extracted from sea-salt.—Its use in calico printing, glass-making, soap-making, &c.

9.—[Report from the Select Committee on the Petition of James Keir, *et al.,* on the same subject.   1780 : Journals, vol. 37, p. 913.

> See No. 12, *infra* ; and likewise *Salt,* No. 42, under Head XII.

Morton's Patent Slip :

10.—Report from the Select Committee on the expediency of extending the Patent for that Invention.   Sess. 1831-32, (380.) vol. 5, p. 295.

> Subjects.—Advantage of the invention.—Expense of placing a ship to be repaired in the old method, 170 *l.* ; by this invention, 3 *l.*—Inadequate profit derived from the patent. —Objection to extension of the period of any patent. —But recommendation of affording him some other means of recompense.——Description of the machinery, and mode of applying it, by placing a cradle under the ship, and drawing her up an inclined plane or railway.—Inquiry as to its originality.—Description of the old method of hauling ships on slips.—Observations on the nature and effect of rollers and wheels.—Comparative merits of Captain Brown's machinery for transporting ships overland.

Patents for Inventions :

11.—Report from the Select Committee on the Law and Practice relative to granting Patents for Inventions.   Sess. 1829, (332.) vol. 3, p. 415.

> Subjects.—Process of taking out a patent.—Designed ambiguity of description given by the title.—Difficulty of drawing a correct specification.—Difficulties in preventing the defeat of the inventor's interest by disclosures during the process.—On the duration of patents ; and expediency of allowing it to be shortened at the will of the inventor.— Expense of a patent.—Impolicy of refusing patents to any but the actual inventor.—On granting patents for abstract *principles.*—On establishing a commission of scientific men for examining inventions.—Improvements proposed in the manner of taking out patents.— On registering and publication of patents.—On searching for and inspecting them.—Admissibility as evidence.—Grounds on which patents may be rendered invalid.—Imperfections of the present tribunal for deciding on patent rights.—On questions of law relating to patents, and its unsettled state.—Instances of collusion to defeat patent rights.— Instances of valuable processes kept secret or lost, from the insecurity of the present law of patents.—Valuable medical secrets uncommunicated,—and important mechanical inventions not remunerated by patent privilege :—which should be purchased by the public.— Law of patents in France.—Patents taken out for short periods, and at little expense.— Commission established for examining their originality.—Law in Austria.—In the Netherlands.—In Spain.— In America. — Foreign law compared with the law of England.— A list of various Acts of Parliament relating to patents and grants of monopolies, with a summary of their enactments, and a history of their objects.—Grants by Parliament of rewards for useful inventions and discoveries.—A list of the most important cases of trials at law respecting patent rights, with extracts from the arguments of counsel, and quotations of the decisions of the judges.—Forms of petition, affidavit, patent, and specification.

Pot and Pearl Ashes, 1751–1755 :

12.—[Report from the Select Committee on the Manufacture of Pot and Pearl Ashes.   Journals, vol. 26, p. 239 ; vol. 27, pp. 233. 264.

> Subjects.—Whence the supply for England is imported.—Different kinds.—Uses to which applied.—Materials for manufacturing them.——*See* likewise No. 8, *supra.*

Sea Water rendered Fresh, 1772:

13.—[Report from the Select Committee respecting Dr. Irving's Method for rendering Sea-water Fresh.   Journals, vol. 33, p. 661.

> Subjects.—Statement of the effects of this method.—Evidence in its favour.— Approbation of the Admiralty.

Size :

14.—[Report from the Select Committee on the Petition of Thomas Foden, respecting his discovery of a Crystalline Size.   1800. Journals, vol. 55, p. 564.

> SUBJECTS.—Ingredients and manner of making described.—Use in sizing cotton goods, &c., and as a substitute for flour.—Various uses for which it is applicable.—Experiments.

Steam-Boats :

15.—Report from the Select Committee on Steam-Boats, &c.
Sess. 1817, (422.) vol. 6, p. 223. [81.]

> SUBJECTS.—On the means of preventing mischiefs arising from the explosion of the boiler of engines on board steam-boats.—Proposed improvement in the construction of safety valves.—In the introduction of steam-engines for propelling boats, many accidents have happened from the insufficiency of the boiler to resist the expansive force of the steam; particularly in the case of a passage-boat plying from Norwich to Yarmouth.——— And *see* under Head XIX. No. 117. 120.

Steam Engines and Furnaces :

16.—Report from the Select Committee on Steam Engines and Furnaces.
Sess. 1819, (574.) vol. 8, p. 271. [81.]

> SUBJECTS.—Inconvenience to the public from the great quantity of smoke discharged by the chimnies of steam-engine furnaces.—Practicability of so constructing the furnaces as to diminish the quantity of smoke.—Description of several plans of furnaces for consuming their own smoke.—Several engravings of the proposed plans.

17.—Report from the Select Committee on Steam Engines and Furnaces, &c.
Sess. 1820, (244.) vol. 2, p. 235. [81.]

> SUBJECTS.—*Annoyance from the Smoke of Steam-Engine Furnaces.—Improved Construction of Flues.*—Continuation of the subject of the preceding Report.—Effectual contrivance of Mr. Parkes of Warwick, for consuming smoke.—Less consumption of coals. —Small expense of adaptation.—Boilers less injured.—Experiment at Messrs. Barclay's brewhouse.—Account of observations made on Mr. Parkes's apparatus, by Michael Angelo Taylor, Esq. the chairman.—Description of Mr. Brunton's apparatus.—Mr. Wakefield's.— Manchester police regulation as to smoke-burning.

Steam Navigation :

18.—Report from the Select Committee on the frequent Calamities by Steam Navigation.
Sess. 1831, (335.) vol. 8, p. 1.

> SUBJECTS.—On accidents happening to steam-vessels.—To sea-steamers and river-steamers.—From bursting of boilers, and undulation occasioned by the motion of the vessels.—Construction of vessels—of American vessels—of paddle-wheels.—Power of engines. —Suggestions for preventing danger, by regulating the speed of vessels.
> *See* likewise under Head IX. No. 12.

Steam-Carriages :

19.—Report from the Select Committee on the proportions of Tolls which ought to be paid by Carriages propelled by Steam or Gas; on the present state and future prospects of Land-carriage so propelled; and on their probable utility to the Public.   Sess. 1831, (324.) vol. 8, p. 203.

> SUBJECTS.—State of the science of propelling carriages on common roads by steam.— Inquiry into the security of such carriages, and as to any annoyance from noise, smoke or steam.—Effect on roads, as requiring an increased rate of toll.—Probability of increased success of this mode of communication.—Successful experiments.—Perfect controllableness of steam compared to horse power.—Construction of engines and boilers.—On the relative wear and tear of roads by wheels and horses' feet.—Action of wheels on roads, of draught and steam carriages.—Doubtfulness of the applicability of steam-power to heavy and slow draught.—Summary of advantages of the application of steam for draught on common roads.

Gurney's Locomotive Steam-Carriage :

20.—Report from the Select Committee on the Mr. Goldsworthy Gurney's case, as set forth in his Petition.   Sess. 1834, (483.) vol. 11, p. 223.

> SUBJECTS.—History of the steam-engine, as applicable to propelling carriages on common roads.—Experiments made by Mr. Trevithick, and result thereof.—Improvements made by Mr. Gurney in steam-carriages.—No accident can possibly occur unless through carelessness.—Loss sustained by Mr. Gurney from several contracts for steam-carriages being given up, in consequence of the heavy tolls inserted in turnpike road bills.—Contract for the sale of the Scotch patent not carried into effect from the excessive tolls levied on steam-carriages in Scotland.

Sugar Refining :

21.—Report of Experiments by Dr. Andrew Ure, M. P. F. R. S., Professor of Chemistry, made by directions of the Lords of the Committee of Privy Council, appointed for the consideration of all matters relating to Trade and Foreign Plantations.   Sess. 1833, (590.) vol. 33, p. 551.

> SUBJECTS.—These researches undertaken for the purpose of ascertaining the amount of extracts from a cwt. of sugar.—Difficulty of finding competent workmen to conduct the experiments.—Description and plan of the premises hired.—Description of the process. —Art of assisting the granulation.—Object of Government in instituting the experiments to determine a question respecting drawbacks.—Circumstances on which the whiteness depend.—Use of animal charcoal.—Sources of loss in the process of refining.—Narrative of the experiments, and tabular statement of the results.

Unloading Engine :

22.—[Report from the Select Committee on the Petition of Mr. Cox for extending his Patent.   1757. Journals, vol. 27, p. 859.

> SUBJECTS.—Application to unloading ships.—Utility in unloading coal vessels.— Description of persons employed.—Evidence of its utility.

XIX.

Public Works;

Buildings—Roads—Bridges—Harbours.

ENGLAND.

Palaces:

Windsor Castle, 1830–31:

1.—Report from the Select Committee on the expense of completing the alterations and improvements of Windsor Castle.

Sess. 1830, (656.) vol. 9, p. 357.

> SUBJECTS.—Nature and extent of the works in progress, and expense of completing them.—Additional works necessary.—Relative importance of the several proposed works. —The restoration of Windsor Castle as a royal residence considered as a national concern.— Reason for the variation of the estimates, with the actual cost.——Manner and circumstances under which the plans were formed and sanctioned.—Expediency of executing the work progressively.—Cause of exceedings in estimates.—Description of the decayed state of the building.—History of the commencement of the repairs.—Manner of paying the tradesmen employed.

Windsor Castle and Buckingham Palace:

2.—First Report of the Select Committee of Inquiry into matters connected with Windsor Castle and Buckingham Palace.   Sess. 1831, (272.) vol. 4, p. 1.

> SUBJECTS.—Amount of Parliamentary grant for furniture at Windsor Castle.—Money paid, and balance due.—Excess of Morel & Seddon's demand beyond the estimates.— Arrangements for settling their claims.—Remarks on the mode of superintending the expenditure.

3.—Second Report from the same Committee.   Sess. 1831, (329.) vol. 4, p. 5.

> SUBJECTS.—Estimated amount of the expense of the proposed alterations in Buckingham Palace.—Inquiry into the reasons for the inaccuracy of the estimates, and the causes of the excess of expenditure.—Conduct of Mr. Nash in making contracts.—In selling materials to tradesmen employed.—Censure of his conduct.—Ineligibility of the site.—Recommendation to complete the palace.——Manner of forming the estimates—Of entering into contracts—Arrangements for obtaining a supply of stone; particularly for supplying marble.—Qualities and kind of marble.—Expense of making and laying down the parquette floors.—Contracts for cast-iron work; quality of castings.—On the construction of the arch at the entrance to the palace, and on the sculpture thereof, and statue intended to be placed thereon.

Houses of Parliament:

Approaches to the House, 1793:

4.—[Report from the Select Committee on Improving the Approaches to the House.

Journals, vol. 48, p. 848.

> SUBJECTS.—Necessity of removing the projecting buildings adjoining the Court of Exchequer.—Purposes for which those buildings are used.—Records kept there; their danger from fire.—Records in the custody of the King's Remembrancer.—In the Augmentation Office; Pipe Office.—Plan for removing the Records to Somerset-house, and consideration how far it would be convenient to the public.——*See* infra, *Westminster Hall*; and likewise under the Head XVII. *Cottonian Library*, No. 1.

House of Commons Buildings, 1831:

5.—Report from the Select Committee on the possibility of making the House of Commons more commodious and less unwholesome.

Sess. 1831, (308.) vol. 4, p. 655.

> SUBJECT.—Deficiency of accommodation; impossibility of altering the present building —Necessity of a new building.

Houses of Parliament—continued.
In 1833 :

6.—Report from the Select Committee on House of Commons Buildings, to whom the preceding Report was referred.   Sess. 1833, (269.) vol. 12, p. 487.

> SUBJECT.—Proposed plans for rebuilding the Houses of Parliament, with more extensive accommodation.——*Twenty-three Plans are attached.*

Westminster Abbey, 1807–1811 :

7.—Report from the Select Committee on the Petition of the Dean and Chapter.   Sess. 1807, (23.) vol. 2, p. 27. [71.]

> SUBJECTS.—Necessity of reparation, and probable cost.

8.—Report from the Select Committee, and Minutes of Evidence, on the Petition of the Dean and Chapter of Westminster Abbey, on the Repairs thereof.   Sess. 1810, (155. 170.) vol. 2, pp. 131. 135. [71.]

> SUBJECTS.—Appropriation of the money voted for the repairs, and the probable amount of sums wanted for continuing them.

9.—Report from the Select Committee on Petitions for repairing Henry the Seventh's Chapel in Westminster Abbey.   Sess. 1810–11, (90.) vol. 2, p. 209. [71.]

> SUBJECT.—Same as preceding.

Westminster Hall, 1788, 1789 :

10.—[Report from the Select Committee as to how far Westminster Hall may be secured from Fire, likely to arise from the contiguity of the other buildings.   1788. Journals, vol. 43, p. 531.

> SUBJECTS.—Inspection of the buildings and various public offices.—Great importance of the Records deposited in them.—Extreme danger.—Recommendation of the removal of the adjacent buildings.

11.—[Report from the Select Committee on the same subject.   1789. Journals, vol. 44, p. 548.

> SUBJECTS.—Continued from the preceding.—Ruinous state of the buildings;—Consequent danger from fire.—Importance of the subject.—The adoption of some noble plan recommended.—Opinions of surveyors.——See *Approaches* to the House, *supra*; and *Records* and *Cottonian Library*, for observations on the state of the Repositories of Public Records, under Head XVII.

Westminster Improvements, 1808–1814 :

12.—Reports of the Select Committee on the Report and Memorial of the Commissioners under the Act 46 Geo. 3, for the Improvement of the Access to Westminster Hall and the Houses of Parliament.   Sess. 1808, (293. 328.) vol. 3, pp. 71. 75. [71.]

13.—Report from the Select Committee on the Improvements in Westminster.   Sess. 1809, (272.) vol. 3, p. 407. [71.]

> SUBJECTS.—Progress of the improvements; and steps taken for procuring designs of intended buildings.

14.—Reports from the Select Committee on inspection of Lords' Journals, with relation to Proceedings on Improvements in Westminster.   Sess. 1810, (198. 294.) vol. 2, pp. 147. 151. [71.]

> SUBJECT.—On the principles to be observed in prosecuting the improvements.

15.—Report of Select Committee on Memorials respecting Improvements in Westminster, and on the Reports of the Committee appointed to inspect the Lords' Journals.   Sess. 1810, (331.) vol. 2, p. 155. [71.]

> SUBJECT.—Progress of the improvements.

16.—Report from the Select Committee on Public Buildings at Westminster.   Sess. 1824, (307.) vol. 6, p. 485. [71.]

> SUBJECTS.—*Style and Taste in the Architecture of Public Buildings.*—Observations on the buildings lately erected for the new Law Courts in New Palace-yard, adjoining Westminster Hall.—Alterations proposed to harmonize the appearance of the elevation of the buildings.—Estimate of expense.—Remarks on the general style of public buildings;—and on the want of taste in their construction.

Westminster Improvements—continued.

17.—Report and Memorials of the Commissioners for executing Act 46 Geo. 3, for improving the Streets near Westminster Hall and the Houses of Parliament.

Sess. 1808, (231.) vol. 3, p. 1. [72.]

Subjects.—History of the Commissioners' proceedings.—Topographical information.—Information connected with architectural planning.

18.—Further Report and Memorials, on the same subject.

Sess. 1810, (31.) vol. 2, p. 83. [72.]

19.—Reports and Memorials of the Commissioners, &c., and Reports by Select Committees of the Houses of Lords and Commons thereupon.

Sess. 1810-11, (251.) vol. 2, p. 225. [72.]

20.—Further Reports and Memorials, from 8 May 1811 to 31 December 1813.

Sess. 1813-14, (340.) vol. 3, p. 61. [72.]

N. B.—Most of the Reports respecting the Improvements at Westminster have *Maps* and *Plans* attached to them.

New Law Courts, 1824:

21.—Report from the Select Committee on the New Law Courts building at Westminster, and on the style and taste of Architecture of Public Buildings.

Sess. 1824, (307.) vol. 6, p. 485.

Subjects.—Propriety of keeping all buildings in the vicinity of Westminster Hall subordinate to the northern entrance of that noble monument of antiquity.—Objection to the style of the buildings opposite the eastern end of St. Margaret's Church, in continuation of Mr. Kent's design made between 1730 and 1740.—Proposed increase of accommodation for depositing the Records of the King's Bench court.—Amended design, removing the objectionable style of building.—The Gothic style recommended to be adopted in all buildings contiguous to Westminster Hall.—Observations on the character of public buildings in the metropolis.—Advantage of a general and superintending power, with talent and original invention.—Example pointed out of the Banqueting-house.—Necessity, in a national point of view, of paying more attention to public edifices.

Approaches to the Houses of Parliament, 1832:

22.—Reports, First and Second, from the Select Committee on improving the Approaches to the Houses of Parliament, and to the Courts of Law ; and also of improving the immediate neighbourhood of Buckingham Palace.

Sess. 1831-32, (567. 614.) vol. 5, pp. 425. 427.

Subjects.—Proposed plan for improving the neighbourhood of Buckingham Palace, and the approaches to the Houses of Parliament.—Inexpediency of erecting barracks in Bird-Cage-walk.—Importance of improving the locality of Westminster.—Necessity of the proposed plans to remedy the defective state of sewage.—Importance to the salubrity of the metropolis, and rendering the Palace more befitting its illustrious inmates.——*With Plans.*

Public Buildings :

Post-Office :

23.—Report from the Select Committee on Petitions respecting the building of a new Post-Office.

Sess. 1813-14, (338.) vol. 3, p. 155.

Subjects.—Insufficiency of the present building.—Necessity of rebuilding it on the present or a new site.—Proposed building in Aldersgate-street, and formation of a new street connected therewith.

24.—Report from the Select Committee on the same subject.

Sess. 1820, (290.) vol. 2, p. 253.

Subjects.—Application of the Corporation of the City of London for a further grant to carry into effect powers granted to them to provide a site for the new Post-office in Aldersgate-street, and forming a new street connected therewith ; which the Committee do not think it expedient should be complied with.

25.—Report from the Select Committee on the intended Improvements of the Post-office.

Sess. 1814-15, (235.) vol. 3, p. 179. [71.]

Subjects.—On plans and papers.—Eligibility of the different plans compared.—Observations on surveyor's per-centage ; and on the propriety of the style of architecture to be adopted.

Cremill Point :

26.—Report from the Select Committee on the Victualling Establishment at Cremill Point.

Sess. 1831-32, (272). vol. 5, p. 359.

Subjects.—Purchase of land in anticipation of vote by Parliament.—Mode of contracting for the works, and providing the machinery.

Public Buildings—continued.

Register House, Edinburgh:

27.—First Report of the Commissioners for completing and fitting-up the Buildings of His Majesty's General Register House at Edinburgh.

Sess. 1826, (347.) vol. 11, p. 43.

SUBJECTS.—Progress in completing the building.—Arrangement of fees of office of Lord Registrar.—Advance by Bank of Scotland on the Register fees.—Plan observed in the work.

28.—Second Report of the Commissioners.   Sess. 1826–27, (384.) vol. 7, p. 103.

SUBJECTS.—State of the funds appropriated to the work.—Necessity of enlarging the plan.—A further grant required.

Office of Works:

29.—Report from the Commissioners of Inquiry into the Conduct of Business in the Office of Works.   Sess. 1812–13, (258.) vol. 5, p. 321. [99.]

SUBJECTS.—Commission appointed by Act 51 Geo. 3, c. 19.—Manner in which the business of the office is conducted.—Mode of executing work.—Account of the Board in 1705—continued down to the year 1782.—Constitution of the office by the 22 Geo. 3, c. 82.—Instructions for its management.—Manner of conducting the business of the office. —Establishment of officers and salaries.—Residences claimed in right of office.—Other allowances.—Clerks of the works.—Labourers in trust.—Constant carpenters; objectionable mode of allowance.—Mode in which the business of the department is conducted. — Annual survey of public buildings.—Repairs of apartments in the palaces held by favour. —Extraordinary works.—Preparation of estimates.—Great exceedings in several instances. —Contracting for and pricing work.—Rate of prices allowed reasonable.—Measurement of work should be on an uniform principle.—Checking of day-work.—Application of stores of materials.—Checks against embezzlement and mischarging in measured work.— Superintendence of work and making up accounts.—Mode of check commended.—Lord Chamberlain, as connected with the Board of Works.—Deductions from tradesmen's bills. —Rents due.—Suggestions for future management.—Works at the Royal palaces.—System of conducting public works.

30.—Code of Instructions for the Government of the Office of Works in all its branches.   Sess. 1814–15, (158.) vol. 10, p. 13.

31.—Report from the Select Committee on the state of the Public Buildings in the Department of the Office of Works.   Sess. 1828, (446.) vol. 4, p. 315.

SUBJECTS.—Manner of conducting the public works and buildings.—Management by the office of works.—Establishment of the office of surveyor-general.—Salaries and allowances of architects.—Proposed arrangements for obtaining designs, and making models of intended buildings.—Mode of remuneration by per-centage.—Question of contracts for prices or contracts in gross.—Mode of contracting either with one or separate tradesmen. —Contracting in gross preferred by the Committee.—Observations on the style of building of the council-office.—Origin of the undertaking; and objections to the plan.—On the palace in St. James's Park.—Discussions on the plans.—Enrichments of the building.—Manner of providing materials.—Manner of conducting the works at Windsor Castle.—Buildings on the site of Carlton House.—Proposed terrace and fountain.—Objections; and proposed access to the Park by a flight of steps.—Failure of the foundation of the Custom-house; cause of the defect, and mode of remedying.—The Mint.—Objection to allowing public departments to incur any other building expenses than incidental repairs.—Successful management of the Regent's Park.—Improvements at Charing-cross.—National Gallery suggested, by converting the Royal Mews.—Expenditure on building and furnishing official residences. — Recommendations for improved management of the public buildings.———Improving the plantations of St. James's Park.—Formation of Regent-street. — Estimated and ultimate cost.—Cause of excess.—The Quadrant.—Origin of the employment of Mr. Nash.—Mode of his remuneration as sanctioned by the Treasury.—Improvements in the Strand.—Other projected improvements in the direction of the Museum, Lincoln's-inn-fields and Holborn.—Introduction of Mr. Decimus Burton.—Improvements in Hyde Park.—Reasons for building the Parliamentary Mews.—Management of the Lord Chamberlain's department.

Roads, Highways and Turnpike Trusts:

Highways, 1763:

32. — [Report from the Select Committee on the application of Money, collected within Eleven Years last past, for repairing any particular Highway.

Journals, vol. 29, p. 646

SUBJECTS.—The management of the following trusts: Hackney; Islington; Kensington; Marylebone; New Cross; Surrey.

Roads, Highways and Turnpike Trusts—continued.

Highways, 1765 :

33.—[Report from the Select Committee respecting the management and application of Money collected for repairing the Highways of the Kingdom.

First Series, vol. 11. p. 465.

SUBJECTS.—State of the Bath road—Islington—Kensington—Marylebone—New Cross —Park-lane or Tyburn-lane — Piccadilly—Stamford-hill — Surrey. — Appointment of trustees.

Highways and Turnpike Roads, 1796 :

34.—[Five Reports from the Select Committee on the state of the Public Highways and Turnpike Roads ; and the Acts relating thereto.

First Series, vol. x. pp. 748. 749. 757. 758. 759.

SUBJECTS.—The appointment, duties and qualifications of commissioners. — On the form of wheels, as affecting the condition of the roads.—Weighing-engines ; their utility, and manner of conducting them.

Highways, Wheels and Carriages, 1806–1819 :

35.—Two Reports on Acts regarding the use of Broad Wheels, and other matters relative to the Preservation of the Turnpike Roads and Highways of the Kingdom.

Sess. 1806, (212. 321.) vol. 2, p. 241. 249. [79.]

SUBJECTS.—Construction of wheels and carriages ; and preservation of roads.

36.—Reports on the state of the Highways of the Kingdom, from the Committee appointed to take into consideration the Acts now in force regarding the use of Broad Wheels, and to examine into what Shape is the best calculated for ease of Draught, and the Preservation of the Roads.

Sess. 1808, (225. 275. 315.) vol. 2, pp. 333. 459. 527. [79.]

SUBJECTS.—On the construction of wheels and carriages, with respect to the preservation of turnpike roads.—Formation of roads.—Legislative provisions for their preservation. —Construction of carriages for economizing the labour of draught.—Form of wheels least likely to injure the surface of the road.——Many *Plans* and *Diagrams*.

37.—Three Reports from the Committee on the Acts now in force regarding the use of Broad Wheels, and on the Preservation of the Turnpike Roads and Highways of the Kingdom.

Sess. 1809, (179. 238. 271.) vol. 3, pp. 411. 449. 453. [79.]

38.—Report on the Acts now in force regarding the Highways, &c., in England and Wales, and the expediency of additional Regulations for the Preservation thereof.

Sess. 1810–11, (240.) vol. 3, p. 855. [79.]

SUBJECTS.—Plan of a general law for regulating the construction and management of turnpike roads.—Account of carriages and horses in England.—Advantages of improving the roads by rendering a less number of horses necessary.—Question of high wheels and low wheels.—Difference between the power of progressive wheels of carriages, and stationary wheels of mechanical machinery.—Spokes and levers not analogous.—Comparative advantages of low and high wheels.—Spokes compared to the legs of animals—Sustaining the load alternately as they advance.—Effect of broad wheels on the materials of the roads. —Construction of roads. — Field-paths. — Weighing-engines. — One-horse carts.—— Regulation of the number of passengers and luggage to be carried by stage-coaches. ——Centre of roads near the metropolis proposed to be paved.—Highgate Archway.— Exemption of mail-coaches from toll ;—Regulation of their drivers.—General view of the information collected on the subject of roads and carriages.—Formation of roads and construction of carriages.—Tracks of wheels.—Regulations for safety of passengers.—As to tolls and tollgates.—Plan for raising a tax on carriages and horses.—Parliamentary Commission or Board for Roads. — Construction of carriages and mode of draught.— Springs ; application to carts and waggons.—Railroads of iron or stone might be applied to general use.—Durability of the Roman roads.—Mechanical modes of the action of the horse.—Comparative advantages of the breadth of wheels.—Of harness.—On forming and repairing roads.—Action of conical and cylindrical wheels.—Mode of harnessing horses.— Use and rationale of springs.—May be applied to heavy waggons.—Use of oxen for draught.—Best way of yoking them.—Shoeing and management of them.—On breaking road-materials to a certain size.—Preservation of footpaths.—Further observations on the advantage of cylindrical wheels.

Highways and Turnpike Trusts, 1819–1821 :

39.—Report from the Select Committee on the Highways of the Kingdom.

Sess. 1819, (509.) vol. 5, p. 339. [80.]

SUBJECTS.—On the prevailing mode of conducting highway trusts.—Defective methods of forming and repairing roads.—Improvements adopted by several skilful persons.—A particular description of their practice.—Kinds and size of materials described.

Roads, Highways and Turnpike Trusts—continued.

40.—Report from the Select Committee on the Turnpike Roads and Highways in England and Wales.   Sess. 1820, (301.) vol. 2, p. 301. [80.]

    Subjects.—Consolidating trusts near London. — Opposition and prejudice.—Computation of the superficial extent of roads in England.—Mr. M'Adam's road-making, and claims.

41.—Report from the Select Committee on Acts now in force regarding Turnpike Roads and Highways in England and Wales.

                                        Sess. 1821, (747.) vol. 4, p. 343. [80.]

    Subjects.—*Improvements in the Management of Roads.*—Object of the Committee in framing the Bill for consolidating the road-trusts near London.—Effect of wheels according to their construction.—Flat cylindrical wheels.—Narrow wheels.—Observations on spring carriages, by Mr. Edgeworth.——Great part of the Appendix consists of table-returns relative to the funds, and their application, belonging to turnpike trusts.

On the Management and Construction, 1823–1827 :

42.—Report from the Select Committee on Mr. M'Adam's Petition, relating to his improved system of constructing and repairing the Public Roads of the Kingdom.   Sess. 1823, (476.) vol. 5, p. 53. [80.]

    Subjects. — *Improved Construction of Public Roads, on Mr. M'Adam's System.*— Mr. M'Adam's claims.—Testimony of Postmaster-general in favour.—Recommendation of the Lords of the Treasury.—Favourable opinion of the Committee of 1819.—Similar opinion in 1820.—Proposal for converting the pavement of London streets into smooth roads.—Experiments to be made in St. James's-square and over Westminster Bridge.— His progress towards road-making.—Extent of turnpike-roads in the kingdom.—Amount of tolls and debt.—Inefficacy of statute labour.—Operations of road-making explained.

    see *Holyhead Roads*, and *Highland Roads and Bridges*, for matters relating to the Construction of Roads.

43.—Report from the Select Committee on the Receipts, Expenditure and Management of the several Turnpike Trusts within Ten Miles of London.

                                         Sess. 1825, (355.) vol. 5, p. 167. [80.]

    Subjects.—*Condition and Expense of the present Trusts, and benefit of the proposed Consolidation.*—Defective state of accounts.—Income raised not applied in the most beneficial manner.—Improvement in the surface of the roads since 1819.—Opinions of Messrs. Telford and M'Adam.—Best materials for making roads.—Expense of lighting in some places paid by the parish, and in others out of the tolls.—Remarks on St. George's and Marylebone, as to the state of the pavement and allowances received from tolls.— Existing debt, and rate of interest.—Estate of Harrow trust, independent of revenue from tolls.—Impolicy and inconvenience of independent trusts for short portions of road.— Opinions of former Committees on the advantage of consolidating the trusts—recommended by this Committee.—Inconvenience and annoyance of numerous gates described. ——Management of the trust.—Salaries.—Special jurymen chosen from the trustees very frequently.—Management of the toll-collectors.—Wages paid them.—Annoyance of Sunday-tolls.—Materials used on Highgate trust.—Material best suited for road-making. —Capability of obtaining a supply.—Cost of forming and keeping in repair.—Comparative quality of granite, whinstone and gravel.—Kentish ragstone.—Amount of toll collected. —Farming tolls,—method of managing, when so done.—Greatest proportion of toll paid by residents in London.—City toll at Temple-bar, &c.—Imperfect state of accounts of the Brentford trust.—Stamford-Hill trust.—Harrow trust.—Quality and quantity of stone to be procured from the Northumberland coast.—Stones may be broken by machinery.— The principles of road-making stated.—Importance of draining.—On the possibility of levying the road-revenue by other means than by tollgates.—Calculations of the amount of toll paid by horses and carriages of all descriptions.—On the system of patrol under the direction of road-trustees, and as established by the police.—Management of roads near Scotland.

44.—Report from the Select Committee on the practicability of reducing the Expenses attending the procuring Bills for continuing Turnpike Trust Acts.

                                       Sess. 1826–27, (383.) vol. 6, p. 1.

    Subjects.—Proposed abolition of Parliamentary fees.—Printing to be defrayed by the public.—Consolidation of trusts.

Turnpike Trusts, 1833 :

45.—Report from the Lords respecting Turnpike Returns, and on what alterations can be usefully made in the Laws relating to Turnpike Trusts.

                                       Sess. 1833, (422.) vol. 15, p. 407.

    Subjects.—Recommendation for a Bill to be brought in for continuing for one year the several Acts for regulating Turnpike Roads, which will expire at the end of Session 1834. ——Also, a Bill requiring the annual transmission of statements to the Secretary of State.

Roads, Highways and Turnpike Trusts—continued.

46.—Second Report from the Lords respecting Turnpike Returns; and on what alterations can be usefully made in the Laws relating to Turnpike Trusts.

Sess. 1833, (703.) vol. 15, p. 409.

SUBJECTS.—Advantages from the Metropolitan Trust Commissioners.—Evil of the number of trusts.—Consolidation of local trusts recommended.—Duration of local Acts not to be limited.—Limitation of the amount of money to be borrowed.—Weighing-engines to be discontinued.—Abuse of power of compounding with trustees for toll.—A system of general control recommended.

Whetstone Roads, 1828:

47.—Report from the Select Committee on the state of the Roads under the Whetstone and St. Alban's Turnpike Trusts. Sess. 1828, (546.) vol. 4, p. 255.

SUBJECTS.—Bad state of the roads.—Composition of the road.—Destruction of horses by the extreme labour.—Amount of funds applicable to the repairs.—Inefficient attention of the trustees.—Recommendation to place the road under the care of the Parliamentary Commissioners for a limited time.—Loss in consequence of the refusal of trustees, in 1823, to accept the assistance of the Commissioners in the improvement of the road at Barnet.—Information of the method of road-making, and the best materials for that use.

Metropolis Turnpike Roads, 1827 to 1834:

48.—First Report of the Commissioners, under Act 7 Geo. 4, c. 142, for management of the Roads North of the Metropolis. Sess. 1826-27, (339.) vol. 7, p. 23.

SUBJECTS.—Preliminary arrangements for commencing the business of the commission trust.—Inquiry into the state of the trusts, placed under the management of the commissioners.—Existing debts.—Removing of tollgates and remission of Sunday foot-toll.—Reasonableness of equalizing the rates of toll in different districts.—Diversity in management of the funds for lighting, watching and watering.—Propriety of removing turnpike-gates from the streets in the outskirts of the Metropolis.——*Three Plans* of present roads, and proposed improvements.

49.—Second Report of the Commissioners. Sess. 1828, (311.) vol. 9, p. 23.

SUBJECTS.—Proceedings of the commissioners.—Removal of tollgates and weighing-engines near London.—State of funds.—Plans of proposed alteration at Snaresbrook, Holloway, Hanwell and Smallbury Green.

50.—Third Report of the Commissioners. Sess. 1829, (219.) vol. 5, p. 21.

SUBJECTS.—Proceedings of commissioners.—Abolition of night-tolls.—Removal of turnpike-gates from the streets of the Metropolis.—Revenue and expenditure.

51.—Fourth Report of the Commissioners. Sess. 1830, (362.) vol. 15, p. 135.

SUBJECTS.—Equalization of tolls on similar distances of road.—Removal of turnpike-gates on the northern verge of the Metropolis.—New roads completed.—Regulation as to cylindrical wheels.—State of accounts.

52.—Fifth Report of the Commissioners. Sess. 1831, (41.) vol. 12, p. 1.

SUBJECTS.—Beneficial effects of the provision respecting the form and breadth of the tires of wheels.—Progress of intended new roads.—Burthen of night-watching the roads should be removed from the commissioners' funds.—Amount of receipts and expenditure.

53.—Sixth Report of the Commissioners. Sess. 1831-32, (449.) vol. 23, p. 541.

SUBJECTS.—Progress of improvements.—New road from Camden-town to Tottenham, and from Shepherd's Bush to Turnham-green.—Financial statement.——*Seven Plans* of improvements, and proposed new roads.

54.—Seventh Report of the Commissioners. Sess. 1834, (237.) vol. 40, p. 211.

SUBJECTS.—Satisfactory progress of the objects of the commission.—Purchase of the annuity on the Lea Bridge tolls completed.—Liquidation of loan.—Financial arrangements successfully carried on.—Old debts done away with.—One principal debt only remaining, the liquidation of which is provided for.

55.—Eighth Report of the Commissioners. Sess. 1834, (238.) vol. 40, p. 223.

SUBJECTS.—Progress of the business of the commission.—Completion of the road from Camden-town to Tottenham.—Reduction of the bonded debt.

Northern Roads, 1830:

56.—Report from the Select Committee on the state of the Northern Roads between London and Edinburgh, and London and Portpatrick.

Sess. 1830, (172.) vol. 10, p. 189.

SUBJECTS.—Description of the lines of road.—Examination of the means of shortening the distances.—Mr. Telford's plans and surveys for that purpose.—Recommendation to intrust the improvements to a board of commissioners.——Description of the proceedings of the commission on the Holyhead-road, showing the success attending their mode of management.

Mail-Coach Tolls :

57.—Report from the Select Committee on Mail-Coach Exemption from Toll.

Sess. 1810-11, (212.) vol. 3, p. 707. [134.]

SUBJECTS.— Diminution of the revenue of turnpike road trusts, by the exemption.—Expediency of its repeal.

Bridges :

Blackfriars Bridge, 1756 :

58.—[Report from the Select Committee respecting the proposed Plan for building that Bridge.   Journals, vol. 27, p. 514.

SUBJECTS.—Opinions as to the utility of the plan, and its explanation.—Estimated to cost 140,000 *l.*—Opinions as to the effect of a bridge so situated on the navigation.—State of London Bridge.—Plan for improving it by taking down the houses thereon.—Opinions as to its durability.—Evidence of an inspection of its foundations afforded by an exceedingly low tide in 1718.—Bridge-house Estate consisted of the houses standing on the bridge.—Resolutions of the Committee in favour of a new bridge at Blackfriars, and recommending taking down the houses on London Bridge.

London Port and London Bridge, 1796–1801 :

59.—[Report from the Select Committee on the best mode of providing accommodation for the increased Trade and Shipping of the Port of London.

First Series, vol. XIV. p. 267.

60.—[First Report of the Select Committee on the consideration of Evidence on Bills for improvement of the Port of London.   First Series, vol. XIV. p. 444.

61.—[Second Report on the same subject.   First Series, vol. XIV. p. 461.

62.—[Report from the Select Committee on further measures necessary for rendering more commodious, and for better regulating, the Port of London, and for the improvement of London Bridge.   First Series, vol. XIV. p. 543.

63.—Second Report on the same subject.   First Series, vol. XIV. p. 604.

and Sess. 1801, (102.) vol. 3.

SUBJECTS.—I. *Trade and Navigation :* Progressive increase of the exports and imports of London for the last century.—The coal trade in the river.—Increase of the coasting trade, and its removal from the legal quays recommended.—Foreign trade, and the accommodation of its shipping in the Pool; regulations of foreign ports.—The West India trade —difficulties in delivering their cargoes—facilities for smuggling and plunderage—advantages of wet docks in landing cargoes.—East India Company's trade and shipping.—East-country, or timber trade—and its proposed removal below Limehouse.—Mediterranean trade.—African trade.—On the bonding system.—Rates and risks of insurance.—State of the Thames, and obstructions to navigation from the increase of shipping, and plans for removing them.—State of the moorings and shipping stations in the River.—The effect of tides on navigation—and the causes of alteration—experiments on their rapidity.—Plans for the improvement of quays, wharfs and warehouses.—Plan for turning the channel of the Thames at the Isle of Dogs—and for embankments.—Plan for the protection of river craft, and formation of a company of lightermen. — Removal of Billingsgate.——— II. *Docks :* Advantages of wet docks—and various plans for constructing them—great security from fire and plunderage.—Plans for improving this part of the river, and constructing docks.———III. *Bridges :* State and structure of London Bridge.—An iron bridge proposed in lieu of London Bridge, with remarks of scientific men respecting it.—Plans of various other new bridges, plates and explanations.—State and structure of Blackfriars Bridge.—State of the navigation between Blackfriars and London Bridges.—Expense of maintenance of Westminster Bridge.——*With many Plans and Sections.*

Rebuilding London Bridge, 1820–1832 :

64.—Report from the Select Committee on the state of London Bridge.

Sess. 1820, (304.) vol. 3, p. 24. [71.]

SUBJECTS.—*Necessity of rebuilding the Bridge.*—States the impossibility of completing their inquiry ; but hopes in a re-appointment of the Committee in the following Session.

65.—Minutes of Evidence taken before the Committee of 1820, on the state of London Bridge.   Sess. 1821, (609.) vol. 5, p. 415. [71.]

66.—Report from the Select Committee on the state of London Bridge.

Sess. 1821, (569.) vol. 5, p. 281. [71.]

SUBJECTS.—*Necessity of rebuilding the Bridge.*—Proposed plan of enlarging the water-way by substituting four large arches for eight of the present ones.—Estimated expense of constructing coffer-dams for the examination of the piers.—Examination of a pier by excavation.—Difference of opinion.—A new bridge recommended.—Supposed beneficial effects of removing the bridge on the navigation.—The water-works condemned.—State of the bed of the river.—Danger in navigating barges through the arches of the bridge.—Bridge-house estates,—officers, &c.—Estimated expense of altering the present and rebuilding a new bridge.—Description of present foundation.

Bridges—London Bridge, 1832—*continued.*

67.—Report of Thomas Telford, James Walker, W. T. Clarke, Sir J. Rennie, and Messrs. Jolliffe and Banks, relative to the Stability of New London Bridge.
Sess. 1831-32, (61.) vol. 45, p. 99.

SUBJECT.—The new bridge was opened 1st August 1831, and soon after some of the piers of the new bridge had sunk out of the level, and fears were entertained of defects in the workmanship.—This survey states the extent and causes.

Rochester Bridge :

68.—Report from the Select Committee on the present state of Rochester Bridge, &c.
Sess. 1820, (267.) vol. 3, p. 29. [71.]

SUBJECTS.—*State of the River Medway.*—*Effect of obstructions on the Beds of Rivers.*—Gradual decay of the river Medway, by the filling up of the channel.—Decrease of the soundings—Ascribed to the obstructions occasioned by the bridge to the flow of the tide, and the consequent diminution of the velocity of the current at the ebb, rendering it less able to keep the channel open.—Reason for the gradual diminution of depth of all navigable rivers.—Proposed improvements of the river.——The *Report* is comprised in a short paragraph, but the *Evidence* and documentary part is of much interest, not only as applicable to the state of the river Medway, and the naval arsenal at Chatham, but as relative to rivers generally.

Thames and Isis Navigation, 1793 :

69.—[Report from the Select Committee on the progress made towards the improvement thereof ; and the state of the Trade upon that Navigation.
First Series, vol. XIV., p. 230.

Harbours :

Ramsgate Harbour, 1748–1755 :

70.—[Reports from the Select Committee respecting building Piers, and other Improvements.
Journals, vol. 25, p. 761 ; vol. 27, pp. 213. 463.

SUBJECTS.—Examinations of the trustees and other persons, as to the suitableness of the plans proposed.—Peculiarities of the harbour, as to the tides and winds affecting vessels entering it.—Opinions as to the best position for opening the harbour's mouth.—Different opinions on the proposed construction of the harbour.

Rye and Dover Harbours, 1699–1764 :

71.—[Reports from the Select Committee on Petitions for extending the Powers of Acts for Repairing those Harbours.
Journals, vol. 27, p. 449 ; vol. 29, pp. 82. 403.

SUBJECTS.—State of the harbour, and progress made in repairs.—Reports read, made to the House on 12 Feb. 1699, Journals, vol. 13, p. 201 ; 25 Feb. 1722, Journals, vol. 20, p. 150 ; and 24 Feb. 1723, Journals, vol. 20, p. 269.

72.—[Report from the Select Committee respecting Rye and Dover Harbours.
First Series, vol. II., p. 385.

Milford Haven, 1757–1758 :

73.—Report from the Select Committee respecting Milford Haven.
Journals, vol, 27, p. 921.

SUBJECTS.—Its situation well adapted for the protection of trade.—Capacity.—Geographical advantages of the harbour.

74.—[Report from the Select Committee respecting the fortifying of the Haven.
First Series, vol. II., p. 405.

1826–1827 :

75.—Report from the Select Committee on the Communication with Ireland by Milford Haven.
Sess. 1826–27, (258.) vol. 3, p. 551.

76.—Second Report on the same subject.
Sess. 1826–27, (472.) vol. 3, p. 649.

SUBJECTS.—Proposed improvement of the packet establishment.—Erection of a pier recommended ; and improvement of the ferry over the Severn.—*With Plans.*

77.—Accounts relating to the Trade of Milford Haven.
Sess. 1826, (154. 178.) vol. 3, p. 739.

Plymouth Harbour :

78.—Report from the Select Committee on the Embankment at Catwater.
Sess. 1806, (298.) vol. 3, p. 1109. [71]

Harbours—Plymouth Harbour—*continued.*

79.—Papers relating to Plymouth Sound.

Sess. 1812, (44. 65.) vol. 10, pp. 175. 205. [71.]

SUBJECTS.—Structure and probable expense of the proposed *Breakwater* for sheltering Plymouth Sound.

Lyme Regis Harbour :

80.—Report on Lyme Regis Harbour Petition.

Sess. 1817, (356.) vol. 3, p. 165. [71.]

81.—Report on re-committed Report on Lyme Regis Harbour Petition.

Sess. 1817, (463.) vol. 3, p. 167. [71.]

SUBJECT.—Damage occasioned to the Cobb, from a violent storm on the 20th January 1817.

82.—Report on the Repair of the Cobb at Lyme Regis.

Sess. 1818, (432.) vol 3, p. 367. [71.]

SUBJECT.—Progress made in the repairs.

83.—Reports from the Officers of the Royal Engineers employed to conduct the Repairs of the Cobb at Lyme Regis.   Sess. 1818, (242.) vol. 3, p. 373. [71.]

84.—Account of Sums expended in the Repairs of the Cobb.

Sess. 1818, (243.) vol. 3, p. 389. [71.]

85.—Copy of the Authority under which a Sum of Money was expended for the Repairs of the Cobb ; together with Correspondence relative thereto.

Sess. 1821, (422.) vol. 21, p. 351. [71.]

86.—Estimate of Sum required for the Repairs of the Cobb.

Sess. 1825, (131.) vol. 18, p. 361. [71.]

87.—Number of Vessels wrecked within the Harbour, driven thereout, stranded, &c., &c.   Sess. 1825, (316.) vol. 21, p. 275. [71.]

88.—Value of Imports and Exports from the Port of Lyme Regis.

Sess 1825, (324.) vol. 21, p. 281. [71.]

89.—Sums of Money paid on account of the Cobb, by Votes of Parliament, or from the Civil List.   Sess 1825, (326.) vol 21, p. 261. [71.]

90.—Tonnage of Vessels cleared inwards, outwards, and coastwise, at Lyme Regis Cobb, and Tonnage of Sixty-six Vessels which sought Refuge from Stress of Weather, in Three years.   Sess. 1825, (218.) vol. 21, p. 259. [71.]

ENGLAND AND SCOTLAND.

Roads communicating between England and Ireland, and England and Scotland :

Glasgow and Portpatrick Roads, 1823–24 :

91.—Report from the Select Committee on Glasgow and Portpatrick Roads, &c.

Sess. 1823, (486.) vol. 5, p. 133. [69.]

SUBJECTS.—*Communication between Scotland and Ireland.*—State of the revenue of the roads.—Importance of the communication between Scotland and Ireland.—Would facilitate the transmission of the mail-packets.—Lines of road proposed.—Survey of them recommended. — Consolidation of trusts considered advantageous. — Establishment of steam-packets recommended.—Improvement of Portpatrick Harbour to be completed.

92.—Report from the Select Committee on Glasgow and Portpatrick Roads, &c. —Girvan to Stranraer.   Sess. 1824, (428.) vol. 7, p. 151. [69.]

SUBJECTS.—*Communication between Scotland and Ireland.*—Survey of new lines of road made.—Comparative advantages of the lines of road from Girvan to Stranraer, and from Girvan to Ballantrae.—Failure of the bill for carrying into effect the recommendation of the Committees of last Session, as to a road from Edinburgh, Glasgow, &c. to Portpatrick. —Intended establishment of steam-packets at Portpatrick rendered unavailing by that failure ; and the proceedings of the Committee have thereby become useless.———*A Map* of the proposed roads is inserted.

Roads communicating between England, Ireland and Scotland—continued.

Highlands of Scotland, 1802-3 :

93.—Four Reports from the Select Committee on the Survey of the Central Highlands of Scotland.   Sess. 1802-3, (80. 94. 110. 118.) vol. 4. [69.]
> These Reports are connected with those made by the Commissioners of the Caledonian Canal, and Highland Roads and Bridges.
> The SUBJECTS are :—1. Emigration.—2. Roads and Bridges.—3. Caledonian Canal.—4. Naval Stations and Fisheries.

94. — Survey of the Coasts and Central Highlands of Scotland, made by command of the Right Honourable the Lords Commissioners of His Majesty's Treasury, in the Autumn of 1802, by T. Telford, civil engineer, Edinburgh, F. R. S.   Sess. 1802-3, (45.) vol. 4, p. 1. [69.]
> *See likewise* under *Caledonian Canal,* and *Highland Roads and Bridges, infra.*

Morpeth and Edinburgh Roads, 1822–1825 :

95.—Report from the Select Committee on the Road from Morpeth to Edinburgh.   Sess. 1822, (506.) vol. 8, p. 381. [69.]
> SUBJECTS.—*Communication with Scotland.*—Advantage of the line of road by Wooler.—Delivery of letters at Edinburgh inconvenient.—Proposed improvement. — Expense.—Proposed mode of defraying it.—The formation of a general trust on the new line of road recommended.—Description of traffic.—Mail on existing line of road not likely to be injured.

96.—Report and Estimate of proposed Line of Road from Morpeth by Wooler; by Thomas Telford, civil engineer.   Sess. 1822, (166.) vol. 8, p. 409. [69.]

97.—Report of Mr. Telford to the Lords of the Treasury, respecting the Mail Road between Edinburgh and Morpeth, by Berwick and Alnwick.   Sess. 1825, (282.) vol. 15, p. 81. [69.]
> SUBJECT.—State of the line of road, and proposed improvements.

Carlisle and Portpatrick Roads, 1809–1811 :

98.—Report from the Select Committee on Mr. Telford's Report and Survey relative to the Communication between England and Ireland, by the North West of Scotland.   Sess. 1809, (269.) vol. 3, p. 593. [69.]
> SUBJECTS.—This Report describes generally the necessity of improving the line of road in the proposed direction. The Appendix contains a detailed account of the projected works.———*There are 16 charts and plans referred to.—They form a separate portfolio.*
> [XV. *of Maps and Plans.*]

99.—Report from the Select Committee upon the Roads between Carlisle and Portpatrick.   Sess. 1810–11, (119.) vol. 3, p. 789. [69.]
> SUBJECT.—Continuation of the preceding Report.—*With Plans.*

Carlisle and Glasgow Road, 1815 :

100.—Report from the Select Committee on the Carlisle and Glasgow Road.   Sess. 1814–15, (463.) vol. 3, p. 331. [69.]
> SUBJECTS.—1. The present state of the road.—2. The advantage of making a good road.—3. The merits of the proposed plan.———*A Plan* is attached.

Holyhead Harbour, 1808–1816 :

101.—Report from the Select Committee on Papers respecting Holyhead Harbour.   Sess. 1808, (273.) vol. 2, p. 91. [69.]

102.—Two Reports from the Select Committee appointed to inquire into the state of the Road from Shrewsbury to Holyhead, and to inquire into the state of Holyhead Harbour.   Sess. 1810, (166. 352.) vol. 4, pp. 33. 41. [69.]
> SUBJECTS.—Dangerous state of the road from Shrewsbury to Holyhead.—Plans of improvement proposed.—Bridge over the Menai Strait suggested.———These Reports are interesting, from being the commencement of a subject which frequently engaged the attention of Parliament in succeeding Sessions.

103.—Report from the Select Committee appointed to inquire into the state of the Road from Shrewsbury to Holyhead; and from Chester to Holyhead; and into the manner of conveying the Mail from Holyhead to London.   Sess. 1810–11, (197.) vol. 3, p. 801. [69.]
> SUBJECTS.—Continuation of the preceding Reports.———There are in this several *Plans* for constructing bridges over the Menai.

Roads communicating between England, Ireland and Scotland—continued.

104.—Report from the Select Committee on Holyhead Harbour.
Sess. 1816, (462.) vol. 8, p. 71. [69.]

Subject.—Utility of the harbour in affording accommodation to the packets employed in sustaining the communication with Ireland.

Holyhead Roads, 1815–1823 :

105.—Two Reports from the Select Committee on Holyhead Roads.
Sess. 1814–15, (363. 395.) vol. 3, pp. 355. 383. [70.]

Subjects.—On the safe and expeditious communication between England and Ireland.—State of the road from London to Holyhead.—Conveyance of the mail with more expedition.—Harbour accommodation of the packets.

106.—Five Reports from the Select Committee on the Roads from London to Holyhead, &c.   Sess. 1817, (313. 332. 411. 459. 469.) vol. 3. [70.]

Subjects.—Same as the preceding.

107.—First Report from the Select Committee on the Road from London to Holyhead.   Sess. 1819, (78.) vol. 5, p. 115. [70.]

Subjects.—Examination of Mr. Telford as to the state of the road between Chirk Valley and Bangor Ferry.—Beneficial effects on the mutual interests of England and Ireland, from providing every facility to a rapid and safe communication between the two countries.

108.—Second Report from the same Committee.
Sess. 1819, (217.) vol. 5, p. 121. [70.]

Subjects.—*Road over Anglesea.*—Reference to Reports of 1810, 1811, 1815, and 1817.—Its state of too much importance to be left subject to local interests.—Mr. Telford's plan for improving the road.—*With a Map.*

109.—Third Report from the same Committee.
Sess. 1819, (256.) vol. 5, p. 135. [70.]

Subjects.—*Proposed Suspension Bridge over the Menai.*—On Mr. Telford's plan for constructing an iron suspension bridge across the Menai Straits.—Bridge described, with its proposed workmanship.—Opinions of several eminent engineers as to its practicability.—With an engraved *Plan* of the design.

110.—Fourth Report from the same Committee.
Sess. 1819, (501.) vol. 5, p. 153. [70.]

Subjects.—*Post-office Packets.*—Interruption of the packets by the ships of war and revenue cutters.

111.—Fifth Report from the same Committee.   Sess. 1819, (548.) vol. 5, p. 157. [70.]

Subjects.—Conveyance of mails, and sailing of packets.—With four *Draughts* of the construction of proposed vessels.

112.—Sixth Report from the same Committee.   Sess. 1819, (549.) vol. 5, p. 223. [70.]

Subjects.—*Turnpike Trusts and Construction of Roads.*—Turnpike trusts between London and Holyhead.—State of the roads.—Observations on road-making.—Mr. Telford's system described and recommended.—General incompetence of road-makers and road-surveyors.—Particular description of an improved piece of road.—*With a Map.*

113.—Papers relating to building a Bridge over the Menai Strait, near Bangor Ferry, &c.   Sess. 1819, (60.) vol. 5, p. 311. [70.]

Subjects.—A detailed account of the suspension bridge proposed by Mr. Telford ; with *two Maps*, and a *Plan* of the proposed bridge.

114.—First Report from the Select Committee on the Road from London by Coventry to Holyhead.   Sess. 1820, (201.) vol. 3, p. 1. [70.]

Subjects.—*Communication with Ireland ;—and improved Method of constructing Roads.*—Bridge at Conway.—Mr. Telford's Reports.—A suspension bridge recommended.—Estimate.—Observations on the necessity of facilitating the communication with Ireland.—Inconvenience of the ferry at Conway.

115.—Second Report from the same Committee.   Sess. 1820, (224.) vol. 3, p. 7. [70.]

Subjects.—*Turnpike Trusts. — Mr. M‘Adam's and Mr. Telford's Improvements.*—Imperfect state of the road from London to Chirk.—Present method of repair ineffectual : Mr. M‘Adam's recommended.—Assistance by issue of Exchequer bills proposed.—Consolidation of trusts from Birmingham to Shrewsbury recommended.—Misapplication of materials.—Difficulty of making the surveyors attend to the rules laid down.—Answers to questions on the state of the roads under several trusts.—Bad state of the Whetstone and Highgate road.—Destruction of horses.—Materials, though indifferent, would make good roads if applied on Mr. M‘Adam's plan.

*Roads communicating between England, Ireland and Scotland—*continued.

116.—First Report from the Select Committee on the Roads from London to Holyhead, and from Chester to Holyhead, &c.   Sess. 1822, (41.) vol. 6, p. 1. [70.]

SUBJECTS.—*Roads in North Wales.*—Great importance of the work.—Superiority of the road now made.—Amount of sums wanted to complete the road.

117.—Second Report from the same Committee.   Sess. 1822, (180.) vol. 6, p. 9. [70.]

SUBJECTS.—*Steam-Packets.*—Advantage of steam-packets in expedition.—Additional ones recommended to be provided by the Post-office.—Accommodation of passengers.— Superiority of steam-packets to sailing packets.—Construction of vessels.—Consumption of fuel.——See *Steam-Vessels*, under Head XVIII.

118.—Third Report from the same Committee.   Sess. 1822, (275.) vol. 6, p 35. [70.]

SUBJECTS.—*Chester Roads.*—State of the road from Holyhead to Chester.—Inattention to its repairs.—Important traffic on it.—Proposed consolidation of the trusts.——*Map* of the present and proposed roads.—*Sections* of the road.

119.—Fourth Report from the same Committee. Sess. 1822, (343.) vol. 6, p. 55. [70.]

SUBJECTS.—*Roads through England, from North Wales to London.*—Mr. Telford's survey of the roads.—Money borrowed by the Parliamentary Commissioners.—Progress made.—Wrong principle of sacrificing the convenience of travellers in a shorter route, in order to favour a town by letting the road pass through it.—Advantages of shortening the line of road, and facilitating travelling to and from Ireland.——*Two Maps* of the present and proposed roads.

120.—Fifth Report from the same Committee. Sess. 1822, (417.) vol. 6, p. 115. [70.]

SUBJECTS.—*Advantages of Steam-Boats.*—Origin of steam-boats.—Their present advanced state, and general use.—Advantages over other vessels used for like purposes.— Precautions to insure safety.—Speed in making their voyages.—I. On the form of the vessels.—II. Strength.—III. Machinery.—IV. Sails.—Fares of passengers.—Searching by Custom-house.—Charges by boatmen.—Delivery of letters at Dublin.——*Plans* for building steam vessels.——see *Steam Vessels* under Head XVIII.

121.—Sixth Report from the same Committee.

Sess. 1822, (513.) vol. 6, p. 241. [70.]

SUBJECTS.—*Roads in Ireland.*—State of them.—Board of Trustees proposed.—Defective state of the mail-coach system in Ireland, compared with the state in England.—Tolls.— Postage.

122.—Reports of Mr. Telford, to the Commissioners for the Improvement of the Holyhead Road, upon the state of the Road between London and Shrewsbury :—with Maps and Estimates.   Sess. 1820, (126.) vol. 6, p. 287. [70.]

SUBJECTS.—*Communication with Ireland.*—*Construction of Roads.*—Describing the present state of the road, and stating the necessary improvements.—Estimates of expenses. —Observations on the best modes of repairs.—These matters are arranged under the heads of the different trusts.——There are *Nine Maps* of the different districts of roads surveyed and described in the Reports.

Northern Roads :

123.—Report of Mr. Telford, to the Lords of the Treasury, on two proposed lines of Road, the one from Catterick Bridge, County of York, to the Carter Fell, on the borders of Scotland ; the other from Catterick Bridge to New Castleton, County of Roxburgh.   Sess. 1820, (279.) vol. 7, p. 57.

SUBJECTS.—Estimates of the two proposed lines of road.——The chief purposes of these are to afford a more direct communication between the city of Edinburgh on the north, and the middle of Yorkshire on the south, and to afford local accommodations to the countries through which they would pass.

124.—Reports of Mr. Telford on the progress and state of the Holyhead Road and Menai Bridge.   Sess. 1821, (574 & 575.) vol. 10, pp. 231. 237.

SUBJECTS.—I. Progress and present state of the Anglesea Road and Menai Bridge, with annual account.—II. Copy of Mr. Telford's Reports, to the Commissioners for improving the Holyhead Roads, upon the state of that road.

125.—Report of Mr. Telford upon the state of the Road from Shrewsbury by Coventry to London.   Sess. 1822, (179.) vol. 6, p. 345. [70.]

SUBJECTS.—*Communication with Ireland.*—Construction of roads.—The improved state of some parts ascribed to the adoption of the method of road-making recommended in former Reports, and to the use of broken materials, not gravel.

126.—Report of Thomas Telford, Esq., dated 9 April 1823, upon the state of the Road from London to Holyhead.   Sess. 1823, (261.) vol. 10, p. 23. [70.]

SUBJECTS.—*Construction of Roads.*—In describing the progress of the road repairs, much information is afforded on the subject of road-making; particularly in the advantage of using broken granite instead of gravel when it can be procured ; and in sorting the materials before used.

Roads communicating between England, Ireland and Scotland—continued.

Reports from Commissioners, 1816–1834 :

127.—Report of Commissioners under Act 55 Geo. 3, for repairing the Roads between London and Holyhead by Chester, and between London and Bangor by Shrewsbury.   Sess. 1816, (459.) vol. 8, p. 61. [83.]

128.—First Report of Commissioners under Act 4 Geo. 4, for the further Improvement of the Road from London to Holyhead.

Sess. 1824, (305.) vol. 9, p. 293. [83.]

SUBJECTS.—*Communication with Ireland.*—First proceedings of Commissioners in taking possession of the works committed to their direction :—Conway and Menai Bridges :— Holyhead and Howth Harbours :—Road from Howth to Dublin.

129.—Second Report of the Commissioners.   Sess. 1825, (492.) vol. 15, p. 63. [83.]

SUBJECTS.—Progress of the works.—Mr. Telford's Reports on the state of the several trusts in the line of the road.

130.—Third Report of the Commissioners.   Sess. 1826, (129.) vol. 11, p. 47. [83.]

SUBJECTS.—On the state of the roads, and progress of improvement.

131.—Fourth Report of the Commissioners.   Sess. 1826–27, (412.) vol. 7, p. 81.

SUBJECTS.—New piece of road from Barnet to South Mims.—Improvements in other parts of the road to Holyhead.—Completion of the Menai and Conway bridges.—Improvements of Holyhead and Howth harbours.

132.—Fifth Report of the Commissioners.   Sess. 1828, (476.) vol. 9, p. 227.

SUBJECTS.—Proceedings of the commissioners, and state of the roads under their management.—Menai and Conway bridges.———*Plans* of road over Flampstead Hill ; of Holyhead harbour ; and *Chart* of Howth harbour.

133.—Sixth Report of the Commissioners.   Sess. 1829, (316.) vol. 5, p. 103.

SUBJECTS.—Progress since passing the Act of last Session in making improvements in several lines of road.—Improvement in navigation of the Menai Straits.—Repairs of Menai and Conway bridges.—Howth and Holyhead harbours.—Dublin to Howth road.—Mr. Telford's survey of improved lines of the Liverpool roads.—Repayment of Exchequer bill loans.—Accounts of receipts and expenditure.

134.—Seventh Report of the Commissioners, 4 Geo. 4, c. 74, and 7 & 8 Geo. 4, c. 35.   Sess. 1830, (659.) vol. 15, p. 23.

SUBJECTS.—Proceedings of commissioners.—State of the roads under their management. —Account of receipts and expenditure from the institution of the commission in 1815.

135.—First Report from the Select Committee on the Money expended, and the progress made, in carrying into effect the recommendations of former Committees.   Sess. 1830, (432.) vol. 10, p. 131.

SUBJECTS.—Accounts of expenditure.—Works executed by the commissioners since 1815. —Present state of the works.—Executed by contract.—Failure of several contractors a proof of the fairness of the prices.—The works afford examples of road-making on perfect principles.———Mode of constructing the roads described.—Advantages to travelling, and in expediting the communication with Ireland.—Observations on milestones.—On tollhouses.—On the state of the roads and bridges.

136.—Second Report from the same Committee.   Sess. 1830, (652.) vol. 10, p. 183.

SUBJECTS.—Measures recommended by Committees from 1810 to 1822, for forming packet harbours at Holyhead and Howth, building bridges and improving roads.—What have been carried into effect ; and what remains.—Steam-packets.—Importance of completing the improvements recommended, and the effect they would have in increasing the speed of the mail, and insuring a more early arrival of the letters at Dublin.

137.—Eighth Report of the Commissioners, 4 Geo. 4, c. 74, and 7 & 8 Geo. 4, c. 35, for the further Improvement of the Road from London to Holyhead.

Sess. 1831, (280.) vol. 12, p. 29.

SUBJECT.—State of the roads under the care of the commissioners.

138.—Report of the Commissioners relative to the origin of their Commission for the Improvement of the Holyhead Roads, and on the present jurisdiction and duties of the Commissioners.   Sess. 1831, (298.) vol. 12, p. 17.

SUBJECTS.—Grant of money in 1815.—Appointment, in 1819, of the commissioners for the Shrewsbury to Bangor roads.—Menai bridge, in 1819.—Conway bridge, in 1821.— Holyhead and Howth harbours.—Road from Dublin to Howth.—Advance of Exchequer bills.—Works effected.—Saving of time in travelling.—Acts passed.—Money expended.— State of the roads under the care of the commissioners.—Expense of establishment for superintending the works.

Roads communicating between England and Ireland—continued.

139.—Ninth Report of the Commissioners under the 4 Geo. 4, c. 74, and 7 & 8 Geo. 4, c. 35, for the further Improvement of the Road from London to Holyhead.   Sess. 1831–32, (584.) vol. 23, p. 573.

SUBJECTS.—State of the harbour of Howth and Holyhead, and of the bridges over the Menai Straits and Conway.—Account of receipts and expenditure.——*Two Plans* of Howth harbour, and mail-road to Dublin.

140.—Tenth Report of the Commissioners.   Sess. 1833, (739.) vol. 17, p. 437.

SUBJECTS.—Condition and repair of the roads.—Account of loans on security of tolls.—Payments in liquidation of principal and interest.

141.—Eleventh Report of the Commissioners.   Sess. 1834, (608.) vol. 40, p. 147.

SUBJECTS.—State, condition and repair of the road.—Bridges over the Menai Straits and river Conway.—Harbours of Holyhead and Howth.—Account of receipts and expenditure.—Mr. Telford's report of the state of the works.

Shrewsbury and Holyhead Roads, 1820–1834:

142.—Annual Reports of the Commissioners appointed under Acts 59 Geo. 3, c. 30.

First, 1820, (127.) vol. 6, p. 351.—Second, 1821, (311.) vol. 10, p. 257.—Third, 1822, (126.) vol. 6, p. 361.—1823, (151.) vol. 10, p. * 22.—Fourth, 1824, (157.) vol. 9, p. 281.—Fifth, 1825, (153.) vol. 15, p. 51.—Sixth, 1826, (181.) vol. 11, p. 97.——Annual Reports, 59 Geo. 3, c. 30, and c. 48 : 1826–27, (196.) vol. 7, p. 61.—1829 (109.) vol. 5, p. 73.—1830, (169.) vol. 15, p. 77.—1830–31, (275.) vol. 4, p. 369.—1831–32, (304.) vol. 23, p. 597.—1833, (124.) vol. 17, p. 427.—1834, (131.) vol. 40, p. 137.

SUBJECTS.—General statement of the receipts and expenditure.—State of the roads; and works for keeping them in repair.

SCOTLAND.

Highland Roads and Bridges, 1803–1821 :

143.—First Report of the Commissioners for Roads and Bridges in the Highlands of Scotland, under Act 43 Geo. 3.   Sess. 1803–4, (108.) vol. 6, p. 715. [73.]

144.—Second Report, on the same subject.   Sess. 1805, (176.) vol. 3, p. 271. [73.]

SUBJECT.—On the progress of the works under the direction of the Commissioners.

Forfeited Estates in Scotland :

145.—Report from the Select Committee on the Funds arising from the Forfeited Estates in Scotland.   Sess. 1806, (221.) vol. 2, p. 305. [73.]

SUBJECTS.—The origin and former application of the funds are stated, and the appropriation of certain sums is recommended to assist the completion of several public works ; and recommends the vesting the balance in the Commissioners for Highland Roads and Bridges. This fund gave support to the Society for encouraging the Fisheries, the Highland Agricultural Society, and to other public works.——*See* under Head XII., No. 45.

146.—Third Report of the Commissioners for Roads and Bridges in the Highlands of Scotland.   Sess. 1807, (100.) vol. 3, p. 231. [73.]

SUBJECT.—On the progress of the works under the direction of the Commissioners.

147.—Fourth Report, on the same subject.   Sess. 1809, (167.) vol. 4, p. 1. [73.]

148.—Fifth Report, on the same subject.   Sess. 1810–11, (112.) vol. 4, p. 393. [73.]

149.—Sixth Report, on the same subject.   Sess. 1812–13, (110.) vol. 5, p. 1. [73.]

150.—Statement of their Origin and Extent.   Sess. 1813–14, (63.) vol. 3, p. 401. [73.]

151.—Seventh Report of the Commissioners for Roads and Bridges in the Highlands of Scotland.   Sess. 1814–15, (205.) vol. 3, p. 427. [74.]

SUBJECT.—On the progress of the works under the direction of the Commissioners.

152.—Report from the Select Committee on Estimate of Sums wanted for Highland Roads and Bridges.   Sess. 1816, (468.) vol. 4, p. 503. [74.]

Highland Roads and Bridges —continued.

153.—Eighth Report of the Commissioners for Roads and Bridges in the Highlands of Scotland.   Sess. 1817, (110.) vol. 9, p. 1. [74.]
>   SUBJECT.—On the progress of the works under the direction of the Commissioners.

154.—Ninth Report of the Commissioners.   Sess. 1821, (432.) vol. 10, p. 37. [74.]
>   SUBJECTS.—*Progress in forming Roads, Bridges, and Harbours.*—This Report contains a general review of the proceedings of the Commissioners.—Origin of the Highland roads and bridges.—Parliamentary grants and local contributions.—Total amount of expenditure.—Cost per mile.—Extreme low contracts discouraged ; yet it was impossible to resist the urgency of many : some of the contractors, in consequence, have been ruined.— General satisfaction of Highland proprietors.—Peculiar character of Highland roads — Repairs. — Statement of money transactions. — Present state of each particular road.— *Highland mail-coach established.*—Bridges.— Harbours.—Ancient instrument for turning up the earth, called *cas-chrom.*——1. *Map of Scotland.*—2. *Sketches of Bridges.*— 3. *Sketches of Harbours.*

155.—Estimates of Highland Roads and Bridges, and South Stein Road ; with Board Minute and Correspondence thereupon.
>   Sess. 1821, (603.) vol. 16, p. 41. [74.]
>   *see* likewise *Carlisle and Glasgow Roads,* No. 101, *supra.*

Roads and Bridges in Scotland, 1818–1834 :

156.—First Report of the Commissioners ;—*see* Appendix to 7th Report on *Highland Roads and Bridges.*

157.—Second and Third Reports of the Commissioners :—*see* Appendix to 8th Report on *Highland Roads and Bridges.*

158.— Fourth Report of the Commissioners.   Sess. 1818, (148.) vol. 10, p. 53. [74.]
>   SUBJECT.—Repair of roads.

159.—Fifth Report of the Commissioners.   Sess. 1819, (147.) vol. 11, p. 49. [74.]
>   Same subject.

160.—Sixth Report of the Commissioners.   Sess. 1820, (19.) vol. 7, p. 45. [74.]
>   Same subject.

161.—Memorials respecting Damage occasioned by a Storm, in October 1819, to Peterhead and Banff Harbours.   Sess. 1820, (242.) vol. 7, p. 331. [74.]

162.—Seventh Report of the Commissioners on Roads and Bridges in Scotland : —*see* Appendix to 9th Report on *Highland Roads and Bridges.*

163.—Eighth Report of the Commissioners.   Sess. 1822, (120.) vol. 8, p. 363. [74.]
>   SUBJECTS.—*Progress in forming Roads, Bridges, &c.* — Difficulties of executing road repairs by contract.—Progress of repairs of roads and bridges.—Repairs of harbours.

164.—Ninth Report of the Commissioners.   Sess. 1823, (112.) vol. 10, p. 1. [74.]
>   SUBJECTS.—*Progress in completing Roads, Bridges, &c.* — General good state of the roads. — Peculiar features of roads in Highland countries. — Evil consequences of low contracts.—Inadequacy of the Commissioners' funds.—Progress in completing roads and bridges.—Accounts of receipts and expenditure.

165.—Tenth Report of the Commissioners.   Sess. 1824, (167.) vol. 9, p. 257. [74.]
>   SUBJECTS.—*Progress in completing Roads, Bridges, &c.*—Additional fund required.— Road-making.—Description and *Plans* of bridges built.

166.—Eleventh Report of the Commissioners.   Sess 1825, (150.) vol. 15, p. 29. [74.]
>   SUBJECTS. — *Progress of the Works.*—*Difficulties to the Workmen in remote Parts.*— *Accounts.*—Proportion of expense borne by the heritors and the public.—Proportion of public aid assigned to the four northern counties.— Erection of tollgates.— Accommodation for working parties in mountainous parts.— Moveable caravans constructed.—Improvements proposed.—Indefatigable character of Mr. John Mitchell, road-inspector : — his death.— Necessity of keeping the cross and side drains clear in Highland roads.—Damage by storm in October 1824.—Increase of traffic on the Glengarry road, in consequence of opening the Caledonian Canal.—South Stein road in the Isle of Skye.—Progress of the Glasgow and Carlisle road, and Lanarkshire road.—State of accounts.

167.—Twelfth Report of the Commissioners.   Sess. 1826, (209.) vol. 11, p. 59. [74.]
>   SUBJECTS.—*Progress of the Works on the Roads.*—Macleod's road in the Isle of Skye.— Torgoyle Bridge well completed. — Junction of Fort William and Laggan roads. — Casualties in the condition of roads, from neglect or weather.—Improved condition of Glasgow and Carlisle road.—Lanarkshire roads well constructed.—Bridge over Cartland Craigs.—Statement of accounts.

Roads and Bridges in Scotland--continued.

168.—Thirteenth Report of the Commissioners, under Act 59 Geo. 3.

Sess. 1826-27, (208.) vol. 7, p. 107.

SUBJECTS.—Injury to roads from snow and sudden thaws.—Effects of river floods.—Destruction of the bridge over the Spey at Kirk-Laggan.—A timber bridge the only kind suitable for replacing it.—Question as to the expediency of establishing toll-gates for raising funds to repair the Inverness roads—Instance of an accident at Bonar-bridge, showing the degree of stability in arches over a rapid tide-way.

169.—Fourteenth Report of the Commissioners.   Sess. 1828, (175.) vol. 9, p. 277.

SUBJECTS.—Placing of toll-gates on several roads.—Objections in some cases.—Difficulties in procuring materials.—Account of expenditure.—Observations of Lord Colchester on the improvements of Highland roads.—Sketch of the present Highland road between Inverness and Perth, and proposed improvements.———*Map* of Scotland, showing the improvements by the Parliamentary Commissioners.

170.—Fifteenth Report of the Commissioners.   Sess. 1829, (114.) vol. 5, p. 135.

SUBJECTS.—State of the roads under the care of the commissioners.—Rebuilding of the timber-bridge over the River Spey at Kirk-Laggan.—General inspection of Mr. Telford.

171.—Sixteenth Report of the Commissioners.   Sess. 1830, (181.) vol. 15, p. 87.

SUBJECTS.—Effects of violent storms of rain, greater than have occurred since 1763.—Amount of damage to the roads and bridges.—Destruction of private property.—Inexpediency of high and extensive roads of approach to bridges, as daming up the torrent and diverting its force to the destruction of the bridge.—Inexpediency of the competition system in road-making.

172.—Seventeenth Report of the Commissioners.   Sess. 1830–31, (286.) vol. 4, p. 379.

SUBJECTS.—Restoration of the public works damaged by the storms of 1829.—State of Lanark roads and Crinan Canal.

173.—Eighteenth Report of the Commissioners.   Sess. 1831–32, (345.) vol. 23, p. 521.

SUBJECTS.—Destructive effects of a water-spout in the vallies of Urquhart and Inverfarigaig upon the shores of Loch-Ness.—Effects of a great flood by raising the water Strath-Fleet, and threatening the destruction of the Mound.—Building toll-houses and parapets; forming drains, and improving the lines of road.

174.—Nineteenth Report of the Commissioners.   Sess. 1833, (114.) vol. 17, p. 405.

SUBJECTS.—Repairs of casualties of former year.—Restoration of Balam Bridge.—Improvement of the pass of Slochmuicht.—Improvement of entrance to Dingwall-town, and rebuilding Craig-bridge.—Arrangement for replacing Ballater-bridge.—District in Inverness taken under the care of the commissioners.—Restrictive but still useful pecuniary assistance to be afforded to local authorities in making roads.—Accounts of receipts and expenditure.

175.—Twentieth Report of the Commissioners.   Sess. 1834, (164.) vol. 40, p. 165.

SUBJECTS.—Application of a considerable sum, by the economy of former years, to several improvements.—Difficulties which have prevented their commencing the intended improvement of the line of road between Inverness and Nairnshire.—Rebuilding Ballater-bridge.—Account of receipts and disbursements.———*Two Plans.*

Caledonian Canal, 1803–1834 :

176.—First Report of the Commissioners for making and maintaining the Caledonian Canal.

Sess. 1803-4, (51.) vol. 5, p. 324. [75.]

SUBJECT.—Progress of the Works under the direction of the Commissioners.

177.—Second Report :—same subject.   Sess. 1805, (151.) vol. 3, p. 191. [75.]

178.—Third Report :—same subject.   Sess. 1806, (193.) vol. 6, p. 496. [75.]

179.—Fourth Report :—same subject.   Sess. 1807, (84.) vol. 3, p. 149. [75.]

180.—Fifth Report :—same subject.   Sess. 1808, (281.) vol. 3, p. 79. [75.]

181.—Sixth Report :—same subject.   Sess. 1809, (246.) vol. 4, p. 69. [75.]

182.—Seventh Report :—same subject.   Sess. 1810, (332.) vol. 9, p. 1. [75.]

Caledonian Canal—continued.

183.—Eighth Report of the Commissioners for making and maintaining the Caledonian Canal.   Sess. 1810–11, (202.) vol. 4, p. 363. [75.]
SUBJECT.—Progress of the Works under the direction of the Commissioners.

184.—Ninth Report:—same subject.   Sess. 1812, (258.) vol. 4, p. 475. [75.]

185.—Tenth Report:—same subject.   Sess. 1812–13, (249.) vol. 5, p. 65. [75.]

186.—Eleventh Report:—same subject.   Sess. 1813–14, (211.) vol. 4, p. 353. [75.]

187.—Twelfth Report:—same subject.   Sess. 1814–15, (344.) vol. 3, p. 487. [76.]

188.—Thirteenth Report:—same subject.   Sess. 1816, (385.) vol. 8, p. 1. [76.]

189.—Report of the Select Committee on the Estimate of Sums wanted for 1816.   Sess. 1816, (463.) vol. 4, p. 495. [76.]

190.—Fourteenth Report of the Commissioners for making and maintaining the Caledonian Canal.   Sess. 1817, (316.) vol. 9, p. 83. [76.]
SUBJECT.—Progress of the Works under the direction of the Commissioners.

191.—Fifteenth Report:—same subject.   Sess. 1818, (390.) vol. 10, p. 1. [76.]

192.—Sixteenth Report:—same subject.   Sess. 1819, (387.) vol. 11, p. 1. [76.]

193.—Seventeenth Report:—same subject.   Sess. 1820, (106.) vol. 7, p. 1. [76.]

194.—Eighteenth Report of the Commissioners.
        Sess. 1821, (599.) vol. 10, p. 173. [76.]
SUBJECTS.—*Progress in executing the Canal.*—In this Report is inserted a *Map* of the Canal.—Description of an antique massy silver chain discovered in digging the Canal.

195.—Nineteenth Report of the Commissioners.   Sess. 1822, (382.) vol. 8, p. 1. [76.]
SUBJECTS.—*Progress in executing the Canal.*—Causes of delay in completing the Canal. —Statement of sums wanted.—Trading vessels on the Canal.—A steam-packet plies between Inverness and Fort Augustus.—How the porousness of the gravelly part of the soil is remedied.—Use of the dredging-machine.—Claim of Colonel Ronaldson Macdonall.— Crinan Canal.

196.—Twentieth Report of the Commissioners.   Sess. 1823, (412.) vol. 7, p. 111. [76.]
SUBJECTS.—*Progress in executing the Canal.*—Opening of the Canal, and passage of vessels from sea to sea.—Account of such vessels.—Tonnage rates.—Depth of the Canal. —Progress of works.—Total expenditure up to 1823.

197.—Twenty-first Report of the Commissioners.
        Sess. 1824, (380.) vol. 9, p. 213. [76.]
SUBJECTS.—*Progress of the Works of the Canal.*—Increased traffic on the Canal.—Comparative length of passage : by Canal, three or four days ; by Cape Wrath, as many months. —Improved average depth from the operation of dredging.—Progress of works in completion of the Canal.—State of Crinan Canal.

198.—Twenty-second Report of the Commissioners.
        Sess. 1825, (394.) vol. 15, p. 1. [76.]
SUBJECTS.—*Progress of the Works.*—Endeavours to obtain a navigable depth of the Canal.—Number of vessels navigating from sea to sea.—Tonnage duty too low.—Progress of the works along the line of the Canal.—Progress of lining the Canal near Muirtown Locks.—Evils from the washing down of gravel, &c. by torrents.—Number of labourers employed.—Expenditure similar to preceding year.—State of Crinan Canal.

199.—List of Claims made of alleged Injuries and Damages occasioned by the Caledonian Canal.   Sess. 1826, (93.) vol. 2, p. 163. [76.]

200.—Twenty-third Report of the Commissioners.
        Sess. 1826–27, (420.) vol. 7, p. 123.
SUBJECTS.—Reparation of damage at Mucomer Lock.—Other repairs.—Rates of tonnage, and amount of sums collected.—Injurious effects of increased rate.—Necessity of deepening the Canal to insure its efficiency.

201.—Twenty-fourth Report of the Commissioners.   Sess. 1828 (384.) vol. 9, p. 345.
SUBJECTS.—Proceedings of Commissioners.—Constant use of the Canal, but insufficiency of the income to meet the expenditure.—Assistance from the Lords of the Treasury.— Width of the canal and locks found suitable to the working of steam-boats.—Transfer of the Crinan Canal to the original proprietors.—Accounts of receipts and expenditure.

Caledonian Canal—continued.

202.—Twenty-fifth Report of the Commissioners for making and maintaining the Caledonian Canal. Sess. 1829, (286.) vol. 5, p. 163.

    SUBJECTS.—Proceedings for maintaining the Canal.—Account of receipts and expenditure.

203.—Twenty-sixth Report of the Commissioners. Sess. 1830, (668.) vol. 15, p. 111.

    SUBJECTS.—Secure construction of the Letterfindlay Road; which enabled it to resist the storms and flood.—Defeat of the claim of Glengarry to compensation for alleged damages to the Loch-Oich.—State of accounts; receipts of tonnage rates.

204.—Twenty-seventh Report of the Commissioners. Sess. 1831, (169.) vol. 12, p. 43.

    SUBJECTS.—Interruption to navigation by the severity of the frost. — Repairs effected.— Advantage that would result from deepening the Canal.—A steam-boat for towing recommended.—Probable annual expense.—Receipts and expenditure.

205.—Twenty-eighth Report of the Commissioners. Sess. 1831–32, (686.) vol. 23, p. 293.

    SUBJECTS.— Inability of the Commissioners to effect the recommended deepening of the Canal.—Increased intercourse by the Crinan Canal.—Failure and repair of the Sea Lock and Tunnel.—Accounts of receipt and expenditure.

206.—Twenty-ninth Report of the Commissioners. Sess. 1834, (489.) vol. 40, p. 191.

    SUBJECTS.— Increase of communication.—Additional steam-boats navigated on the Canal.—Probable adjustment of the claims of Glengarry against the Canal.—Condition of the navigation of Crinan Canal.—Repairs and improvements necessary to be done.

IRELAND.

Bogs in Ireland, 1810–1814 :

207.—Report of the Select Committee appointed to inquire into the Progress made by the Commissioners appointed to consider of the practicability of draining the Bogs in Ireland. Sess. 1810, (148.) vol. 4, p. 103. [71.]

    SUBJECTS.—Progress of the survey under the directions of the Commissioners.—Instructions to the engineer.

208.—First Report of the Commissioners on the practicability of draining and cultivating the Bogs in Ireland. Sess. 1810, (365.) vol. 10, p. 389. [77.]

209.—Second Report, on the same subject. Sess. 1810–11, (96.) vol. 6, p. 579. [77.]

210.—Third Report, on the same subject.⎫
                            ⎬ Sess. 1813–14, (130. 131.) vol. 6, p. 1. 167. [77.]
211.—Fourth Report, on the same subject.⎭

    The Subjects on which these Reports afford knowledge may be enumerated under the heads—Agriculture and Botany:—Draining and engineering employed in such undertakings:—Geology:—Topography.——The *Maps* are numerous, and many of them on a large scale. [XV. *Maps and Plans.*]

    See likewise under *Poor in Ireland,* Head XXI.

Inland Navigation, Ireland, 1812–1818 :

212.—Three Reports from the Select Committee on the affairs of the Grand and Royal Canal Companies; and on the state of Inland Navigation in Ireland. Sess. 1812–13, (190. 266. 284.) vol. 6, pp. 35. 85. 99. [71.

    SUBJECTS relate to the management of the Companies' affairs, and not to the construction of any works.

213.—Survey of the Line of Canal from Lough Allen to the Shannon. Sess. 1818, (267.) vol. 16, p. 457. [71.]

Roads and Bridges, Ireland, 1826–1832 :

214.—First Report of the proceedings of the Commissioners appointed for the execution of the Act 6 Geo. 4, c. 101, for repairing certain Roads and Bridges in Ireland. Sess. 1826, (102.) vol. 11, p. 173.

    SUBJECTS.—Roads under the direction of the commission.—Appointment of the board.—Necessity of keeping up the roads by small and continued repairs.—Directions to accustom the labourers to money payments.

Roads and Bridges, Ireland—continued.

215.—Second Report of the proceedings of the Commissioners appointed for the execution of the Act 6 Geo. 4, c. 101, for repairing certain Roads and Bridges in Ireland.   Sess. 1826–27, (171.) vol. 11, p. 329.

SUBJECTS.—Continued from the preceding report.—Improvement of roads in Clare and Galway.—State of roads in Mayo and Roscommon.———*Map* of roads under the management of the Directors of Inland Navigation.

216.—Third Report of the Commissioners.   Sess. 1828, (126.) vol. 12, p. 339.

SUBJECTS.—Statement of proceedings.—Mode of procuring execution of the work.—A map of Ireland, showing the roads under the management of Directors-general of Inland Navigation.

217.—Fourth Report of the Commissioners.   Sess. 1829, (132.) vol. 13, p. 187.

SUBJECTS.—Proceedings of the commissioners.—Increased traffic from the improved state of the roads.

218.—Fifth Report of the Commissioners.   Sess. 1830, (198.) vol. 15, p. 151.

SUBJECTS.—Proceedings of commissioners.—Cause of increase of expenditure.

219.—Sixth Report of the Commissioners.   Sess. 1830–31, (295.) vol. 4, p. 397.

SUBJECTS.—Completion of part of the road through the Bogra Mountains.—New road through the mountains from Newport to Thurles, placed under the superintendence of the board.

220.—Report on the Roads made at the public expense in the Southern District of Ireland; by Richard Griffith, civil engineer.
                                        Sess. 1831, (119.) vol. 12, p. 61.

Roads in Ireland, 1832:

221.—Report from the Select Committee on the state of Turnpike Roads in Ireland.   Sess. 1831–32, (645.) vol. 17, p. 397.

SUBJECTS.—Desirableness of adopting in Ireland the superior system of English road-management.—Advantages possessed by Ireland of the means of forming good roads.—Failure of road-trusts.—Deficiencies of Acts forming trusteeships.—Imperfect mode of rendering accounts.—Accumulation of debts.—Incompetency of surveyors of roads.—State of roads vested in individuals establishing mails.—Defective of state of cross-roads, and misapplication of money raised by presentment.—Benefit that might result from placing the management of roads under the Board of Public Works.—Proposition of purchasing the interest of roads vested in individuals.—Analytical digest of returns of receipts and expenditure, debt and interest, of road-trusts ——— *Two Maps* of Metropolis Roads, and Roads in Ireland.

Post-Office Communication with Ireland, 1832:

222.—Report from the Select Committee on Post-Office Communication with Ireland, with two Maps.   Sess. 1831–32, (716.) vol. 17, p. 1.

SUBJECTS.—Object of the Committee to ascertain where improvements may be made for the future.—Cause of the deficient state of mails and cross-posts.—Importance of improvements beyond a consideration of expense.—Eligibility of Holyhead as the line of communication.—Communication between Scotland and Ireland through Portpatrick;—with the South of England and Ireland by Milford and Waterford.—Expediency of establishing a packet-station at Bristol to communicate with Waterford.—Construction, power and accommodation of the packets at the several stations.—Transmission of letters by private vessels.—Irish inland communication.—Want of direct lines.—Necessity of improving roads to give effect to plans of more rapid communication.—Importance of these improvements to the prosperity and permanence of the union of the two countries.

Public Works in Ireland, 1832–1833:

223.—First Report of the Commissioners upon the state of the several Roads and Bridges placed under their care by the Act 1 & 2 Will. 4, c. 33, pursuant to Act 6 Geo. 4, c. 101, s. 9.   Sess. 1831–32, (327.) vol. 23, p. 607.

SUBJECTS.—Transfer of powers given to Directors of Inland Navigation to the Board of Public Works.—Satisfactory progress in repair of roads.—Beneficial effect of the new road through the Keeper Mountains to Thurles, by introducing civilization among desperate outlaws.

Public Works in Ireland—continued.

224.—First Report of the Commissioners on Public Works in Ireland, of their proceedings for the year 1832.   Sess. 1833, (75.) vol. **17**, p. 373.

SUBJECTS.—Proceedings of the Commissioners.—Loans and grants.—Repayments.—Inland navigation.—Improvement of the Shannon.—Fisheries.—Construction of roads and bridges.—Improvement of harbours and other public works.——*Plan* of the town and harbour of Galway, and of Antrim Coast Road.

225.—Second Annual Report of the Commissioners for the extension and improvement of Public Works in Ireland.   Sess. 1834, (240.) vol. **40**, p. 233.

SUBJECTS.—1. Loans or grants.—Applications for aid.—Difficulty of avoiding censure in selecting objects.——2. Collection of repayments of old loans.—Considerable arrears remaining.——3. Inland navigation.—Importance of the subject.—Want of it in Ireland.—Great existing facilities for its establishment.——4. Fisheries.—Circumstances have prevented their attaining the full prosperity they are capable of.—Usefulness of the fishery piers.—Improvement of the passage round Galin Head strongly recommended.——5. Roads and bridges.—Their management and condition.—Great advance in civilization from their improvement.—May be done at little expense; but require the aid of Government.——6. Public buildings in Dublin and the Phœnix Park.—Their state of dilapidation, and steps taken for their restoration.——7. Dunmore harbour.—Difficulty of procuring good stone.——8. Kingstown harbour.—Manner of constructing the work.—Advantage of Merkford and Davy's patent fuze for blasting rock.——Observations on the principle on which public aid should be granted.—Difference of private resources in England and Ireland.—Reasons for giving the preference to improvements of roads and navigation of rivers.—Great national importance and capability of the Shannon.——*Nineteen Maps, Plans and Sections* of proposed improvements in roads and bridges, and in the navigation of the Shannon.

226.—Return of Advances by Government for carrying on Public Works, and of Public Works commenced and in progress, and the manner in which the Grants have been expended.   Sess. 1833, (285.) vol. **35**, p. 575.

SUBJECTS.—Statement of works executed, and amount of money expended since 1821, within the counties of Galway and Mayo.——A *Map* of the lines of roads in the western district.

Shannon Navigation, 1832–1834:

227.—Papers respecting the improvement of the Shannon Navigation.

Sess. 1831–32, (731.) vol. **45**, p. 333.

SUBJECTS.—Instructions to Colonel Burgoyne as to the improvement of the navigation of the Shannon.—General observations on the proposed plans.—Instructions to Captain Mudge and Mr. Rhodes.——Captain Mudge's plans for improving the Shannon.—Tarbert, Kilrush and Carrigaholt.—Proposed piers and accommodations of steam-vessels.—Improvements of Foyns island.—State of the navigation of the Fergus.—Proposed piers and bridges; placing of buoys and beacons; removing obstructions to the navigation.—Wellesley bridge and dock.—Navigation from Limerick to Killaloe.—Soundings and heights of water at locks.—Plans for reducing the waters of Lough Derg.—State of the Portumna and Killaloe bridges.—Improvements of rivers Scarriff, Rossmore, &c.—Ballyshrule and Cappagh rivers.—Improvement of Cow Island and Lower Brusna River.——*Twenty-one Maps and Plans* accompany the explanations of the proposed improvements.

228.—Papers respecting the Shannon Navigation; being letters from Col. John F. Burgoyne to the Right Hon. Sir John C. Hobhouse, bart., and further Reports of Mr. Rhodes, on the Improvement of the Navigation of the River Shannon.

Sess. 1833, (371.) vol. **34**, p. 235.

SUBJECTS.—Completion of Mr. Rhodes's reports.—Review of proceedings in surveying the river Shannon.—Description of that river.—State of its navigation.—Lakes connected with it.—Capabilities of improvements.——Mr. Rhodes's reports.—Obstructions proposed to be removed.—Description of the plans of proposed improvements.—Facilities for procuring materials for the works.—Estimates of expenses.—Tables of soundings of the river.——*Forty-two Maps and Plans.*

229.—Report from the Select Committee on the present state of the River Shannon, and on the best means of improving the same.

Sess. 1834, (532.) vol. **17**, p. 141.

SUBJECTS.—Present state of the navigation of the river Shannon, and the different bodies to whose control it is subject.—Great detriment to the navigation thereof from the land floods.—Want of buoys and beacons causes great delay, and frequently endangers the passage of vessels.—Great deficiency of piers and landing-places all along the coast.—Steam-vessels are engaged in towing vessels.—Failure of the Grand Canal Company to perform their agreement with the Directors general of Inland Navigation in 1806.—Measures to be taken to enforce the performance thereof.—Proposed method of raising funds for the improvement of the navigation.—Extent of benefit to be derived from the outlay.—Increasing importance of the trade of the interior of Ireland.

Crown Lands Improvement :

230.—Papers relating to proposed experimental improvements on the *Lands of Pobble-ò-Keefe.*   Sess. 1831–32, (355, 418.) vol 45, pp. 207. 237.

SUBJECTS.—Progress of the improvements.—Eagerness of the people to obtain employment.—Important benefit in opening new lines of communication.—Miserable condition of the inhabitants of the Crown lands.—Proposed new lines of roads.—Suggestions of the manner of carrying the plans into effect.—Estimated amount of improved value.—*Map* of the proposed roads ———Proposition by Government to the grand juries of Cork and Kerry to defray two-thirds of the expense, if the counties will provide for the other third.—Concurrence of the grand juries, and suggested improvements in the line of roads.—Estimate of the expense of the proposed works.

231.—Papers respecting experimental improvements on the Crown Lands at King William's Town, in the Barony of Duhallon, in the County of Cork; and to new lines of Public Roads constructing in the Counties of Cork and Kerry.   Sess. 1834, (173.) vol. 51, p. 69.

SUBJECTS.—Reclamation of waste land belonging to the Crown.—Undertaken as an experiment to afford an example to landed proprietors of Ireland.—Fitness of the lands of Pobble-ò-Keefe, in the county of Cork, for the purpose.—Its desolate state, and cause.—Its capabilities of improvements.—Effects of roads formed in it by Mr. Griffith.—Historical notices.—Designs for houses to be built in the new village of King William's Town.—Manner of conducting the works, and arrangements with the people employed.———*Six Plans and Maps.*———*See likewise* under Head XII., No. 66.

Improvement of Harbours and Canals :

Ardglass Harbour :

232.—Report from the Select Committee relating to Ardglass Harbour.
          Sess. 1809, (113.) vol. 3, p. 581. [**71.**]

Howth Harbour :

233.—Report from the Select Committee appointed to inquire into the state of Howth Harbour.   Sess. 1810, (203.) vol. 4, p. 111. [**71.**]

SUBJECTS.—State of the harbour.—Proposed improvements.—Present inconvenience and danger.—Difficulty of procuring materials, from claims set up by the Earl of Howth.——— *Two Plans* are inserted.

Kingstown Railroad :

234.—Correspondence between the Commissioners of Public Works, Ireland, and the Proprietors of the Kingstown Railroad.   Sess. 1833, (291.) vol. 35, p. 517.

SUBJECTS.—Application for pecuniary advance in aid of the proposed undertaking.—Security for the repayment.—Commercial importance of the projected works.

Dublin and Kingstown Ship Canal :

235.—Report from the Select Committee on constructing a Ship Canal between Dublin and the Harbour at Kingstown.   Sess. 1833, (591.) vol. 16, p. 451.

SUBJECTS.—Expediency and importance of the proposed works.—Operations of the Dublin Ballast Board for improving the port and harbour of Dublin.—Inland navigation connected therewith.—-Great advantage of a ship canal, and opinions of eminent engineers thereon.—Would be expedient in a national and local view, and practicable between Dublin and Kingstown harbours, and would make the port of Dublin the best in Europe.

236.—Memorials and Correspondence respecting the Dublin and Kingstown Ship Canal.   Sess. 1833, (603.) vol. 35, p. 85.

SUBJECTS.—State of the navigation of the river Liffey.—Advantages of a floating-dock and ship canal connecting Dublin and Kingstown harbours.—Estimated expense.—Advantages compared with those of the proposed railroad.—Imperfect state of buoyage of the river.—Alleged omission to mark the situation of the Mumbles shoal.———*Four Maps* of soundings.

Kilkenny Canal :

237.—Report of Mr. Griffith, Government Engineer, respecting an intended Line of Canal between Kilkenny and Inistioge.   Sess. 1833, (723.) vol. 35, p. 507.

SUBJECTS.—Former endeavours and plans to render the river Nore navigable.—Description of the course of the river.—Proposed canal to run parallel to the river.—Commercial advantages.—Preference of a canal to a railroad.—Estimate of the probable expense.——— A *Map* of the proposed canal.

Improvement of Harbours and Canals—continued.

Derry Bridge:

238.—Report from the Select Committee on the Acts of Parliament relating to the Bridge over the Foyle at Derry, and on the application of the Tonnage Dues levied by the Corporation of Derry.   Sess. 1833, (557.) vol. 16, p. 367.

SUBJECTS.—Origin of the claim of toll by the corporation of Londonderry.—Grant by Irish Society under which the bridge was built.—Money raised by toll and tonnage duties, and borrowed on their security.—Its application.—Excess of money raised, and recommendations of the Committee for better management.

Harbours, Ireland:

239.—Copies of such Portions of Evidence taken before the Commissioners of Revenue Inquiry as refers to the Western Harbours of Ireland.

Sess. 1834, (592.) vol. 51, p. 151.

SUBJECTS.—Advantages of embarkation of packets for the west and south of Europe and America generally, by choosing a harbour on the West of Ireland, instead of one within the Channel.—Advantages of inland ports, from the prevalence of westerly winds.———— *A Plan* of the tracks of 30 packets, showing the advantage of the Irish ports.—*Two Maps* of sailing courses.

Port of Limerick:

240.—Report of Thomas Rhodes, esq., civil engineer, upon the Port of Limerick, for the purpose of making Floating Docks.

Sess. 1834, (300.) vol. 51, p. 251.

SUBJECTS.—Description of the town of Limerick.—Its population and trade.—Indifferent accommodation of the port and quays.—Proposed improvements.————*Plans* of the proposed floating-docks, and soundings of the river.—Explanation thereof.

XX.

Town and Parochial Improvement;

and Local Taxation.

ENGLAND.

County-Rates, 1738:

1.—⌈Report from the Select Committee relating to the County-Rates in Middlesex.

First Series, vol. II. p. 1.

> SUBJECTS.—Manner of levying and collecting the county-rates.—Alleged misapplication and embezzlement thereof by the justices, who are charged with misconduct, and by whom.—These accusations are shown to have originated from malice.

1825:

2.—Report from the Select Committee on the Expenditure of County-Rates.

Sess. 1825, (461.) vol 6, p. 1. [97.]

> SUBJECTS.—*Increase.—Mode of Account.—Charges on that Revenue.*—Acts under which the assessments are made.—Purposes to which the rates are applicable.—Increase of charges for prosecuting felons.—Such offences chiefly arise from aggression of chattel, while the expense of prosecutions falls on rates levied on land and houses.—Origin and progress of paying expenses of prosecutions.—Allowance of magistrate and clerks temp. Rich. II.—Recommendation that expenses awarded at sessions should be defrayed by the county-rate, and those of the assizes by the State.—Opinions of Justice Bayley and Baron Hullock on the practice of assizes in allowing expenses of prosecutions.—Returns of the application of county-rates from 1792 to 1823;—of money received by clerks of the peace;—roads kept in repair by the county.

1834:

3.—Report from the Select Committee for inquiring into the County-Rates and Highway-Rates in England and Wales.

Sess. 1834, (542.) vol. 14, p. 1.

> SUBJECTS.—*Highways and Public Buildings.*—General management of highways in England and Wales are exceedingly defective.—Parishes to be formed into districts.—Highway-rate to be substituted for statute labour.—Roads leading to and over county bridges or turnpike roads should be repaired at the expense of their respective trusts.—Contracts for public buildings should in all cases be by open tender.—Committee of magistrates should be appointed to examine plans and specifications previously to their being sanctioned by the court.——*Finance.*—Great increase in the amount levied for county rates since 1792.—Valuation upon which the county-rate is levied varies extremely in different counties.—Process adopted in Lancashire and the West Riding of York to obtain a correct valuation of these respective counties.—Recommendation that new valuations should be made in counties where none has been made within 14 years.—Manner of making it.—Length of time to continue in existence.—Advantages derivable from the appointment of finance committees in every county.—Expenses of collecting the county-rate vary in different counties.—Advisable that the treasurer should be paid by salary rather than by the amount of balances in his possession.——*Criminal Prosecutions.*—Expense of prosecutions at assizes should be transferred from the county-rate to the public revenues.—Provisions made in Scotland for the expenses of public prosecutions.—County-rate should be relieved from the expense of conveying prisoners under sentence of transportation from the several gaols to the depôts for convicts.—Commission to inquire into the fees and emoluments of the several officers connected with the administration of criminal justice.——*Miscellaneous.*—Counties should be divided into districts, and coroners appointed in each district.—Distance they should travel, and mode of remuneration for performance of his duties.—Expense of the militia force should be defrayed by Government.—Expense of shire-halls and lunatic asylums should be left to the discretion of the magistrates.—Counties should be relieved from the payments towards the maintenance of prisoners in the King's Bench, Fleet and Marshalsea.—Great increase in the bills of the clerk of the peace in the several counties, in consequence of the printing of the registers of electors, and remedies proposed for reducing them.—Difference of practice in several counties as to the inspection of weights and measures.—Returns required by Parliament or Government should be paid for out of the public revenue.

County-Rates, Poor-Rates, &c.

Local Taxation.—Returns, 1748–1829 :

4.—Poor-Rates, County-Rates, Highway-Rates, Church-Rates, with the annual value of Real Property, the Population, and Area of the several Counties in England and Wales.   Sess. 1830–31, (52.) vol. 11, p. 205.

The poor-rates and county-rates are for the average of 1748–49–50; 1775–6; 1783–4–5; 1802–3; and 1812 to 1829.—The average price of wheat is stated.—The highway-rate, church-rate and county-rate are for 1827.—The population and square miles are stated.— The amount of assessment for poor and county-rates for 1826, showing the proportion of amount levied on land, dwelling-houses, mills, factories, manerial profits and incidentals.— In the account of highway and church rates, the annual value of Property Tax in 1815, and the rate in the pound thereon, are stated.—The Accounts are explained in observations by Mr. *Rickman.*———This is a comprehensive combination of the facts stated in former accounts.———*See* under Head XXI. for Accounts of Money raised by *Poor-Rates.*

London Orphans' Fund :

5.—Report from the Select Committee on the Orphans' Fund of the City of London.   Sess. 1812, (268.) vol. 2, p. 315, and 1814–15, (292.) vol. 5, p. 1539. [134.]

Subjects.—Origin and nature of the fund.—The Report likewise explains other money transactions of the corporation of the city of London.

6.—Report from the Select Committee on the Orphans' Fund of the City of London.   Sess. 1822, (481.) vol. 4, p. 227. [134.]

Subjects.—*History and present State.*—Origin.—Loss in time of Charles the First, by national troubles, &c.—Inability to pay their debts.—Grant of duties on wine and coals for that purpose.—Improvement of the fund, and surplusses.—Other charges thereon.—Recommendation to appropriate unclaimed monies to the discharge of the debt.

7.—Report from the Select Committee on the present state of the Orphans' Fund of the City of London.   Sess. 1829, (309.) vol. 3, p. 365.

Subjects.—Origin of the fund.—Revenues forming the fund.—Appropriation.—Adequacy of the fund.—Accomplishment of its original purpose, and application to the execution of public works.—Probable unappropriated surplus after 1832.—Interest on Government advances on account of London Bridge Approaches.—Right of the city to the revenue from rent-charges, &c., but not to retain the powers of levying duty on coals or other impositions, after satisfying the objects for which originally granted.———Statements and accounts of the revenue and application of the fund.

Sewers in the Metropolis, 1823–1834 :

8.—Report from the Select Committee on Sewers in the Metropolis.   Sess. 1823, (542.) vol. 5, p. 1. [96.]

Subjects.—*Management.*—*Appointment of Officers.*—*Levying and Application of Funds.*———*Tower Hamlet Division.*—Appointment of commissioners.—Qualification.—Committee of management, how appointed.—Duties.—Establishment, and salaries.—Meetings.— Proposed additional powers.—Public dinners.—Manner of making presentments.—Formation of the jury.—Mode of assessing;—of making rates.—Enforcing orders for repairs on presentments.———*Holborn and Finsbury Division.*—Local Acts.—London 30 feet above the level of high-water mark.—Mode of assessing.—Non-liability of inhabitants on high levels. —Establishment of office.—Annual expense of works done, 10,000*l.*———*Westminster Division.*—List of commissioners.—Establishment of office.—Mode of proceeding when repairs of new work are to be done.—Annual expense for work done, 25,000*l.*—List of levels of various principal streets.

9.—Returns from Clerks of Commissioners of Sewers relative to Fines, Amerciaments and Penalties.   Sess. 1825, (78.) vol. 20, p. 399. [96.]

10.—Account of Charges for Sealing, Writing and Enrolling any one Commission of Sewers.   Sess. 1825, (160.) vol. 20, p. 407. [96.]

11.—Report from the Select Committee on the state of the Laws respecting the Sewers in and near the Metropolis.   Sess. 1834, (584.) vol. 15, p. 197.

Subjects.—Sewers of the metropolis and adjacent districts are under the direction of trustees.—Acts of Parliament by which they are regulated.—Defects in the law regulating them.—Want of publicity.—Equality of rateage with inequality of advantages.—Want of combination between the different trusts.—Changes proposed in the management thereof.— Number of commissioners in each trust to be fixed.—Manner in which vacancies to be filled up.—All works to be performed by public contract.—Commissioners to have the power of raising money on sewers-rate where improvements necessary.

Water Supply to the Metropolis, 1821–1834 :

1821 :

12.—Report and Minutes of Evidence from the Select Committee on the Supply of Water to the Metropolis.   Sess. 1821, (537. 706.) vol. 5, pp. 21. 33. [96.]

SUBJECTS.—*Establishment of New Companies.—Agreements between Rival Companies.—Necessity of protecting the Interests of the Public.—*Various companies.—Their origin.—Competition in such undertakings prejudicial.—Agreement between the rival companies.—Rise of their rates in consequence.—Public dissatisfaction.—Advantages accruing to the public from the new undertakings.—Principle to be observed in estimating their rate of profit. — Parliamentary provisions recommended for restraining any undue advance of rates.

1828 :

13.—Report from the Select Committee on the present system of supplying Water to the Metropolis.   Sess. 1828, (567.) vol. 8, p. 265.

SUBJECTS. — Sources from which the Companies draw their supplies.—Opinions of the commissioners appointed for the consideration of this subject.—Recommendation of the Committee for the employment of Mr. Telford to make surveys for obtaining a supply of pure water.—Observations on the mode of rating the consumers.———Plan for the supply of water from a common source.—Mr. Mills' survey.—Filtration of water by the Chelsea Company.—Overflowing springs reached by boring near London.—Impurities of Thames water from the discharge from sewers and gas-works.—Medical opinions.—Income and expenditure of the Companies.

1828 :

14.—Commission for inquiring into the state of the Supply of Water to the Metropolis, and Correspondence between the Commissioners and the Home Secretary of State on the subject.   Sess. 1828, (145.) vol. 9, p. 47.

SUBJECTS.—Appointment of commissioners.—Object to inquire into the description, quantity and salubrity of the water now supplied by the several Companies.—Expense of taking levels and making surveys.—Analysises of water to be made.

1828 :

15.—Report of the Commissioners on the state of the Supply of Water in the Metropolis.   Sess. 1828, (267.) vol. 9, p. 53.

SUBJECTS.— State of the supply of water.—Extent of means of the different Companies.—Sources of supply.—Estimated quantity daily supplied.—Its sufficiency in the north of London.—State of supply in the southern district.—Analysis of the water.—Practicability of filtration.—Ill effects of manufactories and gas-works.—Quality of the water capable of improvement.—The supply should be drawn from other sources.—Caution necessary to prevent injurious effects to the public from either unrestrained monopoly or competition.—Various plans of remedies.

1834 :

16.—Report of Thomas Telford, Civil Engineer, on the means of supplying the Metropolis with pure Water.—Three *Maps.*   Sess. 1834, (176.) vol. 51, p. 263.

17.—Report from the Select Committee on the Report of Mr. Telford of the 26th March, respecting the Supply of pure Water to the Metropolis.
Sess. 1834, (571.) vol. 15, p. 1.

SUBJECTS.—Demand for water has increased 25 per cent. since 1828.—Water from the Wandle exceedingly fine water.—No part of the Colne would furnish an improved supply except the River Verulam.—Corn-mill property very much reduced latterly.—Reports from Mr. West and Dr. Bostock on the qualities of water procured from different sources in the neighbourhood of London.—Capability of the West Middlesex Company of supplying the metropolis with water.—Plan of filtering water adopted by the Chelsea Company a very excellent one.—Cost of bringing water from the Verulam to the metropolis.—Plan for supplying with pure water the cities of London and Westminster proposed by Mr. Martin.—Results of experiments made by different persons on water furnished by Mr. Martin.—Experiments on the water of the Wandle, as suggested by Dr. Lambe.—Outline of a plan for supplying London with water from the Thames at Teddington Lock.—Suggestions made by the different water companies to improve their supply.—Result of experiments made by the Grand Junction Company, for the purpose of ascertaining in what degree the Thames is affected by the drainage-water of London.—Measurement of the quantity of water passing over the weirs near Denham, on the River Colne.

Public Walks, 1833 :

18.—Report from the Select Committee on the best means of securing Open Spaces in the vicinity of populous Towns as Public Walks and Places of Exercise.   Sess. 1833, (448.) vol. 15, p. 337.

SUBJECTS.—Great increase of the population of large manufacturing districts.—Increased value of property and extension of buildings.—Suggestions for improvements applicable to all large towns.—State of the metropolis as regards public walks or places of exercise for the middle and humble classes.—Places suggested as proper for public walks.—Advantages from the formation of public walks in the neighbourhood of large towns.—Mode of carrying improvements into effect.—Necessity of forming public bathing places.

Select Vestries, 1830 :

19.—Two Reports from the Select Committee on the Laws and Usages under which Select and other Vestries are constituted.

Sess. 1830, (25. 215.) vol. 4, pp. 425. 569.

Subjects.—Manner of keeping accounts.—Expenditure of parochial funds.—Audit of accounts ; and control of expenditure.—Appointment of vestrymen. —On elective vestries.— Making rates.—Dissatisfied state of Marylebone parish.—Good effect of the elective system of Paddington parish.—Districts of St. Martin's parish.—Dinner expenses.—Good management of St. Luke's Chelsea.—St. Anne's Soho.—Management of St. Pancras parish. —Money raised for building churches.—St. George Hanover-square.—St. Mary Lambeth ; effect of management by select vestry, under Sturges Bourne's Act.—St. James's Westminster.—Management of St. James's Clerkenwell by elective boards ; description of the excitement at the elections.

Second Report.—Constitution and evils of select self-elected·vestries.—Management of the joint parishes of St. Giles in the Fields and St. George Bloomsbury ; legal proceedings as to the validity of the joint select vestry ; state of accounts ; of parochial charities.— Management of St. Giles Cripplegate ; and of its charity funds.—Mismanagement of open vestries.—Misapplication of church-funds in the parish of Watford.—Advantage and practicability of parochial government by elective vestries.—Beneficial operation of Mr. Sturges Bourne's Act.—Parochial management of Bristol.—Of St. Paul's Covent-garden.—Successful management of St. Andrews' Holborn by an annually elected board of governors. ——— *See likewise* Head XXI., *Poor,* No. 1.

Gas Lighting, 1809–1823 :

20.—Minutes of Evidence taken before the Committee to whom the Bill for incorporating certain Persons for procuring Coke, Oil, Tar, and Inflammable Air from Coal, was committed. Sess. 1809, (220.) vol. 3, p. 339. [96.]

Subjects.—*Applicability of Gas, extracted from Coal, to lighting Streets, &c.*—Quality of coke produced in gas-making by Mr. Winsor's process.—Pitch and tar produced.— Asphaltum :—fit for japanning, when boiled with linseed oil and resin.—Ammoniacal liquor used in dyeing.—Use of the ammoniacal principle in manure.—Capability of the conveyance of the gas through tubes.—Inflammability.—Comparative intensity of light.—Lighting up manufactories.—Origin of the application of gas for light, from 1795 to 1803.— Applied to lighting streets.—Examination of many scientific men and superior mechanics. ———This Bill incorporated the Gas and Coke Company projected by Mr. Winsor.

21.—Report from the Select Committee to whom the Reports of the Royal Society, &c. were referred. Sess. 1823, (529.) vol. 5, p. 195. [96.]

Subjects.—*Regulations for protecting the Public.*—Improvements in the apparatus have diminished danger apprehended.—Power recommended to be given to the Secretary of State to enforce precautionary arrangements of the gas establishments.— Use of gas recommended, as contributing to the comfort and safety of the metropolis.

22.—Copy of the Report of the Royal Society to the Principal Secretary of State for the Home Department, on the subject of Gas Lights ; and Copies of Two Reports of the Person appointed by the same Secretary of State to inspect the Gas Light Establishments in the Metropolis.

Sess. 1823, (193.) vol. 5, p. 303. [99.]

Subjects.—*Liability to Accident, and Necessity of Precautionary Regulations.—Report of Committee of Royal Society in* 1814.—Probability and effect of explosion.—Gasometer or gasholder.--Remarks on explosion.—Not likely to happen.—Explosive force of gas shown in an accident at Woolwich.—Force of gas explosion compared with gunpowder.— 14,000 cubic feet of gas equal to five barrels of gunpowder.—Necessity of care in superintendents.—Degree of danger in buildings lighted with gas.———*Sir W. Congreve's Report on the State of Gas Establishments in* 1822.—List of gas establishments.—Recommendations neglected.—Danger of explosion,—how to be guarded against.—Superiority of oil-gas.———*Sir W. Congreve's Report in* 1823.—Account of the several companies :— their works :—Gas produced :—Lamps lighted :—Coals consumed ; 33,000 chaldrons annually.—Consumption per lamp, five cubic feet per hour.—Price of coals not increased, being compensated by the coke produced.—One hundred and twenty chaldrons of coke produced from one hundred chaldrons of coal.—Diminution of accidents from improvements in conducting the process.—Improvements.—Experiments on the comparative explosive force of gas and gunpowder :—of one gasometer equal to fifty barrels of gunpowder :—one cubic foot equal to five ounces.—No liability to stoppage in the cast-iron pipes ; but the wrought iron service pipes found choked up.—May be remedied by using lead or block-tin.—Regulations proposed. ——— *Superiority of Oil-gas.*—Portable gaslights introduced :—their danger.

Paving the Metropolis, 1816 :

23.—Report from the Select Committee on the present state of the Pavement of the Metropolis.   Sess .1816, (159.) vol. 5, p. 417. [96.]

> SUBJECTS.—Causes of the defective state of the pavement.—Proposed remedies to be enforced by a Bill to be submitted to Parliament.

Smithfield Market, 1828 :

24.—Report from the Select Committee on the state of Smithfield Market.
                                          Sess. 1828, (516.) vol. 8, p. 1.

> SUBJECTS.—Recommendation for a Bill for preventing carriages passing through Smithfield during market hours.

25.—Second Report from the Select Committee on the state of Smithfield Market.   Sess. 1828, (551.) vol. 8, p. 3.

> SUBJECTS.—Bill for preventing carriages passing through Smithfield during market hours abandoned.—Passing of live stock to and from Smithfield a nuisance.—Not sufficient accommodation for the live stock offered for sale.—Sites proposed in the event of removing the market.—Plans for the enlargement of the present market.—Difficulties in the way of establishing subsidiary markets.—Establishment of slaughter-houses.—Profanation of the Sabbath.—Altering market-day from Monday to Tuesday.—Characters of drovers.— Necessity for the abolition of the horse-market.—Improvements in the market that might be adopted by the city.—Cruelty to cattle in the market—[and *see* under *Miscellaneous*, Head XXVI., No. 6.]—State of slaughter-houses in Whitechapel.—Accidents.—Deterioration of meat —Why Bartholomew fair not abolished.—Slaughter-houses in Leadenhall-market.—Mode of slaughtering by the Jews.—Nuisance to Islington from cattle on Sunday. —Mode of slaughtering adopted in the abattoirs at Paris.—Difficulty in punishing drovers for cruelty.—Injury to cattle from bruises.—Slaughtering at a distance from the place of sale.—Disease from improper feeding of cattle, and from meat being killed and eaten in an unwholesome state.—Slaughter-houses in New York.—Poisonous weeds among grass.— Neighbourhood of markets generally healthy —Business of carcass-butcher.—Attendance of city-officers at Smithfield.—Advantage of Copenhagen-fields as a site for a new market. —Proposal for two markets at the north and west of London, with abattoirs.—Advantages of Mr. Laycock's premises at Islington.—Deterioration of dead meat by carriage in hot weather.—Right of the city to hold Smithfield-market is by prescriptive right, charter, and Act of Parliament.—Applications made by the city to Parliament relative to the market. —Alteration of the day for holding the hay-market.—Duties of a money-taker in Smithfield.—Collection of dues, and expenses of the market.—Loss to publicans by removing the market.—Purchase of cattle for stall-feeding.—Account of receipts and disbursements by the corporation of London on account of Smithfield-market.—Number of cattle and sheep in the market at particular periods.

IRELAND.

Grand Jury Presentments, 1815–1827 :

26.—Report from the Select Committee on Grand Jury Presentments of Ireland.
                                  Sess. 1814–15, (283.) vol. 6, p. 1661. [98.]

> SUBJECTS.—Methods of raising money, and appropriating it.

27.—Two Reports from the Select Committee on Grand Jury Presentments of Ireland.   Sess. 1816, (374. 435.) vol. 9, pp. 1. 5. [98.]

> SUBJECTS.—Methods of raising money, and appropriating it.

28.—Report from the Select Committee on the same subject.
                                          Sess. 1819, (378.) vol. 8, p. 361. [98.]

29 —First Report from the Select Committee on Grand Jury Presentments.
                                          Sess. 1822, (353.) vol. 7, p. 1. [98.]

> SUBJECTS.—*Mode of collecting and applying them.*—Increased amount of money raised. —Inequality.—Proposed general survey of the island, for the purpose of a just apportionment of the assessments.

30.—Second Report from the same Committee.   Sess. 1822, (413.) vol. 7, p. 15. [98.]

> SUBJECTS.—*Salaries of County Officers, &c.*—Proposed to be fixed.—Classification of offices, with scale of salaries proposed.

Grand Jury Presentments, 1815–1827—continued.

31.—Third Report from the Select Committee on Grand Jury Presentments.

Sess. 1822, (451.) vol. 7, p. 25. [98.]

SUBJECTS.—Regulations respecting the office of County Treasurer.

32.—Report from the Select Committee on Proceedings for regulating Grand Jury Presentments of Ireland. Sess. 1826–27, (555.) vol. 3, p. 745. [98.]

SUBJECTS.— *Abuses in the manner of applying the Money raised by Presentments for making and Repairing Roads.*—Inquiries of Parliament, in 1815, 1816 and 1822—particularly of 1825.—Importance of the subject.—Increased amount of levies.— Insufficiency of time allotted to the transacting the business of the grand juries.—Suggestions for an improved method of managing the public business of local taxation.—Mr. Nimmo's description of road making.—Persons who get the applotments or assignments of the presentments, let portions out to their tenants to be done as a set off for rent.—Proposed regulations by the grand jury of the county of Cork.

Dublin Local Taxation, 1822–1825 :

33.—Report from the Select Committee on the Local Taxation of the City of Dublin. Sess. 1822, (394.) vol. 7, p. 159. [98.]

SUBJECTS.— *Mode of assessing and applying Rates.*—Powers granted by Parliament for raising money by assessments.—Great inequality of rates.—New valuation of houses recommended.—Grand juries, formed exclusively of the corporation, disapproved of.—Criminal jurisdiction.—Great increase of expense.—Misapplication of water-supply funds.—Bad state of the gaols.—Oppressive tax on hotel-keepers.—Advantages of the mode of parochial taxation in England, by including all classes in discharge of important duties.

34.—Two Reports from the Select Committee on the Local Taxation of the City of Dublin. Sess. 1823, (356. 549.) vol. 6, pp. 11. 15. [98.]

SUBJECTS.—*Management and Application of Funds.*—Pipe Water and Metal Main.—Resolution on the necessity of inquiry to ascertain the balance due, and the right of the corporation to the pipe-water estates.———The First Report consists entirely of the Minutes of Evidence.—The two are printed together.

35.—Report from the Select Committee on the Local Taxation of the City of Dublin. Sess. 1824, (475.) vol. 8, p. 61. [98.]

SUBJECT.—Management and application of funds.

36.—Report from the Select Committee on the Local Taxation of the City of Dublin. Sess. 1825 (329.) vol. 5, p. 637. [98.]

SUBJECTS.—*Abuses : and Necessity of Parliamentary Remedy.*—Reference to former Reports.—Unequal pressure of local taxation on Dublin.—New valuation necessary.—Foundling tax.—Water rates.—Exclusive system of forming grand juries ; the corporation only considered eligible.—Evils arising from that practice.—Increase of the amount of money raised.—Causes of the increase.—Expenses of criminal jurisdiction.—Fees to officers on convictions.—Superintendence of gaols more than can be attended to by the grand juries.—Disproportion of the medical expenses, compared with the London prisons.—Improvements in prisons, and providing a new gaol, recommended.—Management of the Paving Board—Wide-street Commissioners.—Coal trade.—Watch and police establishments.—Butter trade.—Effect of the union on Dublin.—Few resident persons of rank.—Increased local taxation, and diminished rateable houses.

Dublin Paving, 1806–1827 :

37.—Report of the Commissioners appointed to inquire into the Conduct and Management of the Corporation for Paving, Cleansing and Lighting the Streets of Dublin. Sess. 1806, (17.) vol. 8, p. 473. [99.]

SUBJECTS.—State of the paving of the streets of Dublin.—Want of cleanliness.—Conduct of the Paving Board.

38.—Report of the Commissioners for Paving, Cleansing and Lighting the Streets of Dublin. Sess. 1809, (148.) vol. 7, p. 574. [99.]

SUBJECTS.—Proceedings of the Commissioners, according to Act 47 Geo. 3.

39.—Report of the Commissioners for inquiry into the Management and System of conducting the Affairs of the Paving Board, Dublin. Sess. 1826–27, (329.) vol. 11, p. 417.

SUBJECTS.—Misconduct of some of the commissioners and officers of the Board.—Misapplication of public money for private accommodation.—Mismanagement of work executed for private persons.—Negligent and corrupt conduct of collectors.—Irregularity in conducting the business in the Board-room.—Proper conduct of the supervisor of works.—Mismanagement of the works executed, and of the persons employed.—Mode of making and applotting the assessments.—Suggestions for correcting abuses, and improving the execution of works done under the direction of the Board.—But ineffectual without intelligent and upright persons to carry them into effect.

Richmond Penitentiary, Dublin, 1827 :

40.—Report of Commissioners for inquiry into the State of the Richmond Penitentiary.   Sess. 1826–27, (335.) vol. **11**, p. 567.

> SUBJECTS.—Management and discipline of the prison.—Alleged misconduct of officers.—Accusations of severities and cruelties exercised towards the prisoners who may be Roman-catholics, to induce them to become Protestants.

Tolls and Customs, 1826–1834 :

41.—Report from the Select Committee on Tolls and Customs taken in Ports, Fairs and Markets in Ireland.   Sess. 1826, (170.) vol. **5**, p. 451. [98.]

> SUBJECTS.—*Laws, Practice and Abuse of Market and other Tolls.*—Laws regulating tolls.—Tolls actually claimed.—Remedies.—A consolidation of the laws on the subject recommended.

42.—Report from the Select Committee on the Tolls and Customs at Markets and Fairs in Ireland.   Sess. 1834, (603.) vol. **17**, p. 227:

> SUBJECTS.—Classification of tolls levied at fairs in Ireland.—Mode of levying toll on cattle one of considerable difficulty.—Nature of the stallage toll.—No necessity for a renewal of the registry of schedules of tolls annually.—All dealings in public markets should be restricted to buying and selling by weight.—A modification of the manner of levying tolls in the different parts of Ireland is absolutely necessary.—Meaning of " toll thorough " and " toll traverse."—No prescription for toll within legal memory.—Great abuse of the practice of the right to the collection of tolls.—Principle on which patents for tolls are granted.—Objections to tolls taken at fairs arises as well to the amount collected as the mode of collection.—Uniform schedule of tolls should be formed for the whole of the fairs in Ireland.—Successful opposition to payment of tolls demanded by the corporation of Youghall.

Limerick Local Taxation :

In 1761 :

43.—Report from the Committee (of the late Irish House of Commons, on 23d December 1761) on the Abuses of the Corporation of the City of Limerick.
                                        Sess. 1820, (270.) vol. **3**, p. 355. [98.]

In 1822 :

44.—Report from the Select Committee on the Local Taxation of the City of Limerick.   Sess. 1822, (617.) vol. **7**, p. 235. [98.]

> SUBJECTS.—*Mode of Assessment,—Expenditure,—and Account.*—Population and trade.—Geographical situation.—Municipal jurisdiction and management.—Mode of levying taxes.—Of forming grand juries.—Management of the New Town superior to the Old.—Misapplication of the revenues of the Old Town.—Suppression of corporation records.—Charities.—Defalcation of Mr. Morony, the city treasurer.—Leases of corporate lands granted in their own favour.—Improper persons appointed to offices.—Refusal to admit claimants to the freedom.—A witness reverses his answer when allowed to correct his evidence.—A juryman rewarded for obtaining a verdict in favour of the corporation, by standing out singly.—The committee recommend legislative interference.

XXI.

Poor, and Poor Laws.

ENGLAND.

Rates—Management—Infants :

Rates and Select Vestries, 1715:

1.—⌈Report from the Select Committee appointed to inspect the Poor's-Rates, and Scavenger's-Rates, within the Cities of London and Westminster, and Weekly Bills of Mortality.

Journals, vol. 18, p. 392.

Subjects.—Confined to the maintenance of the poor.—St. Martin's-in-the-Fields chosen for an example for inquiry, as supposed to be most free from abuses.—Immediate interposition necessary to redress inveterate evils even in this parish.—Nature of the funds.—Intermixture of those applicable to the Church with those applicable to the maintenance of the poor.—Difficulty of distinguishing them.—Accounts for 1712, 1713 and 1714.—Money annually collected from door to door distributed without account.—Unsatisfactory state of the accounts.—Impositions in the charges for casual poor, by other charges being blended with them.—Arrears of poor-rate not duly collected.—Surplus in overseers' hands, on quitting office, paid over to the vestry, and not to the succeeding overseers.—Irregularity in collecting and disposing of the sacrament-money.—Vestry constituted by the past churchwardens—who chiefly supply all the articles wanted for the church.—Specimen of account showing the objectionable items of expenditure.—Great proportion in the mortality of children.—Mortality of bastard children imputed to the misconduct of the parish nurses.—Objectionable management in other parishes.—Great misapplication of funds.—Increase of poor and beggars.———Upon this Report leave was given to bring in a Bill for the better regulating Select Vestries.

See likewise *Select Vestries,* under Head XX. No. 19.

1748–1750:

2.—⌈Statement of Assessments for Relief of the Poor in the years 1748, 1749, 1750.——*See* No. 17, *infra.*

Infant Poor, 1767:

3.—⌈Report from the Select Committee on the state of Poor Parish Children.

Journals, vol. 31, p. 248.

Subjects.—Average mortality under the age of twelve months.—Apprentices.—What proportion of the infants live to be apprenticed.—Apprentice fees inadequate.—Mode of nursing censured.—Report of 1715 referred to and quoted.

Relief and Settlement:—County-houses of Industry, 1775:

4.—⌈Report from the Select Committee on the Laws which concern the Relief and Settlement of the Poor ; and relative to Vagrants and Houses of Correction.

First Series, vol. IX., p. 241.

Subjects.—Resolutions on the defective state of the poor laws, and management of the poor.—Increased burden from the amount of money raised; improper expenditure in litigation.—Employment of infant poor.—Evils of the law of settlement.—Plan for establishing county-houses of industry.—Proposed regulation for relieving the lame and impotent poor, and casual poor.—Regulation for maintaining infant poor.—Mode of controlling accounts.—Money to be raised by assessment, made at quarter-sessions, upon the parishes in the county, in proportions to be ascertained by certain rules.

1775:

5.—⌈Second Report from the Select Committee on the same subject.

First Series, vol. IX., p. 243.

Subjects.—Continuation of the preceding Report.—Resolutions for apportioning the number of houses in each county for the general reception of the poor—for appointing governors, and enforcing their attendance—for amending laws relating to vagrants, so as effectually to prevent begging—for providing houses of correction at the houses for the general reception of the poor.—That returns should be made by masters, &c. of houses of industry, according to forms prescribed in the Report.

Maintenance—Management—Infants—continued.

Returns of Expense of Maintenance, &c. 1776 :

6.—[First Report from the Select Committee appointed to inquire how far the Orders of the last session (11 April 1775), respecting the Poor, had been complied with.   First Series, vol. IX., p. 247.

> LIST of places where establishments have been formed for the poor, from which returns have been made ; and list of such as have not made returns.

7.—[Second Report from the Select Committee on the same subject.
                                                                              First Series, vol. IX., p. 249.

> ABSTRACTS of Returns made pursuant to the Resolutions of the Committee and Order of The House of the 11th April 1775, and in the form prescribed by the Report of the Committee of 11th May 1775.—The returns are from the governors and overseers of the poor, for the years 1773, 4, & 5, of the expense of maintaining and employing the poor in houses of industry and workhouses, in hundreds, cities, towns, and *Parishes* ; and from clerks of the peace, concerning vagrants and houses of correction.———The Returns are arranged alphabetically, and therefore form an Index to themselves.

1777 :

8.—[Report from the Select Committee appointed to inspect and consider the Returns made by the Overseers of the Poor in pursuance of the Act of last session, 16 Geo. 3, c. 40 ; together with the Abstracts of the said Returns.
                                                                              First Series, vol. IX., p. 297.

> ABSTRACT of the Returns.—Showing in columns the money raised in 1776, distinguishing the amount expended on account of the poor, from that expended for other purposes.—Payments for rent of workhouses.—Litigations concerning settlements.—Where workhouses are established, and the number of persons which each will accommodate.———Being arranged alphabetically, these returns form an Index to themselves.

Infant Poor, 1778 :

9.—[Report from the Select Committee on the state of Poor Parish Children within the Parishes of London, Middlesex, and Surrey, &c.
                                                                              First Series, vol. IX., p. 541.

> SUBJECTS.—Utility of the Act 7 Geo. 3.—Benefit of amending it.—Guardians of the infant poor.—Their duties imperfectly performed.—No appointment made of guardians in some parishes.—How far the Act has been carried into execution.—Resolutions of the Committee concerning the state of them.

Poor and Charitable Donations, 1787 :

10.—[Report from the Select Committee appointed to inspect and consider the Returns relative to the state of the Poor, and Charitable Donations, made in pursuance of two Acts of last session, 26 Geo. 3, c. 56, and c. 58.
                                                                              First Series, vol. IX., p. 543.

> SUBJECTS.—Complete state of the Returns.—Out of 13,000 parishes only 28 deficient, of which 14 only have made no return.—Abstracts of the Returns annexed to the Report, being the totals of each county.—Observations of the Committee on the arrangement of the statements in columns for the purpose of comparison; and, by bringing particular heads of expenditure under notice, to lead to a plan of more economical regulation in county expenses; overseers' expenses ; charges for entertainments, and for law business.—Small amount of charges for employing the poor.===Charitable Donation Returns defective. —A complete Abstract directed to be made according to a form prescribed.—In order to be made perfect, requisitions directed to be sent to ministers and churchwardens to correct their imperfect returns.———The Returns being arranged alphabetically, form an Index to themselves.———For further matters relating to *Charitable Donations*, see *Education and Charities*, under Head II.

Poor-Rate Returns, 1787 :

11.—[Further Appendix to the preceding Report, being an Abstract of the Returns made by the Overseers of the Poor, in pursuance of the Act 26 Geo. 3, c. 56, relative to the state of the Poor.   First Series, vol. IX., p. 553.

> SUBJECTS.—Heads of expenses of maintaining the poor.—Medium amount of money applied to county purposes ; and setting the poor to work.—Expenses of entertainments. —The charges of overseers.—The medium expense for purposes which do not concern the poor.———*N. B.* Prefixed to the Report is a List of Counties, referring to the page where the particulars respecting each are to be found; and the Returns for the years 1783, 1784, 1785, placed alphabetically. The names of the Hundreds in each County, and the *Parishes* in each Hundred, are likewise alphabetically arranged. The different Classes of Expenditure are disposed in columns, with heads expressing their contents.———The whole, therefore, forming an Index of itself.

Maintenance—Management—Apprenticeships—continued.
Expense and Maintenance, 1804:

12.—Abstract of the Answers and Returns made pursuant to Act 43 Geo. 3, relative to the Expense and Maintenance of the Poor in England.

Sess. 1803-4, (175.) demy folio, vol. **13.** [VIII.]

SUBJECTS.—The total amount of money raised by the poor-rate in 1803, and expended on that account.—The rate per pound.—The money raised and expended is compared with the amounts in 1776, 1783, 1784 and 1785, copied from returns 16 Geo. 3, c. 40, and 26 Geo. 3, c. 56. [*see* 1777 (No. 8); and 1787 (No. 11).]—The money expended in maintaining and employing the poor—in providing materials : of money earnt.—Law expenses ; removals ; and overseers' expenses ; church and county rates ; and other expenses not connected with the poor.—Number of persons relieved ; whether permanent, occasional or casual ; distinguishing infants, children, and persons above 60 years of age.—Number of friendly societies, and members ; and the number of children in schools of industry.—The totals are shown of each hundred, and the general total of the county.—Considerable information is scattered throughout the returns in observations by way of notes, as to the incorporation and peculiar state of some parishes, the manner of management and employment of the poor, the existence of local acts, the state of parochial schools and friendly societies.——— At the end of each county are " twelve concise observations deduced from the returns, and from other sources which may be deemed authentic." 1, on the state of the returns ; 2, on the number of workhouses, and the average expense of each pauper ; 3, on the average expense of each pauper *out* of the workhouse ; 4, on the average expense of each person exclusively parishioners ; 5, money raised and expended compared with the population ; 6, law expenses, removals, &c. compared with 1785 ; 7, purchase of materials for employing the poor ; 8, maintenance by contract ; 9, special acts ; 10, friendly societies ; 11, proportion of rated rental to rack rental ; 12, area of the county.—In the summary, these results are made applicable to the whole kingdom of England and Wales.—There is a very elaborate summary of totals ; and a statement of the amount of charitable donations. —In an appendix containing the amount of the Metropolis, two columns are added, exhibiting the annual expenditure, by poor and church rates, about the year 1725, extracted from *Maitland's History of London.*

☞ The whole arrangement is alphabetical by hundreds under counties, and by *Parishes* under hundreds ; and therefore forms an Index of itself.—The number of parishes and places returned are 14,240 : in 1776 there were 14,113.

1818:

13.—Abridgment of the Abstract of the Answers and Returns made pursuant to Act 55 Geo. 3, c. 42, for procuring Returns relative to the Expense and Maintenance of the Poor in England.   Sess. 1818, (82.) demy folio, vol. **19.** [IX.]

SUBJECTS.—The information contained in these abstracts is disposed in columns, stating the amount of money raised by poor-rate or other rates in 1813, 1814 and 1815.—Amount of the Property Tax, and the average in the pound thereon of the rates raised.—The money expended for the maintenance of the poor.—Suits at law, removals, and overseers' expenses. —Militia expenses.—Money expended for all other purposes, as church-rate, county-rate, &c. —The number of persons relieved.—Members of friendly societies.—Produce of charitable donations, and statement of the schools supported, and other purposes to which the bequests are applied.—There are, with the summary of each county, ten observations, being results deduced from the information contained in the returns ; the number of parishes from which the returns are collected ; average number of persons relieved ; parishes having workhouses, and the number of poor relieved therein ; population of the county, and proportion in 100 relieved ; rate per head of money raised, and rate per pound on the Property Tax ; amount of maintenance of each pauper ; proportion of money expended in law suits, removals, &c. to the money raised ; proportion of members of friendly societies in the 100 of the population ; area of the county ; prevailing employment of the population.—In the general summary these results are aggregated as applied to the whole kingdom.—The summary of England and Wales by counties contains a column of the total amount of sums assessed to the Property Tax, and the total annual value on which such assessments were made, and the average rate in the pound on real property of the money raised by the poor-rate.—In an appendix, all the information relating to the Metropolis is collected into one account.—Another appendix exhibits a comparison of the information contained in the returns relating to the maintenance of the poor made in 1776 ; 1783, 4 & 5 ; 1803 ; and 1815.———The whole is arranged alphabetically, according to counties, hundreds and *parishes*, with proper tables of contents ; and therefore forms an Index to itself.

Poor-houses and Poor-rates, 1813:

14.—Report from the Select Committee on Poor-houses and Poor-rates.

Sess. 1812–13, (113.) vol. 3, p. 463 ; reprinted 1813–14, (27.) vol. 4, p. 375. [84.]

SUBJECTS.—Manner of raising rates.—Settlements.—Powers of churchwardens over the poor and in appeals against rates.—Settlement of bastards.—Vestry books.—Evidence. —Inhabitants competent witnesses.—Relief from rates.——Publicity of making rates.

Parish Apprentices, 1815:

15.—Report from the Select Committee on the Condition of Parish Apprentices bound into the Country from the Parishes within the Bills of Mortality.

Sess. 1814–15, (304.) vol. 5, p. 1567. [84.]

SUBJECTS.—On the condition of those bound to the cotton or similar trades.—Observations and objections to the practice.

Laws—Management—Assessments.

Poor Laws, 1817:

16.—Report from the Select Committee on the Poor Laws.

Sess. 1817, (462.) vol. 6, p. 1 ; reprinted 1819, (532.) vol. 2, p. 287. [84.]

SUBJECTS.—*Operation of the Poor Laws.*—Severity of the antient laws against vagrancy.
—Impotent poor permitted to beg, and laws made enjoining charitable contributions, and
enforcing them if neglected.—Evils resulting from the establishment of compulsory provisions.—The law in Scotland similar, yet its operation beneficially restrained.—Importance
of reviving the moral feelings connected with self support and independence.—Deficient
means of information on the subject in the 17th and 18th centuries. — Comparison of
expense from 1776 to 1815.—Observations on the increase ; which will continue under
the operation of the present system.—Consideration of the plans for making interest of
money and profits of stock liable to assessment.—Intention of 43 Eliz.—Land-tax originally
designed as a tax on income—why failed.—Assessing funded property considered.—
Inequality of poor-rate borne by land.—Rating owners of small tenements instead of
occupiers.—Extra-parochial places.—Decline of aversion to becoming paupers.—Increase
of inherent pauperism.—Proposal to limit the amount of money to be raised.—National
management of poor expenditure.—Advantage of saving-banks.—Parochial benefit societies.
—Bill of 1789 for similar objects, with scales of contributions.—Classification of the poor
by 43 Eliz.—Not intentionally altered by any subsequent law ; but has been by parochial
management.—Observations of Mr. Locke, in 1697, on the employment of pauper children.
—Schools of industry recommended.—Evils of making up wages from poor-rate in proportion to children in a family.—On the application of the principle of 43 Eliz. for finding
work for all who require it.—Interference with local trades.—Parish farms.—Letting small
portions of land.—Road-labour. --Roundsmen.—Difficulty of finding pauper labour in large
towns.—Consequent abuse in the mode of relieving.—Workhouses.—Hardships of the small
farmer.—On the mode of administering the poor laws in Scotland.—Assistant overseers and
select vestries recommended.—Importance of principal inhabitants taking part in the
management.—Assignment of Chelsea and Greenwich pensions.———*Law of Settlement.*—
Effects in restraining the seeking for labour.—Expense of litigation and other purposes
compared from 1776 to 1815.—Proposed alteration to residence of three years.—Usual
points of dispute under existing law.———The Appendix contains a report from the
General Assembly of Edinburgh, on the principle of managing the poor in Scotland ; and
accounts of money raised.—Account of money raised and expended on account of the poor in
England and Wales.—Tables of weekly allowance and contributions on the principle of
friendly societies, being the schedule to a Bill of 1789.—Account of parish and cottage farms.
—Memorial of the magistrates of Suffolk on the inadequacy of labourers' wages, and the
evils of mixing them up with parish relief.

1818:

17.—Report from the Select Committee on the Poor Laws.

Sess. 1818, (107.) vol. 5, p. 1. [84.]

SUBJECTS.—Statements of poor assessments, extracted from returns made in 1748, 1749,
1750, and which were but recently discovered among the records of The House.—Comparative view of money raised by assessments as shown in these returns, and in those of 1813,
1814 and 1815.—Observations of Mr. Rickman on the information contained in the returns
of 1748–1750.—Incorrectness arising from making the poor-rate year end at Easter.—How
rectified.—Deficiencies in these returns supplied from those of 1776.—Successful effect of
an Order of The House in producing returns in 1750.—List of places raising assessments,
made out by The Speaker's directions, preparatory to adopting that method of procuring
returns in future.—Success expected from the authority of The House, and the facilities of
post-office transmissal.═══Abstract of returns of 1748–1750, showing the monies assessed ;
payments on account of the poor ; and for other purposes.

1818:

18.—Second Report from the Select Committee on the Poor Laws.

Sess. 1818, (237.) vol. 5, p. 15. [84.]

SUBJECTS.—Liability of mines to poor assessments.—Recent decisions by courts of law,
declaring landlords rateable to the poor-rate if receiving profits from mines by any reserved
portion of unmanufactured ore, but not so if receiving their profits in manufactured metal
or reserved money rents.—In consequence of this exposition of the law, the landlords reserve
money rents, and so avoid paying poor-rate.—Consequent evil to the poorer parts of mining
districts.—Alteration in the law proposed.

Poor in Scotland, 1818:

19.—Third Report from the Select Committee on the Poor Laws.

Sess. 1818, (358.) vol. 5, p. 23. [84.]

SUBJECTS.—*Management of the poor in Scotland.*—Report of the General Assembly,
being the result of inquiries instituted at the instance of the Committee, and obtained
by communication with the Clergy.—I. Scotch statutes—their object the suppression of vagrancy—introduction of legal provision—characteristic of the application of
Scotch-poor-law, in permitting recourse to legal provision only when other means fail.
—II. Management—by heritors and kirk sessions—source of funds—duties of ministers
and elders not yearly but for life.—III. Result of inquiries : 1, collections at church-
doors ; moral advantages—2, contributions by heritors ; private charities ; prevent the
adoption of parochial assessments—3, expense of management—4, assessments : apprehensions from their progress ; amount ; rule of levying ; personal property made liable in
some

Laws—Management —Assessments.—Poor in Scotland—*continued.*

some cases ; authority by which made ; commencement and increase ; are established only in counties contiguous to England ; progressive rise in assessments ; diminution of voluntary contributions, and increase of claims, immediately on the proposition of establishing assessment ; evil effects in debasing the common people ; comparative allowance under assessment and under contribution ; the progress should be resisted as a disastrous evil ; moral character of the people destroyed by compulsory assessments—5, reluctance of application for relief lessened by legal assessments—6, number of poor ; proportion to 100 of the population: rate of relief given—7, consideration of character in apportioning relief—8, removal of paupers never enforced—9, litigation between parishes generally avoided, and amount of expense inconsiderable—10, deceased paupers effects—11, appeals for increase of allowance seldom occur—12, poor of different religious sects ; proportions to the established church—13, practice of begging ; opinion of its effects ; considerably checked ; badges sometimes worn—14, collections for extraordinary cases ; private contributions ; activity of young persons in collecting, particularly at Christmas-time—15, blind, deaf, and dumb ; number and proportion to the population—16, relief of distress in 1817-18—17, number and beneficial effects of saving banks—18, friendly societies ; decrease in consequence of original inaccuracy in the calculations on which they were founded—19, Sunday-schools ; number of schools and scholars ; interest taken by parents in teaching their children—20, mortifications for educating the poor ; bequests for charitable purposes—21, education ; a school in every parish ; fees 1 s. to 3 s. 6 d. per quarter ; poor scholars gratis ; universality of instruction ; deficiency of religious instruction from extent of parishes—22, importance of the subject of the Report ; exertions of the clergy to collect information.———In the Appendix are a list of the queries circulated to collect information, and the substance of the abridged reports, arranged in columns.———The numbers used in this Abstract of Subjects correspond with similar divisions in the Report, and answers for an Index.

Poor in Scotland, 1820 :

20.—Supplementary Report of the General Assembly on the Management of the Poor in Scotland.
Sess. 1820, (195.) vol. 7, p. 343. [84.]

SUBJECTS.—*Expenditure in Maintenance.*—This paper consists of returns from parishes of the expense of maintaining the poor.—Explanation of the principle on which the returns are constructed.—The information is arranged in columns, with headings expressing their contents ; viz. names of the presbyteries in each synod, and of the parishes in each presbytery—population—number of poor—funds—amount raised by collections at church-doors—by sessions—by voluntary contributions—by legal assessments—expense of levying —of litigation—rate of pay to paupers.—Observations on the peculiarities affecting the money raised and causes of expenses ====At the end of each synod is an abstract of the information obtained, and a statement of the proportion of paupers to the population, and the expense of each individual, distinguishing where assessments are and are not made. —At the end is a general abstract, in totals of synods.———The arrangement forms an Index to itself.

Poor Laws, 1818 :

21.—Report from the Lords' Committees on the Poor Laws.
Sess. 1818, (400.) vol. 5, p. 91. [84.]

SUBJECTS.—View of early laws incorporated in the 43 Eliz.—Scarcity of husbandry labourers in 1349.—Statute 23 Edw. 3, for compulsory agricultural labour.—Other laws relating to labourers and mendicants.—First law imperative on granting poor relief, 27 H. 8, c. 25.—Laws of Edw. 6, and Phil. & Mary, against vagabonds ; and supporting the impotent, aged, and diseased.—Act 3 Eliz. enforcing relief from what is given of will weekly ; and if not so given, to be assessed at what reasonably ought to be given.—Beggars licensed. —Act 5 Eliz. c. 4, for ordering artificers. labourers, &c. formed on the basis that employment should be found by the parish for all who could not find it themselves.—Act 18 Eliz. relating to bastards, removing rogues, providing stock for work, and establishing houses of correction.—Act 31 Eliz. c. 7, respecting building cottages and assigning lands to them.— Act 39 Eliz. relating to overseers.—Act 43 Eliz. combines these provisions—the true spirit sometimes departed from ; but in any improvement of the law, the system must be essentially maintained.—Changed state of the country since the enactment of these laws renders some of the provisions less applicable.—Population then inadequate to supply agricultural labour.—Increase of trading class.—Present distress in agricultural and manufacturing districts.—Objectionable manner of affording relief by roundsmen, throwing part of the amount of wages on poor-rate.—Making up deficiency of wages by allowances to labourers in proportion to the number of children—practice began in 1795—improperly continued.— Increase of other charges not connected with the maintenance of the poor.—Manner of assessing property.—Personal property.—Management of the poor in Scotland.—Power of making compulsory assessment seldom had recourse to.—Law of settlement—to be obtained by a residence of three years, or renting of 20 l.—Removal of Irish.—Permanent overseers and surveyors recommended.—Right of voting in vestries to be in proportion to rate paid.—More regular returns relating to the poor should be obtained.—Advantage of publicity of accounts.—Saving-banks.—Individual exertion necessary to improve the administration of the poor-laws.———The Appendix contains returns of the expenditure on account of the poor in several parishes in Cambridgeshire ; Manchester and Salford ; Norfolk and Suffolk ; and returns from Scotland.

Laws—Management—Vagrants –continued.

Management of the Poor, 1819 :

22.—Report from the Select Committee on the Poor Laws.
Sess. 1819, (529.) vol. 2, p. 249. [84.]

> SUBJECTS.—Evils of the present system, as inducing a reliance on indiscriminate parish support.—Select vestries.—Permanent assistant overseer.—Publishing paupers' names.—Accounts of expenses.—Removals.—On the construction of the Act of Eliz. requiring the parish to find work for all those wanting it.—Ill effects of the poor-laws.—Good effects of the recent law for sending home strangers becoming chargeable.—Recommendation of encouraging emigration.—Beneficial effects anticipated from restricting compulsory relief to the infirm and helpless.—Saving-banks.—Plan of colonizing the Cape of Good Hope.———See *Emigration*, under Head XVI.

Vagrants, 1821 :

23.—Report from the Select Committee on the existing Laws relating to Vagrants.
Sess. 1821, (543.) vol. 4, p. 121. [84.]

> SUBJECTS.—*Apprehension and Passing of Vagrants.*—Laws relating to vagrants.—Rewards for apprehension.—Connivance between constables and vagrants for the sake of the reward.—Vagrants invite apprehension, in order to change their routes at the public expense of conveyance.—Officers connive at their escape while passing.—Inutility of passing professed vagrants to their parishes.—Receive some trifle from the parish officers, and are dismissed, and soon travel through the country back to London.—Manner of passing.—Abuses.—Remedies proposed.—Repeal of present Acts.—Vagrants not to be passed, but more severely punished.—Rewards to be abolished ; and discretionary rewards to be given by magistrates for apprehensions.—An office recommended for registering the names of Scotch and Irish poor passed to their respective countries ; and likewise an office for enforcing the laws against habitual vagrants.

Able-bodied Poor, 1828 :

24.—Report fron the Select Committee relating to the Employment or Relief of Able-bodied Persons from the Poor-Rates.
Ses. 1828, (494.) vol. 4, p. 137.

> SUBJECTS.—Construction of the law—practice and abuses—proposed remedies.—Value of information contained in reports of 1817 and 1819 on the poor-laws, and in 1824 on labourers' wages—of evidence on emigration in 1826, and on criminal commitments in 1827.—Application of 43 Eliz. for setting the poor to work.—Wide range given to the discretion of overseers.—Misconstruction in supposing parishes bound to find work for all who want it.—Evils arising from giving relief to the poor at their homes.—Payment of able-bodied labourers without giving them work—practice of letting them to the highest bidder, and the difference made up by the parish.—Allowance for children without reference to parents being employed—and looked for by the labourer as a matter of right.—Marriage reckoned on as the means of increasing their pittance of allowance.—The consequent redundancy of labourers, and its evils.—Tendency to encourage improvident marriages.—Proposed improvement in the law.—Overseers to be restrained from paying allowances to labourers in work, in addition to wages.—Excepted cases.—Expected rise in wages, and other consequences anticipated.—Objections answered.—Superior condition of labourers where this principle of applying the poor-laws has been observed.

Settlement, 1828 :

25.—Report from the Select Committee on the Law of Parochial Settlement.
Sess. 1828, (406.) vol. 4, p. 201.

> SUBJECT.—Reports of 1817 and 1819 referrd to, and considered to afford sufficient ground, without examination of additional evidence, for founding a recommendation by the Committee for the House to receive a Bill for repealing the Law of Settlement.

Irish and Scotch Vagrants, 1828 :

26.—Report from the Select Committee on the Laws relating to Irish and Scotch Vagrants.
Sess. 1828, (513.) vol. 4, p. 203.

> SUBJECTS.—Great expense of removals—disproportionate to the benefit derived from the labour of the emigrants.—Many obtain parochial relief though not in want, that they may be passed home without diminishing their earnings.—Hardship on the English labourer, from encouraging the emigration of the Irish.—Tends to throw the expense of the pauper population of both islands on England.—Recommendation to repeal laws for passing Scotch and Irish vagrants.—Contrivances of Irish labourers, in taking passage at Liverpool, to pass as having no money.—Money deposited in the hands of agents to estates in Ireland, by labourers working in England, and tenants on such estates, and which is remitted to Ireland on their account, they passing over as vagrants.—Some are beggars, who so transmit money to relations in Ireland.—The same persons come over repeatedly, and return to spend their earnings.—Leave Ireland when the potatoes are planted, and return to dig up the crop.—Brought over in gangs by leaders.—Great increase of numbers coming over.—Manner of granting passes by magistrates.—Pauper-labourers sent over from Ireland, by an association raising passage-money by subscription.

*Laws—Management—Assessments—*continued.

Irish Vagrants, 1833:

27.—Report from the Select Committee on the Laws relative to the Passing of Poor Persons born in Ireland to their own Country.

Sess. 1833, (394.) vol. 16, p. 323.

SUBJECTS.—Increased number of paupers in Middlesex.—Advantages of removing Irish vagrants by contract.—Sum per head for conveyance of vagrants.—Majority of paupers refuse to work.—Irish paupers frequently escape from persons having the charge of them. —Forged passes, and manner obtained.—Sailing vessels not adapted to the conveyance of paupers.—Money frequently found in the possession of vagrants.—Some paupers are often re-passed.—Deceptions practised by pass-masters, and necessity for a check on them.— Receipts taken for vagrants.—Sea conveyance of vagrants.—Stone-yard work not agreeable to Irish paupers.

Poor Laws and Management, 1831:

28.—Report from the Committee of the House of Lords on the state of the Poor Laws.   Sess. 1831, (227.) vol. 8, p. 321.

SUBJECTS.—*Poor and Poor Laws.*—Evils arising from their misadministration.—Demoralizing effect on the habits of the poor.—Bastardy-laws.—Mode of administering relief— magistrates' scale.—Opinions on the expediency of labour-rate.—Evils from paying deficiency of wages out of poor-rate.—Allowances to women and children.—Impolicy of distinction between married and single men.—Condition and employment in various parishes.—Employment of paupers on road-repairs.—Expense of maintenance in particular parishes.— Evils of the present state of the law of Removals and Settlement, and alterations necessary. —Improper class of persons appointed overseers.—Advantages of assistant and permanent overseers.—Imperfect state of parish accounts, and want of a system of book-keeping.— Advantageous management by select vestry.—Management of workhouses.———*Condition of the Agricultural labouring Population.*—Effects of increased population.—Food and clothing of labourers, opinions as to its present and former quality.—Beneficial effects of saving-banks.—Chandlers' shops disadvantageous to the poor.—Rental of cottages.—Want of accommodation afforded.—The distressed condition of labourers ascribed to several causes.—Advantages of friendly societies, if properly managed.—Fuel obtained by the poor. —Advantages of gardens attached to cottages.—Inclosures.—Evils of the truck-system. ———*Circumstances affecting the Demand for Labour.*—Price of labour.—Advantages of piece-work.—Number in want of employment.—Effects of machinery.—Threshing-machines not always thought advantageous.—Rate of wages generally prevailing.—Evils of giving parish allowance in aid of.—Disturbances occasioned by lowness of wages.—Influx of Irish labourers.———*Employment of Women and Children.*—Destroyed by lace-machinery.— Diminishes the aid thereby obtained to assist their families.———*Moral Condition of the Agricultural Classes.*—Degradation produced by pauperism.—Evil tendency of the bastardy-laws.—Beer-shops.—Game-laws.—Evil habits from deficiency of employment.—Injurious mode of hiring, by decreasing domestic farming servants.—Evils of early marriages—promoted by the present mode of administering the poor-laws and bastardy-laws—encouraged by the allowance for children, and by the underpaying single men.—Advantages to the character of the labourer from letting small portions of land.———*State of Agriculture and Condition of Farmers.*—Remuneration afforded for capital employed.—Insufficiency of capital.—Effects of tithes on the cultivation of corn, and retarding improvements.— Supposed effects of the currency.—Advantages of small farms to labourers.—State of cultivation of land.—Neglect of drainage from poverty.—Waste land capable of cultivation. —Productiveness of spade-husbandry.—Difficulties of small farmers in establishing themselves.—Inability to pay higher wages.———*General State of Rental.*—Increase of county-rate.—Increase of poor-rate.———*Emigration.*—Advantages in diminishing pauperism— different modes of carrying it into effect.—Home colonization compared.

Rates and Expenditure, 1821:

29.—Report from the Select Committee on Poor-Rate Returns.

Sess. 1821, (748.) vol. 4, p. 269. [85.]

SUBJECTS.—*Application of Rates.—Improved Method of keeping Accounts.*—Observations on the manner in which the Returns have been made, and on the degree of information they convey.———The Appendix contains, 1, an account of money raised and expended in England and Wales in 1748 to 1819–20, showing the payments for removals and for other purposes than for the poor;—2, an account of expenditure in England and Wales in 1813 to 1820, in totals of counties, showing where select vestries and assistant overseers have been appointed under Act 59 Geo. 3, c. 12;—3, account of the expenditure for the poor only in England and Wales, in totals of counties, in 1750 to 1820; showing the population in 1811, and the property assessed in 1815 under schedule (A.);—4, average price of wheat per quarter in 1812 to 1821.

1822:

30.—Report from the Select Committee on Poor-Rate Returns, made in pursuance of the Orders of The House in 1819, 1820, 1821, and 1822; with a Supplemental Appendix.   Sess. 1822, (556.) vol. 5, p. 517. [85.]

SUBJECTS.—*Expenditure; and Parochial Accounts.*—Returns complete, forming a series of nine successive years.—Reduction of levies.—Expenditure for relief of poor less, but for other purposes more.—Statement of averages.—Appointment of select vestries and assistant overseers.—Accounts of parochial expenditure to be enforced: the State interested in
their

Rates and Expenditure, 1822—continued.

their being kept.—Importance of parish audit.—Classification of relief.—Illegal charges in accounts; as dinners, &c.—Laws requiring overseers to account.—Registry of persons receiving relief.—Why returns defective in utility.—Proposed new form of returns and of accounts.—Repeal of former Acts.—Heads of accounts to be kept.—Observations on the necessity of keeping accounts.—Legislative measures recommended.—Returns of money raised and expended.—Explanation of proposed plan of accounts, with blank forms.
————The Appendix contains a continuation of the accounts in the Report of 10 July 1821 (748.), with forms for an improved and uniform manner of keeping overseers' accounts.
—The Supplemental Appendix contains an account of the expenditure for the relief of the poor in every *Parish* from 18;6 to 1821.————These are arranged alphabetically under counties and hundreds; and therefore form an Index to themselves.

1823:

31.—Report from the Select Committee on Poor-Rate Returns.

Sess. 1823, (570.) vol. 5, p. 345. [85.]

SUBJECTS.—*Expenditure; and Parochial Accounts.*—State of the returns.—Gradual diminution of expenditure.—Parochial accounts should be classed under general heads.—Payments to poor should be distinguished.—Proposed to authorize justices to appoint an examiner of accounts.————The Appendix contains a continuation of the accounts in the two preceding Reports of 1821 (748.) and 1822 (556.) Nos. 29, 30.—Rate of diminution in the expenditure in 1821-22 compared with the preceding years, and with 1817-18.—An account of the proportion which the expenditure in 1812-13 and 1821-22 bear to the population of 1811 and 1821; and the difference of rate per head between the two periods.—A list of counties ranked according to the largeness of their expenditure per head in reference to the population.

1824:

32.—Report from the Select Committee on Poor-Rate Returns.

Sess. 1824, (420.) vol. 6, p. 371. [85.]

SUBJECTS.—*Expenditure; and Parochial Accounts.*—Comparison of the amount of expenditure with former years.————The Appendix contains a continuation of the preceding accounts to 1822-23.—An account of monies levied for the poor-rate on land, houses, factories and manerial property.

1825:

33.—Report from the Select Committee on Poor-Rate Returns; with a Supplement.

Sess. 1825, (334.) vol. 4, p. 39. [85.]

SUBJECTS.—Continuation of those of former years.—Comparison of the amount of sums raised.————The Appendix contains a continuation of the preceding accounts to 1823-24.—Abstract of expenditure for poor only, in totals of counties, commencing with 1750, and is continued down to 1824, with the amount of property assessed under schedule (A.) in 1815.—Accounts of rates of diminution, and proportions of expenditure to population, and other accounts contained in the appendixes to the preceding Reports, are continued down to 1823-24.—The supplemental appendix is an account of the money expended for the relief of the poor in every *Parish* for each of the three years 1822, 1823 and 1824.————These returns are arranged alphabetically under counties and hundreds; and therefore form an Index to themselves.

1826:

34.—Report from the Select Committee on the several Returns of the Year 1825.

Sess. 1826, (330.) vol. 3, p.67. [85.]

SUBJECTS.—Statement of the result of the Returns.————The Appendix contains a continuation of the tables of comparison and proportions inserted in the preceding Reports.

Accounts of Expenditure, 1825:

35.—Account of Money expended in certain Counties in England for Relief of the Poor.

Sess. 1825, (519.) vol. 19, p. 361. [85.]

SUBJECT.—Returns of expenditure for the years ending 25th March 1824 and 1825 respectively, showing the manner in which the latter has been calculated from the returns that have been received; and showing also the per-centage of increase or diminution of expenditure, in the several counties, for the year ending 25th March 1825.

1826-1828:

36.—Account of the Amount of Money levied and expended for the Relief of the Poor in each County in England and Wales,—

In the year ending 25 March 1826; and stating the formation of Select Vestries, and appointment of Assistant Overseers, under 59 Geo. 3, c. 12.

Sess. 1826-27, (316.) vol. 20, p. 673.

Rates and Expenditure—continued.

37.—Account of the Amount of Money levied and expended for the Relief of the Poor in each County in England and Wales,—

> In the year ending 25 March 1827; and stating the formation of Select Vestries, and appointment of Assistant Overseers, under 59 Geo. 3, c. 12; specifying the rate of Increase and Diminution as compared with the preceding year.
> Sess. 1828, (124.) vol. 21, p. 637.

38.—A similar Account for the year ending 25 March 1828;—

> Also an account of the number of Removals and Appeals during the same period.
> Sess. 1829, (78.) vol. 21, p. 99.

Account of Expenditure, 1829–1831:

39.—A similar Account for the Year ending 25 March 1829.
> Sess. 1830, (141.) vol. **31**, p. 49.

> The number of Removals and Appeals are not stated in this Account.

40.—A similar Account for the Year ending 25 March 1830.
> Sess. 1830–31, (219.) vol. **11**, p. 201.

41.—A similar Account for the Year ending 25 March 1831.
> Sess. 1831–32, (216.) vol. **44**, p. 449.

> These Accounts are a continuation of the collection of facts stated in Appendix (B.) to the Report on Poor-rate Returns, May 1, 1826 (330.) No. 34, *supra*, and were compiled from answers to circular requisitions issued under the authority of a Sessional Order of The House.

Tables of Increase, 1776–1815:

42.—Table of Proportions of Comparative Increase, 1776, 1785, 1803, 1815; with explanations and observations: Sess. 1826, (306.) vol. 21, p. 171.

> Being appendix (No. 3), page 638, in the Poor Return Abstract, made in pursuance of Act 55 Geo. 3, and presented to The House 3 March 1818. (82.) No. 13, *supra*.

1801–1821:

43.—A similar Table; also Comparative Statement of the Enumeration of 1801, 1811, and 1821.   Sess. 1826–27, (18.) vol. 20, p. 665.

Account of Poor-Rates and County-Rates, 1826:

44.—Account of the Amount of the Money levied by Assessment for Poor-Rates and County-Rates, in each County in England and Wales,—

> For the year ending 25 March 1826; distinguishing the amount levied on Land, Dwelling-houses, Mills, Factories, Manerial Profits, &c.——This account is in continuation of Appendix (E.) Rep. 15 June 1824, (420.) No. 32, *supra*.
> Sess. 1826–27, (120.) vol. **20**, p. 669.

1776–1823:

45.—Accounts relating to Poor-Rate, being,—   Sess. 1830, (53.) vol. **31**, p. 41. [IX.]

> 1, Appendix (E.) to Report on Poor-Rate Returns, [15 June 1824, (420.)], *i.e.* an Account of monies levied for Poor-Rate and County-Rate, in each county in England and Wales, for the year ending 25 March 1823; distinguishing the amount levied on Land, Dwelling-houses, Mills and Factories, and Manerial Profits;—2, Of the amount levied by assessment of Poor-Rate and County-Rate, in each county in England and Wales, in the year ending 25 March 1826;—3, Tables of Proportions of Comparative Increase, 1776, 1785; 1803, 1815: being Appendix (No. 3), page 638, in the Poor Return Abstract, 55 Geo. 3, 1818, March 3. (82.)——These accounts are a combination of accounts, April 25, 1826 (306.)—November 30, 1826 (18.)—March 1, 1827 (120.)—*See* Nos. 13. 42. 44, *supra*.

Poor-Rate Returns, 1825–1829:

46.—Account of the Money expended for the Maintenance and Relief of the Poor in every *Parish*, &c., in England and Wales, for Five Years, 1825 to 1829; with the Annual Value of Real Property assessed in 1815 for the purposes of the Property Tax.   Sess. 1830–31, (83.) vol 11, p. 227.

> These, with the previous Nos. 7. 11. 12. 13. 30. 33. under this Head, complete the series of Parochial Returns hitherto printed.——*See* likewise under Head XX. *Local Taxation*, No. 4.

Rates and Expenditure—continued.

1828:

47.— Abstract of Returns of the Number of Poor Persons belonging to several Parishes relieved from the Poor-Rates between 25 March 1827 and 25 March 1828 ;—   Sess. 1829, (52.) vol. 21, p. 95.

> Also of the number of Able-bodied Men relieved from the Poor-Rates, whether by making up wages, allowances for children, cottage rent, parish work, or for any other purpose. ———These returns are confined to particular parishes in Bucks, Northumberland, Salop, Sussex, Westmorland and Wilts.

Mendicity, 1815–1816 :

48.—Report from the Select Committee on the state of Mendicity in the Metropolis.   Sess. 1814–15, (473.) vol. 3, p. 231. [87.]

> SUBJECTS.—The Report is but a short paragraph, introductory of the Evidence ; which details the extent of vagrancy, real and fictitious.—Artifices practised.—Conduct of parochial police.—Charitable Institutions.

49.—Report from the Select Committee on the same subject.

Sess. 1816, (396.) vol. 5, p. 391. [87.]

> SUBJECTS.—A digested statement of the facts detailed in the Evidence of the preceding Report.

Poor Laws, 1834 :

50.—Report from the Commissioners for inquiring into the Administration and Practical Operation of the Poor Laws.   Sess. 1834, (44.) vol. 27.

Appendix (A).— Reports of Assistant Commissioners. In Three Parts.		
Part I. - - - - - -	Sess. 1834, (44.)	vol. 28.
Part II. - - - - - -	ib.	vol. 29.
Part III.—Evidence collected by E. Chadwick.	ib.	vol. 29.
Appendix (B 1).—Answers to Rural Questions. In Five Parts.		
Part I. - - - - - -	Sess. 1834, (44)	vol. 30.
Part II. - - - - - -	ib.	vol. 31.
Part III. - - - - - -	ib.	vol. 32.
Part IV. - - - - - -	ib.	vol. 33.
Part V. - - - - - -	ib.	vol. 34.
Appendix (B 2) —Answers to Town Questions. In Five Parts.		
Parts I. & II. - - - -	Sess. 1834, (44)	vol. 35.
Parts III. IV. & V. - - - -	ib.	vol. 36.
Appendix (C).—Communications - - -	ib.	vol. 37.
Appendix (D).—Labour Rate - -	Sess. 1834, (44.) vol. 38, p. 1.	
Appendix (E).—Vagrancy - -	ib.	vol. 38, p. 223.
Appendix (F).—Foreign Communications, Sess. 1834, (44.) vol. 38, p. 321, and vol. 39.		

> SUBJECTS.—The following is the substance of an analysis which precedes the Report.
>
> Statement of proceedings ; progress of the law.———*Administration of the Law :*— I. Out-door Relief: of the able-bodied—in kind, as in house-room—in money, as relief without labour ; by allowance ; by the roundsman system ; by parish employment ; by labour-rate.—Widows.—II. Of the Impotent: general remarks on out-door relief.— III. In-doors Relief: progressive burthen.—Objections to amendment ; by the labourers ; by employers ; by proprietors.———*Operation of the Law as administered :*—I. Effects on proprietors.—II. Effects on employers ; on agricultural labourers ; on manufacturing labourers.—III. Effects on labourers.———*Character of Persons who distribute and award Relief :*—1. Overseers ; annual and assistant.— 2. Vestries ; open, representative, and self-appointed.—3. Magistrates.———*Settlement.—Bastardy.—Legislative measures considered, but not recommended ;* as constituting a national charge ; as enabling labourers to occupy land ; as to labour rates.———*Remedial Measures :*—Distinction between the *Poor* and the *Indigent*—the indigent alone within the province of the law.—Specific effects of the application of this principle in the case of *able-bodied* paupers—who will become independent labours—as tending to a rise of wages—diminution of improvident marriages— content of labourers, and diminution of crime.———*Principle of Legislation.*———*A Central Board recommended.*—Grounds for its establishment—insufficiency of any legislative enactments that are not permanent, and creating independent authority.———*Powers and Duties of the Central Board*—in uniting parishes—regulating officers—contracts—apprenticing—relief of vagrants.———*Further Legislative Amendment*—on Settlement ; Bastardy ; Emigration ; Rating ; Militia ; Charities ; Education.

IRELAND.

Condition and Employment :
In 1819:

51.—First Report from the Select Committee on the State of Disease, and Condition of the Labouring Poor in Ireland. Sess. 1819, (314.) vol. 8, p. 365. [86.]

    SUBJECTS.—Reports of the medical inspectors commissioned to inquire into the state of disease in several provinces.—Nature of the prevailing disease.—Causes.—Methods of prevention.—Prevalence of the epidemic fever.—Its first extensive appearance in 1817. —Valuable information collected from the returns of the medical inspectors.—Necessity of attending to cleanliness of streets, and purification of dwellings.—Measures proposed for that purpose—appointment of officers of health in towns for removing nuisances—suppression of wandering beggars.—Employment of the labouring poor would counteract the malady.——The Appendix contains the reports of Drs. Barker, Crampton, Clarke and Cheyne, respecting the state of disease in the provinces of Munster, Connaught, Ulster and Leinster, arranged under heads of inquiry furnished by the Irish Government, as to its prevalence ; occurrence ; origin ; character ; contravention ; relapses and distant recurrence ; constitutional effects ; extension ; account of progress.

52.—Second Report from the Select Committee on the State of Disease, and Condition, of the Labouring Poor in Ireland. Sess. 1819, (409.) vol. 8, p. 457. [86.]

    SUBJECTS.—Drainage of bogs recommended.—Reference made to the Reports of the Commissioners on that subject, 1810–1814.—Extracts from those Reports.— Making of roads through the mountain districts.—Causes of the want of capital in Ireland.—Increase of population.—Possibility of increasing agricultural employment.—Fisheries.—Improvements in harbours and public works suggested.——*See* likewise *Bogs in Ireland*, under Head XIX.

In 1820:

53.—Report of the Commissioners appointed by the Lord Lieutenant of Ireland to inspect the House of Industry, and to report upon the Management thereof.

Sess. 1820, (84.) vol. 8, p. 227. [86.]

    SUBJECTS.—Establishment of Houses of Industry by Act of Parliament in 1772.—Funds for their support raised partly by presentments, and partly by voluntary contributions.— Formed local corporations for the support of the poor.—As a general measure failed.— Counties where partially established.—Dublin House of Industry supported by national grants in 1777.—Great increase of applicants from indiscriminate admission.—In 1816 restricted to certain classes.—Further restraint on admission to the locality of Dublin.—Its generality attracted paupers from all parts of the kingdom.—Proposed changes.—Review of the departments of the establishment.—Management.—Number of governors and salaries.—Proposed retrenchments.—Medical officers.—Estimate of the whole expense of the establishment.——The Appendix contains the manager's account of the establishment ; statement of expenses ; dietaries.—Account of the officers ; their duties and emoluments. —Observations on the management of the poor.

1823:

54.—Report from the Select Committee on the Employment of the Poor in Ireland. Sess. 1823, (561.) vol. 6, p. 331. [86.]

    SUBJECTS.—*State of the Agricultural Population.*—Distressed state of Ireland in 1822.— Exertion in England to afford relief by subscriptions.—Character of the distress.—Deficiency of potato crop, but abundance of other food.—The peasantry unable to buy, from want of employment.—Approbation of the principle adopted in distributing relief, making labour the medium.—Description of the mode of living of the peasantry,—their anxiety to procure labour.—Increase of population.—Smallness of farms :—a great proportion from five to twenty acres only.—Deficiency of capital.—Wretched state of farming implements in use.— Money-payments for labour not made ; but the amount set off against rent due.—Mr. Owen's plan explained :—its impracticability.—Encouragement of manufactures, and improvement of public roads, recommended.—Emigration.——And see *Emigration*, under Head XVI.

1823:

55.—Copies of the Reports made to the Irish Government by the Civil Engineers employed, during the late Scarcity, in superintending the Public Works ; and an Account of the Appropriation of the Sums expended, to find Employment for the Irish Poor, during the last Year.

Sess. 1823, (249.) vol. 10, p. 437. [86.]

    SUBJECTS.—*State of the Agricultural Population.*—Object on which the money was expended.—Description of the *Southern District*—Limerick, Cork and Kerry.—Remarks on the nature of the soil.—Collieries.—New roads proposed, and old ones repaired.— Wheeled carriages not used in some parts.—Mode of contracting—not with intermediate persons.——*Western District.*—Description of the country.—State of the roads —Abuses of presentments.—Numerous cross-roads in Connaught.—Improvements of the roads, &c. in that district.——*Central District.*—State of the roads, &c. in the county of Clare.— Wretched condition of the inhabitants of the coast.—Wickerwork boats covered with hides in use.—Evil of jobbing in road repairs.—High rents.—Good effects in Tipperary of the money advanced by the London and Dublin Committees.—Proposed improvements.

Condition and Employment—continued.

1830:

56.—Three Reports from the Select Committee on the State of the Poor in
Ireland; viz.   Sess. 1830, (667. 589. 654. 655.) vol. 7.

I. Summary Report.—II. First Report of Evidence.—III. Second Report of Evidence.—
IV. Third Report, with Documents.

SUBJECTS.—*Condition of the Labouring Population.*—Means and manner of living.—
Miserable state of their cabins.—Improvident and early marriages.—Sufferings from want
of employment.—Clothing and habitations better—habits improved from intercourse with
England.—Advantage from the migration of reapers to England.—State of wages, and rates
paid in various parts.———*Their Moral Condition.*—State of education—increasing desire
of parents to educate their children.—Evils of the multiplicity of oaths.—Crime diminished.
—Evil tendency of the Foundling Hospital.———*Provision for the Poor.*—On the probable
effects of compulsory assessment for their relief, and on the applicability of the poor-laws to
Ireland.—Management of charities and public institutions defective.—Lunatic asylums;
their defective state till lately.—Good effects of mendicity asylums.—On the removal of
the poor from England.—On the applicability of the law of settlement to Ireland.—Inapplicability of workhouses to Ireland.—Increase of paupers.—State of vagrancy.—Strolling
beggars chiefly relieved with food—great amount of potatoes given away.———*Emigration.*
—Advantages to Ireland compared with England.—Vacancy occasioned by in England filled
up from Ireland.—Plans proposed for assisting.———*State of Agriculture.*—Effect of the
consolidation of farms—advantages—bad effect of small farms on cultivation.—Condition
of farmers.—Improved state of farm-houses—of farming machinery.—Improved management of land and letting.—Importance of potatoes as food for the people.—Improved
stock in husbandry by intercourse with England.—Free trade with England in corn of great
advantage to Ireland.———*General grievances.*—Evils of non-residence.—State of tenantry.
—Distress occasioned by altered management of land.—Miserable condition of ejected
tenantry.—Miserable condition of cottiers.—Effect of subletting.—Benefits that would
result from the better management of landlords.—Bad effects of management by middlemen.—Difficulties of paying rent.—Rate per acre.—Amount of rental paid, and proportion
paid to absentees.—Grand Jury system; its management, and proposed amendment.—
Church-rate should be borne by Protestant landlords.—Heavy burthen of county-rates.—
Improvements made in the administration of justice.—Unequal as to the recovery of small
debts.—Advantages of petty session system.—Abuses in sheriff-office.—Discontent produced
by Vestry Acts.—Effect of Tithe Composition Act.—Evils of existing tolls and customs at
fairs.—Deficiency in the law of wills and intestacies for small sums—cheap mode of redress
required for the relief of the peasantry.———*State of Trade and Manufactures.*—Great
improvements from spreading of capital.—Introduction of English capital discouraged by
insecurity of investment.—Distress from want of employment.—State of the linen manufacture.—Want of machinery.—Increased consumption of British manufactures.—Improved
state of revenue from customs and excise.—Increase of tonnage of ships.———*Public
Works for general Improvement and Employment of the Population.*—Their extension recommended—benefits produced.—Capability of reclaiming the bogs.—Necessity of introducing
capital—causes of discouragement.—Experimental drainage recommended at the public
expense.—Embankments of rivers recommended.—Improvement of fisheries.—Inland navigation.—Grand Canal.—Improvements of the Shannon earnestly recommended.—Improvement of roads to be encouraged.—Importance and increase of steam navigation.

Houses of Industry, 1828:

57.—A Return of the Corporations in the Counties, Cities and Towns in Ireland, instituted for the Relief of the Poor, and for punishing Vagrants and
sturdy Beggars, in pursuance of Act 11 & 12 Geo. 3, c. 30; also, of Hospitals and Houses of Industry for the Relief of the Poor.

Sess. 1828, (291.) vol. 22, p. 453.

An abstract of the returns is prefixed; and the substance of the returns given in an
abridged form, stating the facts of their being any or no establishments for the relief of the
poor: in some the destitute condition of the sick and needy is mentioned, and in others the
police existing for suppressing vagrancy; one states that the corporation keeps a constable,
called a *bang beggar,* to drive the vagabonds out of the town.

XXII.

Crime, Police, Gaols, and Punishment.

ENGLAND.

Criminal Commitments, 1827–1828 :

1.—Report from the Select Committee on the increase of Criminal Commitments and Convictions.   Sess. 1826–27, (534.) vol. 6, p. 5.

> SUBJECTS.—Low rate of agricultural wages.—Making up the deficiency of wages from the poor-rate.—Game Laws.—Evils of summary convictions under the Tresspass Act.—Inefficiency of prison discipline in producing reform.

2.—Report from the Select Committee on the cause of the increase of Criminal Commitments and Convictions.   Sess. 1828, (545.) vol. 6, p. 419.

> SUBJECTS.—Cause of the increase in agricultural and manufacturing districts.—Not in proportion to distress, as seen in the condition and conduct of the population in Lancashire.—Increase of commitments not indicative in the same proportion of an increase of crime.—Petty offences more sought for than formerly.—Character of crime less atrocious, but carried on more artfully against property.—Suggestions for making the office of high constable more efficient. —Evil operation of the poor-laws and bastardy-laws in agricultural districts.—Effects of the game laws, and class of persons who become poachers. —Comparative state of farming labourers now and formerly.—Disadvantage to morals from not lodging servants in farm-houses, and in manufacturing towns from the practice of out-door apprenticeships.—Juvenile offenders.—Demoralizing effect of factory-employment.—On summary punishment of petty offences.—Comparison of offences and punishment of boys of the higher and lower classes of society.—Increased consumption of spirituous liquors.—Defective state of the police in populous towns, and the state of crime therein.—Ill effects of the numerous sentences of death.—Effects of secondary punishments. —Transportation.—The hulks.—Improved state of gaols.—Comforts injudiciously afforded, and consequent less dread of gaol punishment.—Necessity of good prison discipline, and its fitness to improve offenders.—Effects of solitary confinement.—Good effects of the tread-mill.—Importance of training children by education in habits of industry and morality.—Evidence of its good effects.—State of crime in France.

Police of the Metropolis, 1770 :

3.—[Report from the Select Committee of Inquiry concerning Burglaries and Robberies.   Journals, vol. 32, p. 878.

> SUBJECTS.—Number of robberies from 1766 to 1770, stated by Sir John Fielding.—Cause of their increase.—Pawnbrokers effectually detect them by stopping the goods. — Police effectual in discovering footpads and highwaymen.—Parish watch-police defective ; insufficiency of their pay.—Sir John's proposal for making the constables and watchmen more efficient.—Manner of choosing constables.—Ballad-singers.—Gaols.— Magistrates.— Brothels ; prostitutes.—Rules observed in granting public-house licences.

1812–1818 :

4.—Report from the Select Committee on the Nightly Watch and Police of the Metropolis.   Sess. 1812, (127.) vol. 2, p. 95. [92.]

> SUBJECTS.—*Nightly Watch and Police.*—The Committee mention the " apprehensions excited by late occurrences;" which may allude to the murder of Marr's family, and of a victualler's at Ratcliff-highway.—State of the police.—Proposed improvements.

5.—Report from the Select Committee on the State of the Police of the Metropolis.   Sess. 1816, (510.) vol. 5, p. 1. [92.]

> SUBJECTS.—General conduct of the police.—Parochial watch.—Public-house licensing. —Public offices.—Parliamentary rewards.

Police of the Metropolis— continued.

6.—First Report from the Select Committee on the State of the Police of the
Metropolis.   Sess. 1817, (233.) vol. 7, p. 1. [92.]
    SUBJECT.—On licensing public-houses.
      see *Beer and Breweries,* under Head VII., Nos. 8 to 12.

7.—Second Report from the same Committee.   Sess. 1817, (484.) vol. 7, p. 321. [93.]
    SUBJECT.—On rewards on conviction.

8.—Third Report from the same Committee.   Sess. 1818, (423.) vol. 8, p. 1. [93.]
    SUBJECTS.—Tothill-fields, Clerkenwell, and Coldbath-fields prisons.——And see *infra,*
Nos. 20. 21.

9.—Report from the Select Committee on the Police of the Metropolis.
                                      Sess. 1822, (440.) vol. 4, p. 91. [93.[
    SUBJECTS.—*On Licensing Public-houses.—Rewards on Conviction.— Penitentiaries.—
Prostitution.—Expenditure of Police Establishment.*—Arrangements of the City police.—
Westminster police.—Police-office establishments.—Horse, dismounted and foot patrol.—
Parish police ;—want of concert with the general police.—Pay of police officers.—Proposed improvement.—Superannuated allowances recommended.—Head-constable of police
officers recommended.—Solicitors not to be clerks at police offices.—Illegal fairs—provisions for suppressing.—Bullock-hunting.—Fear lest an established day-patrol would give
an excuse to the parishes to withdraw their police.—Inefficiency of the parish constables.
—Evil effects of fairs.—No regular highway robbers.—Tables showing the police establishment of the parishes in London.
    See likewise *Licensing,* under Head VII., Nos. 8 to 12.

      In 1828 :

10.—Report from the Select Committee of Inquiry into the Cause of the
Increase in the Number of Commitments and Convictions, and into the State
of the Police of the Metropolis.   Sess. 1828, (533.) vol. 6, p. 1.
    SUBJECTS.—Inquiry whether the increase of commitments arises from increase of crime,
or from the state of society bringing offences more conspicuously under notice.—Classification of offences.—Effect of increase of population.—Evils of low-priced spirituous
liquors.—Neglect of children.—Education not sufficient to check juvenile depravity.—
Expediency of a separate prison for the correction of young offenders.—Advantages of
prompt summary punishment.—Advantage of more frequent holding of sessions of the
peace.—Compromises for restitution of stolen property.—Extent of the practice, and robberies of bankers.—Practice and execution of Jonathan Wild.—State and discipline of
prisons.—Inconvenience arising from the necessity of " backing" warrants, to give them
validity in distant jurisdictions.—Defect in the law of forgery.—Extensive evils of flash-
houses.—Compromises of convictions on penal statutes by common informers.—Utility of
the Police Gazette.—Marine-store shops.—Present system of parochial watch described.—
State of the metropolis and its vicinity.—Plan of a New Police establishment.——
Increase of petty offences, but not of higher crimes.—Causes of increase; want of employment ; youthful depravity ; cheap spirits.—Organized gangs of juvenile thieves.—Good
effect of day patrol in suppressing street robberies.—Burglaries less frequent.—Inefficiency
of the parochial police.—Parish constables and nightly watch.—Duties of the mounted,
dismounted, and street patrol.—State of the magistracy, and defectiveness of the police
near the metropolis, and insufficient means of affording assistance.—Plans for compulsory
employment of young vagrants training up for thieves.—On the expense of sending officers
to detect thefts in the country.—On employing men to mingle with thieves, in order to
detect their plans of robberies.—Assistance to thievery by chaise-carts.—Turnpike-keepers
might be made auxiliary to the police.—Part of the increase of commitments attributable
to paying prosecutors' expenses.—Use of the publication called the " Hue and Cry."—Evil
of association of boys in prison.—Utility of summary punishment of them.—Ill effects of
education without employment.—Most thieves are educated.—Good moral effects of the old
parish charity schools.—Conduct of prostitutes less offensive.—Deteriorated conduct of
domestic servants.—Depredations of petty thieves about the theatres.—Tally-shops encou-
rage theft in domestic servants, and extravagance in others.—Inquiry into the moral conduct of boys attending the national schools.—Marine society.—Jealousy and want of
co-operation between officers of the different police establishments.—Management of the
Refuge for the Destitute.—State of the River police.

      In 1833–1834 :

11.—Report from the Select Committee on the state of the Police of the
Metropolis.   Sess. 1833, (675.) vol. 13, p. 401.
    SUBJECTS.—Economy observed in every department of the Metropolitan police.—Great
care taken in the selection of the men employed.—Efficient manner in which the duties of
the commissioners are discharged.

*Police of the Metropolis—*In 1833-1834—*continued.*

12.—Report from the Select Committee on the Petition of Frederick Young and others.   Sess. 1833, (627.) vol. 13, p. 407.

SUBJECTS.—Alleged improper employment of policemen in watching the proceedings of certain meetings.—Reprehensible conduct of Popay for the manner in which his reports were made up.—Not sufficient caution used by the persons to whom his reports were submitted in checking the occasional diffuseness of their contents, and in warning him against having recourse to undue means for supplying them.—Occasional employment of policemen in plain clothes, as laid down by the Commissioners, affords no just matter of complaint.—The employment of them as spies strongly deprecated.

13.—Report from the Select Committee on the Conduct of the Police on the 13th of May last, in dispersing a Public Meeting in Coldbath-fields.
                                                    Sess. 1833, (718.) vol. 13, p. 589.

SUBJECTS.—No blame to be attached to the Commissioners of Police in the arrangements made by them for carrying into effect the instructions they received relative to dispersing the public meeting in Coldbath-fields.—Conduct of the police not attended with greater violence than became necessary by the resistance they met with.—Police engaged in clearing the surrounding ground were suffered to follow persons to a greater distance than necessary.—Sufficient notice given of the illegality of the meeting, and that interference from the police might be anticipated.—Offensive weapons of a dangerous nature carried and used by some of the persons composing the meeting.

14.—Report from the Select Committee on the state of the Police of the Metropolis, and on the state of Crime therein.   Sess. 1834, (600.) vol. 16, p. 1.

SUBJECTS.—Management and conduct of the Metropolitan Police since its first establishment.—Objections made against the police.—Charges of want of attention by Commissioners to complaints.—Nature of complaints made, and manner attended to.—Advantages of complaints being heard by magistrates instead of Commissioners.—Inconvenience arising from the discharge of policemen from the force between commitment and trial of prisoners, and means the Commissioners have of knowing that the men discharged would be wanted on the trial.—Evening sittings at police offices.—Manner in which accounts are kept of the amount of fines, fees and penalties received at the different police offices.—Number of magistrates might be reduced if the powers now vested in two magistrates were transferred to one.—Particular cases in which the jurisdiction of magistrates should be extended.—Evils of diversity of decisions and practice at different offices.—Magistrates have not sufficient power over the police.—Advantage of policemen doing duty at the police-offices instead of the present officers.—Suggestions for amendments in the police, in the event of a new police Act.—Increased expense of the new over the old police.—Evils arising from the concentration of the force on public occasions.—Advantage to be gained from an extension of the police-district.—Officers belonging to the police offices, their pay and emoluments.—Qualification, duty and pay of police constables.—Extent and nature of the complaints against the collection of the police rate.—Situations, receipt and expenditure, internal management and manner of performing duties at the different station-houses.—Jurisdiction of the Thames police might be extended.—Number of the nightly watch in the city; power given to magistrates of suspending watchmen often evaded by the parish authorities.—By whom private watchmen employed.

For further concerning *Police*, see under Head X. No. 4.

Prisons, and Pretended Privileged Places :

Fleet, and King's Bench, 1696 :

15.—[Reports from the Select Committee on the Abuses of Prisons, and pretended privileged Places.—Fleet and King's Bench.   Journals, vol. 11, pp. 641. 675.

SUBJECTS.—Endeavours to obstruct inquiries before Parliament.—Extortions practised by gaolers,—and illegal protections given to debtors, by connivance with the keepers.—Counterfeiting the coin carried on in the prisons.

Prisons, 1699 :

16.—[Report from the Select Committee on Abuses in the King's Bench and the Fleet.   Journals, vol. 12, p. 684.

SUBJECT.—Negligence of the warden, and corrupt conduct of the keepers, who suffer prisoners to be at large, or escape for bribes received.

Privileged Places, 1705–1722 :

17.—[Report from the Select Committee touching the late riotous Proceedings in the Mint.   1705: Journals, vol. 15, p. 169 ; and in 1722, vol. 20, p. 155.

SUBJECTS.—Outrageous conduct of persons harbouring there.—The execution of magistrates' warrants resisted, and the officers attempting to enforce them maltreated.—Set up a mock police among themselves, for inflicting punishment on those who attempt to resist their lawlessness.—Rescue persons arrested, and rifle the house of the officer arresting.—Rescue a man committed for murder, and by a gross assault on a constable, intimidate a coroner's jury summoned to take inquest on a murdered child.

Prisons, and pretended Privileged Places—continued.

The Fleet and Marshalsea, 1728–1729 :

18.—⌈Reports from the Select Committee of Inquiry into the state of Prisons.—
Fleet and Marshalsea.   Journals, vol. 21, pp. 274. 376. 513.

> Subjects.—*The Fleet.*—Antiquity of that prison.—For what originally used.—Its ori-
> ginal jurisdiction abrogated.—Becomes a prison for debtors.—Its original oppressions
> ingrafted on the present use of the prison.—Acts for the government of prisons;—not ob-
> served in the Fleet.— Patents for granting the wardenship of the Fleet.—It becomes a free-
> hold property.—Abuses.—Connivance at the escape of prisoners, and at their having liberty
> to go to foreign parts to trade.—Severity used by the warden.—Bad state of repair of the
> prison.—Its state detrimental to health.—Exactions by gaolers.—Day rules.—Prisoners
> kept at sponging-houses at exorbitant charges, instead of being admitted into the prison.—
> Illegal use of irons.—Particular instances of cruelty to prisoners. Journals, vol. 21, p. 274.
> ———Statement of some progress in remedying these evils. Journals, vol. 21, p. 513.
> ———*The Marshalsea.*—To what jurisdiction attached.—The marshal, how appointed.—
> Abuses and oppressions.—Charities ;— their perversion.—The practice of the Marshalsea
> Court, in selling the offices belonging to it, condemned.—Disinterested conduct of the Dukes
> of Argyle and Dorset.—Cruelties practised on the prisoners.—Instrument of torture used.
> Vol. 21, p. 376.

The King's Bench, 1752–1753 :

19.—⌈Report from the Select Committee on the state of the King's Bench Prison,
as affected by or arising out of the vested interest of it as Private Property.
                                       Journals, vol. 26, pp. 505. 680.

> Subjects.—1. As being incommodious, unhealthy, and insecure.—2. As to the mort-
> gage under which the marshalship is held.—3. As to the inconvenience arising therefrom
> to the public.

Coldbath-fields, 1799 :

20.—⌈Report from the Select Committee on the state of His Majesty's Prison
of Coldbath-fields, Clerkenwell.   Journals, vol. 54, p. 441.

> Subjects.— General state of the prison, and plan of its management.—Satisfactory con-
> dition.—Healthy state of the prisoners—but journals irregularly kept.—Examination of the
> complaints of E. M. Despard, a state prisoner.—Personal inspection of the prison by the
> Committee.—Satisfactory opinions of its condition, and management.——And see *supra,*
> No. 8.

In 1809 :

21.—Report from the Commissioners on the state of Coldbath-fields Prison.
                              Sess. 1809, (216.) vol. 4, p. 215. [95.]

> Subject.—This Report is not connected with the subject on the general state of prisons ;
> but is an inquiry into the hardships stated to be suffered by prisoners in this prison.

Penitentiaries, 1811–1812 :

22.—Two Reports from the Select Committee on the Laws relating to Peniten-
tiary-houses.   Sess. 1810–11, (199. 217.) vol. 3, pp. 569. 691. [89.]

> Subjects.—Approbation of the penitentiary system.—Gloucester.—Necessity of one
> in London.—Newgate.—Evil of admission of the prisoners' friends.—Of the indiscriminate
> mixture of prisoners.—Building a penitentiary recommended.—Mr. Bentham's plans and
> contracts with the Treasury.—Gloucester and Southwark gaols.—Principles of managing
> penitentiaries.

23.—Third Report from the Select Committee on the Laws relating to Peni-
tentiary-houses.
              Sess. 1812, (306.) vol. 2, p. 363 ; reprinted 1813–14, (35.) vol. 4, p. 391. [89.]

> Subjects.—Establishment and management of the hulks.—State of morals.—Sugges-
> tions of improvements.—Estimated value of labour, and cost of the establishment.

Lancaster and Lincoln, 1812 :

24.—Reports from the Commissioners on the state, condition and management
of His Majesty's Prisons in Lancaster and Lincoln ; and of the Prisoners
confined therein.   Sess. 1812–13, (3. 4.) vol. 5, pp. 115. 213. [95.]

> Subjects.—Messrs. Finnerty and Drakard, and some others, were confined in these
> gaols for political libels. These persons urged great complaints about the prison dis-
> cipline. To examine into the truth of these complaints the commission was appointed.
> The alleged misconduct of the gaolers, and mismanagement of the prisons, are not
> proved.

Gaols in London, 1814–1818 :

Newgate :

25.—Report from the Select Committee on the state of the Gaols of the City of London.   Sess. 1813–14, (157.) vol. 4, p. 249. [89.]

> SUBJECTS.—State of Newgate.—Admission of visitors.—Debtors.—Garnish.—Fees.— Criminals.—Exposure of the convicts in the chapel previous to execution.—Deficiency of classification.—Libellists.—Chaplain.——Other prisons.

King's-Bench, Fleet, and Marshalsea :

26.—Report from the Select Committee on the King's-Bench, Fleet and Marshalsea Prisons, &c.   Sess. 1814–15, (152.) vol. 4, p. 531. [89.]

> SUBJECTS.—Constitution, state and management.—Conduct of the officers.—Fees.— Chumming.—Day and other rules.—Other permissions of absence.—Charities.—Abuses of them.—Voluntary preference of remaining in prison.—Moral state.

Newgate, Giltspur-street, Whitecross-street, Borough Compter and Bridewell :

27.—Reports from the Select Committee on the state of the Prisons within the City of London and Borough of Southwark.

                              Sess. 1818, (275. 392.) vol. 8, pp. 297. 545. [89.]

> The SUBJECTS of the First Report are arranged under the heads—1. Newgate.— Classification.—Boy's School.—Cleanliness.—Bedding.—Food.—Clothing.—Treatment.— Infirmary.—General health.—Religious instruction.—-Dartmoor prison.——Those of the Second Report are— 2. Giltspur-street prison.—3. Whitecross-street prison.—4. Borough Compter.—5. Bridewell.

Fleet, Marshalsea, &c., 1819 :

28.—Report from the Commissioners appointed to inquire into the state of the Prisons of the Fleet, Marshalsea, &c.   Sess. 1819, (109.) vol. 11, p. 325. [95.]

> SUBJECTS.—General state of the prisons. — Management.—Regulations.—Officers.— Fees.

Prison Discipline, &c. :

State of Gaols, 1819 :

29.—Report from the Select Committee on the state of Gaols, &c.

                              Sess. 1819, (579.) vol. 7, p. 1. [90.]

> SUBJECTS.—State of the gaols as to the accommodation afforded for classification of prisoners.—Morals. – State of the colony of New South Wales.—Transportation.

30.—An Account of all the Gaols, Houses of Correction, or Penitentiaries in the United Kingdom, as far as relates to England and Wales.

                              Sess. 1819, (135. 136. 137.) vol. 17, pp. 371. 475 493.

> SUBJECTS.— Name and situation of the gaol.—Superintendence.—Capacity and assification.—Number and description of prisoners.—Labour performed and value thereof.— Dietary and allowances.

31.—Return from all the Gaols, Houses of Correction, or Penitentiaries, in England, Wales and Scotland.   Sess. 1821, (400.) vol. 21, p. 481.

> SUBJECTS.—Name of prison.—Number and classes of prisoners.—Observations on the state of the prisons.—On alterations in the buildings to establish the means of employment, and the better classification of the prisoners.

Laws relating to Prisons, 1822 :

32.—Report from the Select Committee appointed to consider the Laws relating to Prisons, &c.   Sess. 1822, (300.) vol. 4, p. 67. [90.]

> SUBJECTS.—*Prison Discipline.*—This Report refers to former ones on the same subject. —A decided opinion expressed of the necessity of providing the means of constant labour in every prison.—Inconvenience of small prisons having local jurisdiction.—Recommends a Bill for enforcing a good system of prison discipline.—The Appendix contains returns relative to the jurisdiction of the prisons in each county.

Ilchester Gaol, 1822 :

33.—Report from the Commissioners appointed to inquire into the state of Ilchester Gaol.   Sess. 1822, (7.) vol. 11, p. 277. [94.]

34.— Appendix to Report of Commissioners :—with Six Plans of the Buildings.

                              Sess. 1822, (54.) vol. 11, p. 313. [94.]

*Ilchester Gaol—*1822—*continued.*

35.—Reports of the High Sheriff and Magistrates of the County of Somerset, on an Inquiry into Charges preferred against the Keeper of the said Gaol, by Mr. Henry Hunt, a Prisoner confined therein.

Sess. 1822, (30.) vol. 11, p. 733. [94.]

36.—Papers relating to the same subject; being Reports of Coroner's Inquests on Persons dying in the Gaol.   Sess. 1822, (70.) vol. 11, p. 757. [94.]

> SUBJECTS.—*Prison Discipline.*—These Papers relate to various charges of misconduct made against the keeper by Mr. Hunt, who was confined in Ilchester gaol by sentence of the court of King's-Bench, for matters arising out of the Manchester riots. The alleged unhealthy state of the gaol is likewise a subject of inquiry.

Penitentiary at Milbank, 1823–1824:

37.—Report from the Select Committee on the State of the Penitentiary at Milbank.   Sess. 1823, (533.) vol. 5, p. 403. [91.]

> SUBJECTS.—*Prison Discipline.—Diet.—Disease.*—History of the Penitentiary establish-ment—Observations on mental recreation.—Books exclusively religious should not be the only ones supplied to the convicts.—On the kind of labour supplied.—Prevalence of sickness.—Causes of disease.—Dietary reduced.—Sea-scurvy.—Dysentery.—The situation of the prison not insalubrious.—Medical treatment.—Observations on French prisons.—The moral discipline of a prison debilitates the body.—Observations on the term of imprison-ment.—Class of prisoners fitted for penitentiary punishment.—Favourable opinion of the establishment, as having answered its intention.—Conduct of the officers.

38.—Report of the Physicians on the state of the General Penitentiary, Milbank.

Sess. 1823, (256.) vol. 5, p. 379. [91.]

> SUBJECTS.—*Prison Discipline.—Diet.—Disease.*—State of the health of the prisoners.—Inquiry into the prevailing disease.—Decline of health.—Appearance of scurvy:—the same as the *sea scurvy.*—Rise and progress of the disease.—Cause, independent of situation.—Mainly ascribed to the lowness of diet, and partly to the cold of the winter.—Remedies employed.—Suggestions with regard to diet.

39.—Report of the Committee of the General Penitentiary at Milbank.

Sess. 1823, (150.) vol. 5, p. 365. [91.]

> SUBJECTS.—On the state of the prisoners.—General regulations.

40.—Further Papers relating to the Penitentiary at Milbank.

Sess. 1823, (309.) vol. 5, p. 387. [91.]

> SUBJECTS.—On the dietary and health of the prisoners.—Correspondence with Mr. Hutchinson, medical superintendent.—Appointment of two visiting physicians.—Dismissal of Mr. Hutchinson.

41.—Extracts from the Minutes of the Superintending Committee.

Sess. 1823, (545.) vol. 5, p. 401. [91.]

42.—Report from the Select Committee on the Penitentiary at Milbank.

Sess. 1824, (408.) vol. 4, p. 407. [91.]

> SUBJECTS.—*Prison Discipline.—Diet.—Disease.*—Present condition of the prisoners lately in the Penitentiary, and now at Woolwich.—In what degree the recent disease is to be ascribed to the situation of the building.—Treatment of the prisoners.—Improvements in the arrangement, diet and discipline.—Nature of the disease prevalent in the Peniten-tiary.—Mode of treatment.—As to the prevalent disease being contagious—and the influence of locality on it.—Probable fitness of the prison for future habitation.—On the state of health of the surrounding neighbourhood.—Tothill-fields prison.—On fevers arising from marshy situations.—Walcheren.—On army sickness, under particular moral causes, as advance and retreat.—On simulated diseases.—Recreation by active sports recommended.—Arrangements for the temporary removal of the convicts.——The subject is illustrated by a section of the level of the river and buildings, and by a general ground Plan of the Penitentiary.
>
> *For* the Annual Reports of the Committee of Management of the Penitentiary at Milbank, from Sess. 1817 to Sess. 1834,—*see* the GENERAL INDEX.

Bradford Gaol, 1825:

43.—Correspondence relative to the Abuses and Mismanagement of Bradford Gaol.   Sess. 1825, (330.) vol. 21, p. 83. [90.]

Tread-wheels :

44.—Communications respecting the use of Tread-wheels in Gaols and Houses of Correction.   Sess. 1823, (113.) vol. 15, p. 307. [91.]

> SUBJECTS.—*Prison Discipline.*—Reports and opinions of magistrates, gaolers and medical persons, on the moral and physical effects of that labour.

Tread-wheels—continued.

45.—Correspondence respecting the introduction of Tread-wheels into Gaols.

SUBJECTS.—Prison discipline.   Sess. 1824, (45. 247.) vol. 19, p. 147. [91.]

46.—Papers showing the result of Inquiries as to the effect of the Tread-wheel in the Prisons where it has been established.   Sess. 1825, (34.) vol. 23, p. 567. [91.]
Same subject.

Returns under Gaol Act, 1824–1834:

47.—Copies of all Reports, and the Schedule (B.), transmitted to the Secretary of State from the several Counties, Cities and Towns, in England and Wales, under the provisions of the " Gaol Act," of the 4 Geo. 4, c. 64.

Sess. 1824, (104.) vol. 19, p. 359.--Sess. 1825, (5.) vol. 23, p. 1.—Sess. 1826, (10.) vol. 24, p. 1.—Sess. 1826–27, (46.) vol. 19, p. 365.—Sess. 1828, (2.) vol. 20, p. 327.—Sess. 1829, (2. 4.) vol. 19, pp. 1. 401.—Sess. 1830, (5.) vol. 24, p. 1.—Sess. 1830–31, (41.) vol. 12, p. 1.—Sess. 1831–32, (167.) vol. 33, p. 197.—Sess. 1833, (12.) vol. 28, p. 1.—Sess. 1834, (1.) vol. 46, p. 1.

SUBJECTS.—Capacity of the prisons.—Number and classes of prisoners.—Offences.—Sex and age.—Employment.— Punishments within the prison.— Health.—Dietary and allowance.—Description of labour and number of hours at work.—Amount and application of earnings.—Duties of chaplain, and progress of instruction.—Attendance of surgeon, and accommodation for the sick.—Reasons for punishments.—Insane prisoners.——These Reports are arranged under counties.

SCOTLAND.

Jails in Scotland, 1818–1826:

48.—Report from the Select Committee on the Petition of the Royal Burghs of Scotland, respecting the providing of Jails.   Sess. 1818, (346.) vol. 6, p. 199. [90.]

SUBJECTS.—Condition of the jails.—Inability of many of the royal burghs to make adequate provision for their support.—Proposed extension of power of the commission of supply at the different counties to grant aid where necessary.

49.—Report from the Select Committee on the state of Prisons in Scotland, and on the means of maintaining Prisoners confined therein under Criminal Warrants.   Sess. 1826, (381.) vol. 5, p. 1. [90.]

SUBJECTS.—*Defective State.—Inadequacy of Funds.*—Inquiry into the condition of prisons.—Funds applicable to the maintenance of prisoners, and for erecting gaols.—Necessity of a speedy remedy.—District prisons recommended.—Importance of the subject requires a revival of the inquiry next Session.—Accounts from the royal burghs procured, and abstracted.—Abstracts of the income and expenditure of the royal burghs for 1824–25.

IRELAND.

State of Prisons, 1809:

50.—Report from the Commissioners of Inquiry into the Condition and Government of State Prisons and other Gaols in Ireland.
Five plans are annexed to this Report.   Sess. 1809, (265.) vol. 7, p. 575. [95.]

Inspectors' Reports, 1808–1834:

51.—Reports of the Inspectors-general of Prisons in Ireland, from 1808 to 1834; together with Correspondence relating to that subject.

Inspectors'-general Reports; Sess. 1808, (239¹. 239².) vol. 9, p. 351.——Correspondence on the state of gaols; Sess. 1810, (58.) vol. 12, p. 423.——Abstracts of Inspectors' Reports, 1815 to 1820; Sess. 1821, (620.) vol. 20, p. 159.——Inspectors' first report; Sess. 1823, (342.) vol. 10, p. 291.—Second; Sess. 1824, (294.) vol. 22, p. 269.—Third; Sess. 1825, (493.) vol. 22, p. 223.—Fourth; Sess. 1826, (173.) vol. 23, p. 395.—Fifth; Sess. 1826–27, (471.) vol. 11, p. 335.—Sixth; Sess. 1828, (68.) vol. 12, p. 349.—Seventh; Sess. 1829, (10.) vol. 13, p. 421.—Eighth; Sess. 1830, (48.) vol. 24, p. 719.—Ninth; Sess. 1830–31, (172.) vol. 4, p. 269.—Tenth; Sess. 1831–32, (152.) vol. 23, p. 451.—Eleventh; Sess. 1833, (67.) vol. 17, p. 307.—Twelfth; Sess. 1834, (63.) vol. 11, p. 69.

SUBJECTS.—State of the buildings.—Regulations, management and discipline.—Dietary.—Moral conduct and education.—Health and cleanliness.—Expenditure.

Richmond Penitentiary, Dublin.   See Head XX. No. 40.

SECONDARY PUNISHMENTS.

Convicts ; and Hard Labour :

In the Hulks, 1778 :

52.—⎡Report from the Select Committee on the Punishment of Convicts by
Hard Labour.   Journals, vol. 36, p. 926.

    Subjects.—Construction of the hulks.—Manner of accommodating the convicts.—
Expense.—Allowance of food.—Employment.—Evidence of John Howard, Esq. and Dr.
Solander.

By Transportation to Botany Bay, 1779 :

53.—⎡Report from the Select Committee on Returns presented to The House
respecting Convicts.   Journals, vol. 37, p. 306.

    Subjects.—Those treated on in the preceding Report are in this continued.—The follow-
ing arrangement is adopted by the Committee : On the maintenance and employment of
convicts : On the execution of the Act authorizing the confinement and employing in hard
labour transportable offenders aboard the hulks : On punishment by transportation : Observations by the Committee.——Mr. Howard is examined, and states the result of his
observations in visiting the prisons in this country and those in foreign states.   Joseph
Banks, Esq. (afterwards Sir Joseph Banks) is examined as to the practicability of forming
a new colony ; and recommends *Botany Bay.* He gives a general account of that country,
with interesting observations.

In Penitentiaries, 1784 :

54.—⎡Report from the Select Committee respecting the Laws for the Punishment
of Offenders.   Journals, vol. 39, p. 1040.

    Subjects.—Plan for building a Penitentiary for convicts.—Estimates.—Proposed to be
built near Wandsworth.

By Transportation to Africa, 1785 :

55.—⎡Report from the Select Committee respecting the Transportation of
Convicts.   Journals, vol. 40, p. 954.

    Subjects.—As to the expediency of transporting convicts to Africa.—Number of
criminals in confinement waiting transportation.—Difficulty of carrying the sentence of
transportation into effect.—Plan of sending convicts to the Island of *Lemane* in the river
Gambia.—On the climate, and its effects on Europeans.—Obstacles from these causes to
sending settlers to Africa.—Ill effects from the conduct of a colony of criminals as influencing the behaviour of the natives towards other Europeans.

56.—⎡Another Report on the same subject.   1785 : Journals, vol. 40, p. 1161.

    Subjects.—Fulness of the gaols.—Bad effects of the hulks on the moral habits of the
convicts.—Executions, though they remove the bad, produce no effect as to example.—
Transportation does not operate as example, as the sufferings are unseen.—Transportation
to America beneficial ; but difficulties arising from America being shut against receiving
transports.—As to employing them in foreign states.—Impossibility of forming a colony
solely of convicts—" the outcasts of an old society cannot form the foundation of a new
one ;" but under proper government might form a good colony.—All great discoveries
and commercial establishments originate in individual enterprize.—Recommendation in
favour of establishing a colony on the south-west coast of *Africa,* near the river *Des
Voltas.*

By Transportation to New South Wales, 1812 :

57.—Report from the Select Committee on Transportation.

                                                Sess. 1812, (341.) vol. 2, p. 573.

    Subjects.—Formation and general description of the colony.—Trade.—Administration
of justice.—Religion, morals and education.—Manner of transportation.—Selection.—
Treatment in the colony.——*See likewise* under Head XV. *Colonies.*

Secondary Punishments :

58.—Report from the Select Committee on the best mode of giving efficacy to
Secondary Punishments.   Sess. 1831, (276.) vol. 7, p. 519.

    Subjects.—Effect of the punishment of hard labour on agricultural labourers.—Dread
of London thieves to hard labour.—Effect of penitentiary system of confinement and
labour.—Mode of punishment by imprisonment and transportation compared.—Necessity
of the punishment immediately following the crime to be effectual.—Unequal effect of
transportation as a punishment.—Effect of tread-mill punishment.—Prison discipline.—
Effect of solitary confinement.—Classification of prisoners.—Management of the Hulks, and
nature of labour therein, and in the dock-yards.—Diet in prisons.—Systematic training

Secondary Punishments—continued.

or education of London thieves.—Treatment of juvenile offenders better in gaols than at their own homes.—Management of prisons in America.—Treatment of convicts.—The hulks preferred by convicts to the Penitentiary.—Dislike of lower orders to transportation.—Condition of transports.—Relation of master and convict-servant.—Difficulty of managing gentlemen or educated convicts.—Employment of convicts in the Colonies.—Punishment by labour in road-gangs in New South Wales.—Conduct of convicts having tickets of leave.—State of society in New South Wales.—Condition of emancipatists and pardoned convicts.—Many possess wealth.—High price of labour.—State of settlers.—Rapidly increasing from influx of emigrants and convicts.

59.—Report from the Select Committee on the best mode of giving efficacy to Secondary Punishments.   Sess. 1831-32, (547.) vol. 7, p. 559.

SUBJECTS.—*State of Crime.*—Effects of punishment, either in deterring the commission of offence or by inducing reformation.====*Nature of Punishments.*———*Of Transportation.*—Effect on those whose course of crime may subject them to that punishment.—General management of convicts.—Condition at New South Wales, compared with the labouring poor in England.—Difficulty in managing educated convicts.—Punishment at the penal settlements of Moreton and Norfolk Island.—Transportation to Canada.——*Of the Hulks.*—Generally considered.—Nature of employment.—Discipline.—Want of classification.—Clothing.—Instruction.—How far dreaded by offenders, or calculated to deter from crime, and tend to reformation.—Inefficacy of punishment.———*Penitentiary Punishment.*—Effect of solitary confinement.—Superiority of discipline.—Fear of offenders of it, who disregard reformation.———*Corporal Punishment.*—Opinions of its effect on men and boys.———*Labour* applied as a punishment.—In English prisons.—In American.—On board the Hulks.—At the dock-yards.—Its nature and degree.———*Prison Discipline.*—In English gaols.—Necessity, but difficulty of classification.—Instruction.—Evils of local jurisdictions.—In penitentiaries.—Its effects.———In American prisons.———*Female asy*lums and penitentiaries.—Female convicts at New South Wales.—In English prisons.—Difficulty in punishing.———*Juvenile Offenders.*—Necessity of an institution for their correction.—Management on board the Hulks.—In gaols and penitentiaries.

Penitentiaries in the United States:

60.—Report of William Crawford, Esq. on the Penitentiaries of the United States.   Sess. 1834, (593.) vol. 46, p. 349.

SUBJECTS.—Construction of gaols.—Management and discipline.—Effect of punishment.—State of crime.———There are 18 *plans* of gaols annexed.

Preventing Forgery of Bank Notes, 1819–1820:

61.—Report of the Commissioners for inquiring into the mode of preventing the Forgery of Bank Notes.   Sess. 1819, (2.) vol. 11, p. 303. [83.]

SUBJECTS.—Many plans are submitted to the Commissioners.—Prevalence of forgery in America.—Improved notes in circulation in that country.—Observations on the manner in which the system of forgery is carried on.—Difficulty of the subject.

62.—Final Report of the Commissioners for inquiring into the mode of preventing the Forgery of Bank Notes.   Sess. 1819-20, (64.) vol. 2, p. 399. [83.]

SUBJECTS.—Experiment of plans.—Applegath and Cowper's adopted;—and considered as calculated to render forgery difficult.

See likewise *Imprisonment for Debt*, under Head III., No. 47.

XXIII.

Population.

GREAT BRITAIN.

Abstract of Returns in 1801 :

1.—Abstract of Answers and Returns, pursuant to Act 41 Geo. 3, for taking an Account of the Population of Great Britain in 1801.

Sess. 1801, (140.) vol. 6, p. 813. [136.]

ENUMERATION, Part I. *England and Wales.*—Part II. *Scotland* ———The Returns to the Inquiries are arranged in Counties, under the Hundreds.—The Parishes therein are in the order of the alphabet.—The particulars of the answers are placed in columns showing the number of houses inhabited and uninhabited, and by how many families—The number of persons, and distinguishing the sexes—Their occupations, whether in agriculture or trade, and all other persons not comprised in those classes.   There are summaries subjoined to each county, and a general summary of the whole kingdom.

PARISH REGISTERS, *England and Wales.*—The Abstracts are arranged under the Hundreds in each county.—The Baptisms and Burials are shown from 1700 to 1800, in periods of ten years from 1700 to 1780, and yearly afterwards to 1800.—The number of males and females are distinguished.—The parishes from which the Abstracts are made are stated, and where the registers are defective the parish is mentioned.—The Marriages are stated in every year, beginning with 1754, and ending with 1800.—There are summaries of each county ; a summary of London ; and a general summary of England and Wales.—The totals of Baptisms and Burials are stated. ———*Scotland.*—It was found impossible to form a correct abstract of the Baptisms, Burials and Marriages in Scotland ; as only 99 parishes out of 850 made any returns.

Comparative Statement, 1801 to 1811 :

2.—Comparative Statement of the Population of Great Britain in 1801 and 1811.

Sess. 1812, (12.) vol. 10, p. 171. [137.]

THIS was to supply immediate information of general results, till " the larger Abstracts both of Enumeration and Parish Register Returns shall be completed and presented to Parliament."

The Abstract of Returns in 1811 :

3.—Abstract of Answers and Returns, pursuant to Act 51 Geo. 3, for taking an Account of the Population of Great Britain, in 1811.

Sess. 1812, (316. 317.) vol. 11. [138.]

SUBJECTS.—*Preliminary Observations.*—1. ENUMERATION.—Necessity of a comparison of the Results of the Abstracts of 1801 and 1811.—Explanation of the order pursued in compiling them.—Questions by which the facts were ascertained.—Propriety of distinguishing new houses as an indication of prosperity.—Misapprehension of the question of occupation in 1801.—Questions amended in 1811, so as to apply to families.—Comparison of 1801 with 1811.—Increase.———Explanation of the arrangement.—Antiquity of the divisions of Counties.—Origin of the divisions of Hundreds.—Inequality of extent.—Wards, Wapentakes, Latles and Rapes.—Advantage of observing these divisions.—Exceptions as to large towns, and reasons.—This arrangement conformable to that of 1801, and of the Poor Returns in 1776, 1786 and 1803.—Ambiguity from parishes extending into two counties or hundreds.—Origin of Parish boundaries.—Operation of the poor-laws in rendering them immutable.—Largness of parishes in northern counties.—Circumstances legally constituting a parish, according to antient rule.—Modern rule.—Orthography of names of parishes.—Extra-parochial places, and their immunities.—Their evil and remedy.—The complete state of the Enumeration, no place having finally omitted to make a return.—Proportion of sexes.———2. PARISH REGISTERS.—Questions addressed to parochial clergy.—Early origin of parish registers, and ecclesiastical injunctions for enforcing their being kept.—Operation of the Marriage Act of 26 Geo. 2, which began operation in 1754, the year in which these Abstracts commence.—Difficulties arising from duplicate returns.—Comparison of the number of Baptisms, Burials, and Marriages in the returns of 1801 and 1811.—Comparison of the Parish Register Abstract with the Summary of each County in the Enumeration Abstract.———MARRIAGE REGISTRY.—Reasons for considering them correct.—Causes of the variation in the annual number.—Table of the number of Marriages in each year from

1755

Abstract of Returns in 1811—continued.

1755 to 1780.—Medium average of five and ten years.———BURIAL REGISTRY.—Causes affecting their accuracy, and counterbalancing circumstances.—Conclusions afforded of diminished mortality, and ratio stated.———BAPTISMAL REGISTRY.—Causes affecting their accuracy.—Objections to Private and Half-baptism.———INCREASE of the Population.—Deduced from the Baptismal Registers, and compared with the results of the Enumeration.—Table of comparison—of Population in 1700, 1750, 1801, and 1811; Area of each county; Meetings of Magistrates; Number of parishes and parts of parishes; Number of Population Returns.—Annual proportions of Baptisms, Burials, and Marriages.

The ENUMERATION is arranged in columns under the Counties, and the Parishes alphabetically under the Hundreds.—The number of Houses are shown, inhabited, building, and uninhabited, and by how many families occupied; their occupations, whether in agriculture or trade, and those unclassed; their sex and the total number of persons.—There are summaries subjoined to each county, and a general summary of the whole kingdom.

The PARISH REGISTRY Abstracts are arranged under the Hundreds in each county.—The Baptisms and Burials are shown for each year, 1801 to 1810, distinguishing the sex.—The Marriages are shown for the same periods.—A Summary is subjoined to each county. —There is a summary of England, and a general summary of England and Wales.—The Appendix contains statements respecting the Metropolis: a comparison of its Population in 1700, 1750, 1801, and 1811; with a Table of the Baptisms and Burials in every 10 years, beginning with 1700 and ending with 1780, and in every subsequent year, ending with 1810, which is stated according to the Parish Registers, and according to the Bills of Mortality.

The Parishes from which the Abstracts are made are stated, and where the registers are defective the parish is mentioned; and many topographical particulars of union or separation of parishes are pointed out.

Comparison of 1801, 1811, and 1821:

4.—Comparative Statement of the Population of the several Counties of Great Britain, in the years 1801, 1811, and 1821:

Showing the Rate of Increase or Diminution thereof in each County, between the years 1801 and 1811; and between the years 1811 and 1821.

Sess. 1822, (8.) vol. 21, p. 631.

Abstract of Returns, in 1821:

5.—Abstract of the Answers and Returns, made in pusuance of Act 1 Geo. 4, for taking an Account of the Population of Great Britain, and of the Increase and Diminution thereof.
Sess. 1822, (502.) vol. 15. [138.]

SUBJECTS.—*Preliminary Observations.*—Those prefixed to the volume of 1811 are repeated, with such additions as have become necessary from another repetition of the Population Act, which affords a further Comparison of Results. These Returns contain a *new Inquiry regarding the Ages of Persons.* The answer to the question on this subject left optional; but the result shows the good will in execution of the Population Act, as the Returns of Ages embraces eight-ninths of the persons enumerated.—A comparative statement of ages of males and females, deduced from the returns of the specified ages, supposing, for the sake of comparison, the number to be 10,000.———Effect of the Act 52 Geo. 3, c. 146, on the keeping of the Parish Registers.—Received the Royal assent in July 1812, and books prepared for every parish by January 1813.—Careful provision for the preservation of the Registers.——— Advantages from the strictness of the provisions of the Marriage Act in producing correct returns.———Rates of mortality stated.—Causes of the increase in the duration of human life.———Remarks on the increase of the population.—Proximate causes.—In the agricultural and manufacturing classes.—Influence of poor laws and high wages.———The tables of comparison are similar to those in the former volume.

The arrangement and columns of the Enumeration and Parish Register Abstracts are similar to that and those in the Abstracts of 1811.—The Notes contain many topographical particulars, such as the union of parishes; the local connexion and intermixture of parts of parishes; the boundaries of places affected by such localities, and the changes produced by the extensive demolition of houses to form new streets, or to improve old ones.—The causes of increase are frequently stated, and any instances of remarkable longevity are recorded.—*The Table of Ages* is subjoined to each county.

1830—Evidence:

6.—Evidence taken before the Committee on the Bill for taking an Account of the Population.
Sess. 1830, (385. 460.) vol. 4, pp. 721. 733.

SUBJECTS.—(385.)—Statement by Mr. *Rickman* of the method of carrying the Enumeration into effect.—Difficulty of framing questions to obtain plain answers.—Further questions proposed to ascertain the occupations of persons.—Experimental proceedings.—Classification of trades, and number of denominations.—List of proposed questions, and instructions for answering them.———Plan of collecting information from the Parish Registers.—Formula for facilitating that work.

(460.)—Mr. *Rickman's* correspondence with Sir Francis D'Ivernois on the increased length of life apparent from the Population Returns.—Reasons for the decrease of mortality suggested.—Observations on the population, and proportions of burials, in London.—Refutation of Mr. Milne's observations on the proposed mode of taking the enumeration, and ascertaining the duration of life.

Abstract of Returns—continued.

Comparison of 1801, 1811, 1821, 1831:

7.—Comparative Account of the Population of Great Britain in 1801, 1811, 1821, and 1831; with the Annual Value of Real Property in 1815; also, Statement of the progress of Inquiry regarding the Occupation of Families and Persons, and Duration of Life, as required by the Population Act of 1830.

Sess. 1831, (348.) vol. 18, p. 1.

Abstract of Returns in 1831:

8.—Abstract of the Answers and Returns, made pursuant to an Act 2 Geo. 4, for taking an Account of the Population of Great Britain, and of the Increase and Diminution thereof.

Sess. 1833 (149.)

Vol. I. Enumeration Abstract, vol. 36.—Vol. II. Enumeration Abstract, with an Index to the Names of Places, vol. 37.—Vol. III. Parish Register Abstract, vol. 38.

SUBJECTS.—*Preface.*—I. ENUMERATION ABSTRACTS.—Completion of the national investigation on the subject of the Population for 1801, 1811, 1821 and 1831.—Explanation of the method pursued in digesting and connecting the subject-matter of the Enumeration and Parish Register Abstracts.—Explanation of the official machinery of taking the census, to justify the accuracy of the results.—Endeavour to render useful the inquiry as to the occupation of males.—New question to ascertain the number of retail and handicraft population; and accuracy of the returns relating thereto.—Calculation of increase from the ratio of increase of females.—Notices of topographical divisions of Counties, Hundreds, &c. and arrangement of the Returns in their order.—Ecclesiastical divisions, and population of Dioceses.—Comparison of the Metropolis with Edinburgh and other great cities and towns.—Reason for the number of females exceeding males in great towns.—Population of the Metropolis.—Assumed limits.—Compared with Paris.—Reasons for, and advantage of, an eight-mile radius for the environs of the two metropolitan cities.—That quantity coincides with seven meridian geographical miles; propriety of undisturbing the lineal measure inferred therefrom.

II. PARISH REGISTER ABSTRACT.—Questions and formula of abstracting the ages of Burials.—Inquiry as to the dates and deficiencies of Registers.—The answers abstracted and inserted; and the answers themselves deposited in the British Museum.—Antiquity of the registers advantageously compared with those of foreign nations.—Corrected Table of the proportions of Births, Burials, and Marriages.—Useful for facilitating comparisons of the duration of human life, and the proportion of marriages.—Use of the MAPS of proportions inserted in the Parish Register Abstracts.———*Registry of Marriages.*—Table of Marriages for each year since 1754, ending with 1800, and since the Marriage Act, in periods of five and ten years.———*Registry of Burials.*—Excess in the decenniary years explained.—Tables of ages of persons buried in England and Wales in 7 years and 18 years.—Of the ages of persons enumerated.———*Registry of Baptisms.*—Proportions of registered baptisms to population.—Proportion of legitimate births in London and foreign metropolitan cities.—Reasons for the apparent excess in the latter.

III. INCREASE of Population.—Remarks on the materials for estimation.—Statement of its progression.—Mr. Finlaison's inquiries.—Probability of life in different counties.—Average duration of life.—Effect of the poor laws.—Population censuses of Ireland and France.—Table of comparison of the population of 1801, 1811, 1821 and 1831.—The increase per cent.—The area of each county.—Divisional meetings.—Number of magistrates.—Number of returns.—Table of the prices of wheat from 1595 to 1833 inclusive.—Average number of registered burials.—Table of comparison of the expectation of life.

An *Index* to where the places will be found in the Enumeration, and Parish Register Abstracts, is attached to the Second Volume.

In the *Notes* to the Parish Registers are stated the particulars of what years' Registers are incomplete, and at the end of each county the results of the three decennial periods are entered in comparison.—There are 16 maps, each containing the outline of a county, and some of two or more counties, on which are entered the totals of the four censuses, with the areas of the counties, and several other particulars, for the sake of more easy comparison.—There are likewise at the end of each county, Table of Ages, of Mortality, and of proportions of Burials.

The *Appendix* contains a statement of the Population of the Metropolis, with a brief account of its topographical antiquity.—Antient history of Southwark.—Singular want of a mileage standard.—Remarkable historical events in the contests between the Saxons and Danes for the possession of London elucidated.—Explanation of the origin of the *Bills of Mortality.*—Ravages of the plague.—Increase of the population of London.—A *Map* of the Metropolis and its environs is added.

A writer in a statistical essay, in commenting on this work, says, " Mr. Rickman's Preface is indeed a curious document. It is not alone remarkable in respect of its scientific merits, but is also worthy to be studied, as exhibiting perhaps the most perfect example which is anywhere to be found of practical ability in setting on foot a statistical inquiry of enormous extent." [*Quarterly Review*, No. cv. p.57]. " The nature of the information sought, and so successfully obtained, on the subject of population, will be best understood by specifying the headings of each column in the Returns: 1st, the name of the place, with its designation, as parish, township, hamlet, extra-parochial, &c.; 2d, area in acres; 3d, inhabited houses; 4th, families; 5th, houses, buildings; 6th, other uninhabited houses; 7th, families employed chiefly in agriculture; 8th, trade, manufactures, and handicraft; 9th, all other families; 10th, males; 11th, females; 12th, total of persons; 13th, males above 20 years old; 14th, number of such occupying land and employing labourers; 15th, number of such not employing labourers; 16th, number of males above 20 years old, employed as labourers in agriculture; 17th, in manufactures,

Abstract of Returns—In 1831—*continued.*

manufactures, and making manufacturing machinery; 18th, in retail trade or handicraft, as masters or workmen; 19th, as capitalists, bankers, professional and other educated men; 20th, males above twenty employed in labour not agricultural; 21st, other males above twenty years (except servants); 22d, male servants above twenty; 23d, male servants under twenty; 24th, female servants. The information sought and obtained from the Parish Registers, by requesting each officiating minister to state—1st, the number of baptisms and burials appearing in his register in the several years from 1821 to 1830, both inclusive, distinguishing males from females; 2dly, the number of marriages in each of those years; 3dly, the ages of the deceased from 1813 to 1830, both inclusive; 4thly, the number of illegitimate children born in the parish or chapelry during 1830, distinguishing male and female children; 5thly, any explanatory remarks are requested on any of the subjects, particularly on the annual average number of births, marriages, and deaths, which may have taken place without being registered." [*Ib.* pp. 58, 59].—"The results of the volume of Parish Registers of England and Wales are most highly interesting, not to this kingdom only, but to the whole of the civilized world; furnishing, for calculations of the highest import to philosophy and to practical life, data of an authenticity and minuteness of detail, and on a scale of such magnitude, as had been the wish, rather than the hope, of philosophers; and the publication of which has been anxiously waited for by all the statisticians of Europe. Of the results which this volume presents, Mr. Rickman's lucid arrangements furnishes not only local summaries, but a general summary as regards the whole kingdom. And, in the Preface, he has shown the applicability of the results to the solution of the most important questions, upon which men of the first talents and information have, for want of data, come to very different conclusions, or declared their inability to arrive with certainty at any." [*Ib.* p.67].—"The grand results, as may be collected from the summaries and statements in the Preface, may be thus shortly stated: The ascertainment, 1st, of the ages at which very nearly four million persons (3,938,496) died during eighteen years, 1813–1830, distinguishing the sexes; 2d, of the ages of nearly twelve-and-a-half millions (12,487,377) of the living in 1821, distinguishing the sexes; 3d, the increase of the population in England since 1700." [*Ib.* p. 68.]

IRELAND.

Returns in 1813:

9.—Abstract of the Returns of Population of Ireland, according to the late Census; with a comparative view of the number of Houses and Inhabitants, as taken in 1813.   Sess. 1822, (36.) vol. 14, p. 737.

Returns in 1821:

10.—Abstract of the Answers and Returns, made pursuant to Act 55 Geo. 3, for taking an Account of the Population of Ireland, and for ascertaining the Increase or Diminution thereof, in 1821.   Sess. 1824, (577.) vol. 22, p. 411. [139.]

SUBJECTS.—*Preliminary Observations.*—Account of previous attempts to ascertain the population.—Sir William Petty's, in 1672—subsequent attempts.—Table of the estimated population at the several periods of making these attempts.—Occasion of the failure in 1812.—The present attempt more successful.—Origin of the division of Counties—Baronies—Parishes—Townlands.—Difficulty of finding persons in room of the English overseers to take the census.—Persons employed as enumerators—their manner of proceeding.—Difficulties.—Classification of the returns when procured.———Unsatisfactory endeavours to procure returns of Parish Registers.———Summary of the number of Houses and Inhabitants in the several Counties of Ireland.—Population of the Metropolis.———The information obtained is arranged in Counties under the four Provinces.—The heads of information are, 1, houses inhabited; 2, families; 3, inhabited houses; 4, building; 5, males; 6, females; 7, total; 8, employed in agriculture; 9, in trade, manufacture, or handicraft; 10, other occupations; 11, pupils in schools.—At the end of each county is a table of the Ages of the population.—In the Notes many topographical and statistical particulars are collected.

Returns in 1831:

11.—Return of the Population of the several Counties in Ireland, as enumerated in 1831.   Sess. 1831, (254.) vol. 39, p. 1.

Comparative Statement, 1821–1831:

12.—Comparative Abstract of the Population as taken in 1821 and 1831, arranged in the order of Parishes, Boroughs, Counties and Provinces.

Sess. 1833, (23.) vol. 39, p. 3.

The heads of information in this Abstract are, 1st, the names of parishes, &c.; 2d, the population of 1821 and of 1831; 3d, aggregate population of connected places.

13.—Abstract of Answers and Returns under the Population Acts of 55 Geo. 3, c. 120 ; 2 Geo. 4, c. 30 ; 3 Geo. 4, c. 5 ; 1 Will. 4, c. 19.

Sess. 1833, (634.) vol. 39, p. 59.

The Returns are arranged under the Provinces, Counties, Baronies, and Parishes.—The information obtained is placed under the heads, 1st, area in English statute acres ; 2d, houses, inhabited and uninhabited, and building, and families ; 3d, occupations in agriculture, trade, manufactures, handicraft, and all other occupations ; 4th, total of persons, distinguishing males and females, and their ages ; 5th, those who are occupied in agriculture, who employ labourers, or not so employing, and the number of labourers ; 6th, employed in manufacture or making manufacturing machinery ; 7th, in retail trade or handicraft, as masters or workmen ; 8th, capitalists, bankers, professional and other educated men ; 9th, labourers not agricultural ; 10th, other males twenty years of age, except servants ; 11th, male servants twenty years of age, distinguishing those *of*, from those *under* twenty years of age ; 12th, female servants.—At the end of each county is a summary, and a table specifying the particular trades of all males of twenty years of age, employed in retail trade or handicraft.— In conclusion there is a summary of the population of Ireland, stated in Provinces, and a summary specification of persons employed in trade or handicraft.—The Notes contain many particulars of topographical and statistical information.

Marriages in the Fleet, 1705 :

14.—[Report respecting illegal practices in the Fleet.   1705 : Journals, vol. 15, p. 188.

SUBJECTS.—Clandestine solemnization of marriages, under pretence of privilege.—Registers of marriages concealed, or false certificates given, to suit the sinister practices of the parties.—Sham books of registers kept, to give a colour to the deceit ; and neither licences were produced, nor banns published, to sanction the marriage of the parties.—The number of marriages in a given time stated, with the rate of fees taken by the persons officiating.

Parochial Registration :

15.—Report from the Select Committee on the general state of Parochial Registers, and the Laws relating to them ; and on a general Registration of Births, Baptisms, Marriages, Deaths and Burials, in England and Wales.

Sess. 1833, (669.) vol. 14, p. 5.

SUBJECTS.—History and state of the law respecting Parochial Registration—defects therein.—Forms of registration adopted in foreign countries, compared with those in use in this country.—Necessity for the establishment of a national civil registration of births, marriages and deaths, to be open to persons of every religious denomination.—Mode of carrying the same into effect.

XXIV.

Army and Navy.

ARMY.

Land Forces and Marines, 1746 :

1.—⌈Report from the Select Committee appointed to consider the state of His Majesty's Land Forces and Marines.

First Series, vol. ii. p. 73.

SUBJECTS.—Establishment of the army—its increase—compared with different periods—its general management—abuses.—Agents of the army—nature of their business—emoluments—purchase of their appointments.—Clothing the army—application of off-reckonings to that purpose—responsibility of colonels—and advantages derived by them from the clothing system.—Colonels and officers—advantages derived by them from the clothing—from vacant pay—sale of commissions, &c. &c.—Marine establishment—deficiency of musters—abuse in clothing—delay in issuing the clearings and pay.—Mustering the army—inquiry into the method in practice—defective muster-rolls—abuses—non-effective, warrant, or fictitious men—vacant or respited pay.—Pay of the army—money granted—balances in paymasters' hands—misapplication.—Recruiting—method of carrying on that service—fund for defraying charges, how created.—Stoppages from soldiers' pay.

Military Inquiry, 1806–1816 :

Reports of the Commissioners of Military Inquiry, appointed by Act 45 Geo. 3, c. 47, to inquire into the Management of the Military Department, and into the means of preventing Abuses therein :

2.—First Report of the Commissioners.

Sess. 1806, (46.) vol. 6, p. 1. [125.]

SUBJECT.—*Barrack Office.*—Arrears of Accounts.

3.—Second Report.

Sess. 1806, (317.) vol. 6, p. 115. [125.]

SUBJECT.—*Barrack Office.*—Establishment.

4.—Third Report.

Sess. 1806–7, (4.) vol. 2, p. 201. [125.]

SUBJECT.—*Barrack Department.*—Stores and Supplies.

5.—Fourth Report : with a Supplement to the First and Third Reports.

SUBJECT.—*Barrack Department.*—Buildings. Sess. 1806–7, (99.) vol. 2, p. 213. [125.]

6.—Fifth Report.

Sess. 1808, (6.) vol. 5, p. 1. [125.]

SUBJECT.—*Army.*—Medical Department.

7.—Sixth Report : with a Supplement to the Fifth Report.

Sess. 1808, (327.) vol. 5, p. 275. [126.]

SUBJECTS.—*War Office.*—Establishment.—Regimental accounts.—Agency and clothing.

8.—Seventh Report.

Sess. 1809, (3.) vol. 5, p. 1. [126.]

SUBJECTS.—*War Office.*—Department of Foreign Accounts ; and the Chaplain General.

9.—Eighth Report.

Sess. 1809, (4.) vol. 5, p. 123. [126.]

SUBJECT.—*War Office.*—Department of Miscellaneous Accounts.

10.—Ninth Report.

Sess. 1809, (141.) vol. 5, p. 269. [126.]

SUBJECT.—Army expenditure in the West Indies.

11.—Tenth Report.

Sess. 1810, (78.) vol. 9, p. 189. [126.]

SUBJECT.—Royal Military College.

12.—Eleventh Report : with a Supplement to the Eighth Report.

Sess. 1810, (79.) vol. 9, p. 293. [126.]

SUBJECT.—Adjutant and Quartermaster general's departments.

Military Inquiry, 1806—1816—*continued.*

13.—Twelfth Report of the Commissioners of Military Inquiry.

Sess. 1810, (81.) vol. 9, p. 457. [127.]

Subject.—Treasurer of the Ordnance.

14.—Thirteenth Report.   Sess. 1810–11, (32.) vol. 4, p. 1. [127.]

Subject.—Master-general and Board of Ordnance.

15.—Fourteenth Report.   Sess. 1810–11, (135.) vol. 4, p. 243. [127.]

Subject.—Ordnance estimates.

16.—Fifteenth Report.   Sess. 1810–11, (261.) vol. 4, p. 305. [127.]

Subjects.—*Ordnance Department.*—Fortifications and Buildings.—Barracks.—Small-gun department.—Shipping.

17.—Sixteenth Report.   Sess. 1812, (4.) vol. 4, p. 1. [127.]

Subjects.—*Ordnance Department.*—Contracts, &c.—Royal laboratory.—Inspection of artillery, &c.—Royal Carriage department.

18.—Seventeenth Report.   Sess. 1812, (5.) vol. 4, p. 137. [127.]

Subjects.—*Ordnance Department.*—Military accounts.—Field-train department.—Royal artillery drivers.—Deputy adjutant-general of artillery.—Medical department.—Royal Military Academy at Woolwich.—Trigonometrical Survey of Great Britain.

19.—Eighteenth Report.   Sess. 1812, (119.) vol. 4, p. 247. [127.]

Subject.—Commissariat.

20.—Nineteenth Report.   Sess. 1812, (251.) vol. 4, p. 371. [127.]

Subjects.—Chelsea Hospital, and Commissary of Musters.—Royal Asylum.

21.—General Index to the Nineteen Reports.   Sess. 1816, (51.) vol. 10, p. 371. [127.]

NAVY.

Naval Timber, 1771 :

22.—[Report from the Select Committee on the state of Naval Timber.

First Series, vol. iii. p. 13.

Subjects.—Scarcity; how occasioned.—Means for obtaining a better supply.———
See likewise in Land Revenue Reports, under Head XII., No. 46.

Naval Volunteers, 1780 :

23.—[Report from the Select Committee on the better Regulation of Mariners in the Merchant Service ; and respecting the proposed Plan for the encouragement of Volunteers to enter on board Ships of War.

First Series, vol. x., p. 762.

Subjects.—Proposed plan for a general register to be kept of all persons bound to the sea, not belonging to any of His Majesty's ships or vessels.—A fellowship of seamen to be formed, and the benefits resulting therefrom.—Marine offices to be established in different parts for carrying the plan into execution.

Naval Inquiry, 1803–1806 :

Reports of the Commissioners appointed by an Act of 43 Geo. 3, for inquiring into Irregularities, Frauds and Abuses practised in the Naval Departments, and in the Business of Prize Agency :

24.—First Report.   Sess. 1802-3, (78.) vol. 4, p. 163. [128.]

Subject.—Naval storekeepers at Jamaica.

25.—Second Report.   Sess. 1802-3, (97.) vol. 4, p. 115. [128.]

Subject.—Chest at Chatham.

26.—Third Report.   Sess. 1802-3, (109.) vol. 4, p. 173. [128.]

Subject.—Block and coopers' contracts.

27.—Fourth Report.   Sess. 1802-3, (160.) vol. 4, p. 249. [128.]

Subject.—Prize agency.

Naval Inquiry, 1803–1806—continued.

28.—Fifth Report of the Commissioners for inquiring into Irregularities, &c. in Naval Departments. 　　　　Sess. 1802-3, (174.) vol. 4, p. 327. [128.]
　　　　SUBJECT.—Sixpenny Office.

29.—Sixth Report of the Commissioners. 　　Sess. 1803-4, (83.) vol. 3, p. 1. [128.]
　　　　SUBJECT.—Plymouth and Woolwich Yards.

30.—Seventh Report of the Commissioners. 　Sess. 1803-4, (172.) vol. 3, p. 541. [129.]
　　　　SUBJECTS.—Naval Hospital at East Stonehouse.—Le Caton hospital ship.

31.—Eighth Report of the Commissioners. 　Sess. 1803-4, (179.) vol. 3, p. 637. [129.]
　　　　SUBJECTS.—Victualling Department at Plymouth.—Embezzling casks.

32.—Ninth Report of the Commissioners. 　　Sess. 1805, (1.) vol. 2, p. 1. [129.]
　　　　SUBJECT.—Plymouth Yard.

33.—Tenth Report of the Commissioners. 　　Sess. 1805, (21.) vol. 2, p. 125. [129.]
　　　　SUBJECT.—Treasurer of the Navy.

34.—Eleventh Report of the Commissioners. 　Sess. 1805, (47.) vol. 2, p. 481. [129.]
　　　　SUBJECTS.—Issue of Navy bills for the purpose of raising money.—Loss arising from the mode of paying the interest on Navy and Transport bills.—Money imprested by the Navy Board for secret naval services.

35.—Twelfth Report of the Commissioners. 　Sess. 1806, (1.) vol. 4, p. 1. [130.]
　　　　SUBJECTS.—Purchases of hemp, masts, and fir timber.—Transfer of contracts.—Observations by way of Supplement to First Report.

36.—Thirteenth Report of the Commissioners. 　Sess. 1806, (161.) vol. 4, p. 361. [130.]
　　　　SUBJECT.—Contracts for victualling sick prisoners of war.

37.—Fourteenth Report of the Commissioners. 　Sess. 1806, (256.) vol 4, p. 523. [130.]
　　　　SUBJECT.—Greenwich Hospital.

Treasurership of the Navy, 1805 :

38.—Report from the Select Committee upon the Tenth Naval Inquiry Report of Commissioners. 　　　　Sess. 1805, (140.) vol. 2, p. 535. [131.]
　　　　SUBJECT.—Treasurer of the Navy.

39.—Report from the Select Committee upon the Eleventh Naval Inquiry Report of the Commissioners. 　　Sess. 1805, (184.) vol. 2, p. 659. [131.]
　　　　SUBJECTS.—Issue of Navy bills for the purpose of raising money.—Loss arising from the mode of paying the interest on Navy and Transport bills.—Money imprested by the Navy Board for secret naval services.

40.—Report from the Committee of Secrecy on the Eleventh Report of Commissioners of Naval Inquiry. 　Sess. 1805, (198.) vol. 2, p. 767. [131.]
　　　　SUBJECT.—Advance of 100,000 *l.* for a secret naval service.

41.—Letter from Lord Viscount Melville to the Commissioners of Inquiry ; and Answer. 　　　　Sess. 1805, (72.) vol. 2, p. 773. [131.]

42.—Precepts issued by the Commissioners of Naval Inquiry to the Treasurer of the Navy. 　　　　Sess. 1805, (93.) vol. 2, p. 777. [131.]

43.—Letter from the Comptroller of the Navy to the Lords Commissioners of the Admiralty, on the Eleventh Report of the Commissioners of Naval Inquiry. 　　　　Sess. 1805, (94.) vol 2, p. 793. [131.]

44.—Letter from the principal Officers and Commissioners of the Navy, to the Secretary of the Admiralty ; enclosing a Memorial, in Answer to the First Report of the Commissioners of Naval Inquiry.
　　　　Sess. 1805, (100.) vol. 2, p. 803. [131.]

Naval Revision, 1806–1809 :

Reports of the Commissioners for Revising and Digesting the Civil Affairs of His Majesty's Navy :

45.—First Report of the Commissioners.   Sess. 1806, (8.) vol. 5, p. 1. [**132.**]

46.—Second Report of the Commissioners.   Sess. 1806, (92.) vol. 5, p. 245. [**132.**]

47.—Third Report of the Commissioners.   Sess. 1806, (312.) vol. 5, p. 415. [**132.**]
    SUBJECT.—Dock Yards.

48.—Fourth Report of the Commissioners.   Sess. 1809, (120.) vol. 6, p. 1. [**133.**]
    SUBJECT.—Navy Office.

49.—Fifth Report of the Commissioners.   Sess. 1809, (121.) vol. 6, p. 61. [**133.**]
    SUBJECT.—Foreign Yards.

50.—Sixth Report of the Commissioners.   Sess. 1809, (122.) vol. 6, p. 101. [**133.**]
    SUBJECT.—Dock Yards at the Outports.

51.—Seventh Report of the Commissioners.   Sess. 1809, (123.) vol. 6, p. 121. [**133.**]
    SUBJECT.—Naval Hospitals.

  Eighth Report—not printed.

52.—Ninth Report of the Commissioners.   Sess. 1809, (124.) vol 6, p. 189. [**133.**]
    SUBJECT.—Transport Office.

53.—Tenth Report of the Commissioners.   Sess. 1809, (125.) vol. 6, p. 221. [**133.**]
    SUBJECT.—Victualling Office.

54.—Eleventh Report of the Commissioners.   Sess. 1809, (126.) vol. 6, p. 261. [**133.**]
    SUBJECT.—Victualling Establishments at Outports.

55.—Twelfth Report of the Commissioners.   Sess. 1809, (127.) vol. 6, p. 389. [**133.**]
    SUBJECT.—Victualling Department Abroad.

56.—Thirteenth Report of the Commissioners.   Sess. 1809, (128.) vol. 6, p. 413. [**133.**]
    SUBJECT.—Transport Board.

Army and Navy Appointments :

57.—Report from the Select Committee on Army and Navy Appointments.
                      Sess. 1833, (650.) vol. 7, p. 1.

SUBJECTS.—No accurate account of the origin of the home garrisons.—Number of foreign garrisons in which permanent non-residence is permitted.—No garrison appointments in future to be made where no efficient military duty is performed.—Recommendation that the King should be empowered to grant rewards for distinguished services in the army, and condition on which they are to be granted.—Pay and allowances of general officers holding the situation of colonels of regiments.—All profits under the head of non-effective allowances for warrant-men should be abolished.—Some arrangement necessary by which off-reckonings might be issued to colonels at an earlier period, and so reduce the rate of interest now charged by their clothier.—Allowance to colonels of cavalry in India for wear and tear of accoutrements ought to be discontinued.—Staff-pay of general officers has undergone no change since 1685.—Pay and emoluments of other general officers.—No addition should be made to the present list of general officers.—Reductions suggested in the pay of certain officers.—Situations of vice-admiral and rear-admiral of England should remain on their present footing.—Generals and colonels of marines may with propriety be abolished as they become vacant.—No addition to the number of flag-officers in the navy in future to be made, except upon very strong grounds of public necessity.——*See likewise* further concerning *Army,* under Head XV., No. 54.

XXV.

Public Offices.

Fees, Perquisites, &c. in England, 1786–1788 :

1.—Ten Reports of the Commissioners appointed by Act 25 Geo. 3, c. 19, to inquire into the Fees, Perquisites and Emoluments which are, or have been lately, received in the several Public Offices therein mentioned. Dated in 1786, 1787, and 1788.
Sess. 1806, (309.) vol. 7. [28.]

SUBJECTS.—

First Report ; Secretaries of State	p. 3.
Second Report ; Treasury	p. 49.
Third Report ; Admiralty	p. 93.
Fourth Report ; Treasurer of the Navy	p. 131.
Fifth Report ; Commissioners of the Navy	p. 165.
Sixth Report ; Dock-yards	p. 277.
Seventh Report ; Sick and Hurt Office	p. 507.
Eighth Report ; Victualling Office	p. 549.
Ninth Report ; Naval and Victualling Departments Abroad	p. 723.
Tenth Report ; Post-office	p. 755.

Fees, Perquisites, &c. in Ireland, 1806–1814 :

Reports of the Commissioners appointed to inquire into the Fees, Gratuities, Perquisites and Emoluments which are, or have been lately, received in certain Public Offices in Ireland ; and also to examine into any Abuses which may exist in the same ; and into the present mode of receiving, collecting, issuing and accounting for Public Money in Ireland.

2.—First Report of Commissioners of Inquiry. Sess. 1806, (6.) vol 8, p. 1. [29.]
SUBJECT.—Customs.

3.—Second Report of Commissioners of Inquiry.
SUBJECT.—Stamps. Sess. 1806, (270.) vol. 8, p. 387. [29.]

4.—Third Report of Commissioners of Inquiry. Sess. 1806-7, (1.) vol. 6, p. 1. [29.]
SUBJECT.—Assessed Taxes.

5.—Fourth Report of Commissioners of Inquiry.
SUBJECT.—Land Revenue of the Crown. Sess. 1806–7, (2.) vol 6, p. 45. [29.]

6.—Fifth Report of Commissioners of Inquiry. Sess. 1806–7, (124.) vol. 6, p. 139. [29.]
SUBJECT.—Excise—Distillation.

7.—Sixth Report of Commissioners of Inquiry. Sess. 1808, (4.) vol. 3, p. 461. [29.]
SUBJECT.—Excise—Malt.

8.—Seventh Report of Commissioners of Inquiry. Sess. 1809, (15.) vol. 7. p. 1. [29.]
SUBJECTS.—Excise—Auctions ; Cards and Dice ; Glass Bottles ; Hides and Skins ; Paper ; Paper Hangings ; Tobacco and Wrought Plate.

9.—Eighth Report of Commissioners of Inquiry. Sess. 1809, (52.) vol. 7, p. 83. [29.]
SUBJECT.—Mode of accounting for Excise Duties.

Fees, Perquisites, &c. in Ireland, 1806–1814 —*continued.*

10.—Ninth Report of Commissioners of Inquiry into Public Offices, Ireland.

SUBJECT.—General Post-Office.   Sess. 1810, (5.) vol. 10, p. 1. [30.]

11.—Supplement to the Ninth Report of the Commissioners, on the same subject.

Sess. 1810, (366.) vol. 10, p. 94. [30.]

12.—Tenth Report of Commissioners of Inquiry.

Sess. 1810, (234.) vol. 10, p. 141. [30.]

SUBJECT.—Arrears and Balances.

13.—Memorial of the Attorney and Solicitor Generals of Ireland on the Eighth and Tenth Reports.   Sess. 1812, (70.) vol. 5, p. 385.

14.—Supplement to the Eighth and Tenth Reports of Commissioners of Inquiry.

Sess. 1812, (35.) vol. 5, p. 295. [30.]

SUBJECT.—Reply to the Memorial of the Attorney and Solicitor Generals.

15.—First Part of the Eleventh Report of Commissioners of Inquiry.

Sess. 1810–11, (55) vol. 6, p. 939. [30.]

16.—Second Part of the Eleventh Report of Commissioners of Inquiry.

Sess. 1812, (34.) vol. 5, p. 432. [30.]

17.—Third Part of the Eleventh Report of Commissioners of Inquiry.

SUBJECT.—Arrears and Balances.   Sess. 1812–13, (123.) vol 6, p. 241. [30.]

18.—Twelfth Report of Commissioners of Inquiry.

SUBJECT.—Board of Works.   Sess. 1812, (33.) vol. 5, p. 191. [30.]

19.—Thirteenth Report of Commissioners of Inquiry.

SUBJECT.—Inland Navigation.   Sess. 1812–13, (61.) vol. 6, p. 317. [30.]

20.—Fourteenth Report of Commissioners of Inquiry.

SUBJECT.—Treasury.   Sess. 1813–14, (102.) vol. 7, p. 1. [30.]

Sinecure Offices, 1810–1812 :

21.—First Report from the Select Committee on the Second, Third and Fourth Resolutions of the House on the Third Report of the Committee on Public Expenditure.   Sess. 1810, (362.) vol. 3, p. 591. [45.]

22.—Second Report from the same Committee.

Sess. 1810–11, (246.) vol. 2, p. 961. [45.]

23.—Third Report from the same Committee.   Sess. 1812, (181.) vol. 2, p. 191. [45.]

see *Public Expenditure,* and *Finance,* under Head X.

1834 :

24.—Report from the Select Committee on Papers and Returns respecting the Nature, Tenure and Emoluments of all Sinecure Offices within the United Kingdom.   Sess. 1834, (519.) vol. 6, p. 339.

SUBJECTS.—Number of returns of offices.—How many effective offices and sinecures.—Objectionable nature of offices with emoluments and without duty —Under what tenure or condition held.—Should be abolished, making compensation to holders.—Others should be regulated —Grants of offices to be bought up —Patent of the Customs' bill of entry.—Nature of grant and emoluments —Suitors of King's Bench money in the hands of the chief clerk.—Interest of balances should not be his perquisite, but be carried to the public account ——Total number of sinecures, and annual amount of income.

Reduction of Salaries :

For Report of Offices held during the pleasure of the Crown by Members of either House of Parliament—see *Members,* under Head IV., No. 27.

Official Houses :

25.—First Report from the Select Committee on the practicability of Diminishing the number of Houses and Apartments now occupied by Public Officers at
the Public Expense.

Sess. 1834, (480.) vol. 11, p. 449.

SUBJECT.—Expediency of providing some accommodation for the Librarian of the House
of Commons.—The house in Cotton-garden, temporarily occupied by Mr. O'Hanlon,
might conveniently be appropriated as a residence for the Librarian.

26.—Second Report from the Select Committee on the practicability of diminishing the number of Houses and Apartments occupied by Public Officers at
the Public Expense.

Sess. 1834, (558.) vol. 11, p. 453.

SUBJECTS.—No necessity for any of the officers of the Ordnance in Great Britain and
Ireland to have houses, with the exception of the storekeeper and barrack-master.—The
duties of the paymaster of the forces does not require that he should reside on the spot.—
Very necessary for the public service that the Lords of the Admiralty should have official
residences.—Number of official apartments, &c. occupied by the different officers of the
Royal Hospital, Chelsea.—Inconvenient to transfer the Recruiting-office to the Horse-
guards.—Necessity for the Physician of the Navy having a residence attached to his office.
—Duties of the comptroller of the Victualling and Transport require constant attendance
at Somerset House.—Number of houses in the Tower occupied by officers in the civil
department of the Ordnance.—Officers connected with the public service that require to
be furnished with official houses.

XXVI.

Miscellaneous.

Arigna Mining Company, 1827 :

1.—Report from the Select Committee on the origin, management and present state of the Arigna Iron and Coal Mining Company.

Sess. 1826–27, (234.) vol. 3, p. 37.

SUBJECTS.—On the contrivances used to originate speculative joint-stock companies, and the artificial modes of raising the nominal value of shares, for the benefit of the contrivers, by jobbing them.—Fictitious sale of property in Ireland from one of the projectors to the Company, and division of the difference between the nominal and real price among the directors.—Prevalence at this period of schemes for forming fictitious companies, for the purpose of giving an opportunity of the schemes to take advantage of the eagerness of the public to possess themselves of shares, and pay high premiums above the subscribed price.

Baron de Bode :

2.—Report from the Select Committee of Inquiry into the Claim of the Baron de Bode upon the Fund received from the French Government for indemnifying British Subjects for the Loss of Property unduly confiscated by French Authority.

Sess. 1834, (583.) vol. 18, p. 359.

Calcutta Journal :

3.—Report from the Select Committee for considering the circumstances connected with the Suppression of the Calcutta Journal in 1823, and as to the Loss of Property by Mr. Buckingham in consequence.

Sess. 1834, (601.) vol. 8, p. 1.

SUBJECTS.—Circumstances under which the Calcutta Journal was established.—Prosperous condition thereof.—Mr. Buckingham ordered to quit India by the acting Governor-general.—Suppression of the Journal by order of the Governor-general.—Injury sustained by Mr. Buckingham.—Compensation should be made him for the loss of his property.

Charitable Corporation, 1732–1733 :

4.—[Two Reports from the Select Committee on the Petition of the Proprietors of the Charitable Corporation for Relief of Industrious Poor, by assisting them with small Sums on Pledges at legal Interest.

First Series, vol. 1., pp. 363. 537.

SUBJECTS.—Objects and incorporation of the Establishment. and who had the chief management.—-Abuses in the management.—Misconduct of the directors.—Embezzlement and misapplication of property by officers or servants.

Conveyance and Porterage of Parcels :

5.—Report from the Select Committee on the Conveyance and Porterage of Parcels.

Sess. 1825, (498.) vol. 5, p. 255. [134.]

SUBJECTS.—*Inconvenience from the present Regulations.*—Laws on the subject.—Competition has superseded the necessity of statute laws.—Repeal of them recommended.—Act respecting porterage from coach-offices requires amendment.

Cruelty to Animals :

6.—Report from the Select Committee on the Bill relating to the cruel and improper treatment of Animals, and the mischiefs arising from the driving of Cattle.

Sess. 1831–32, (667.) vol. 5, p. 73.

SUBJECTS.—Cruelty to animals by stealers of cats and dogs in skinning them alive ; reasons for so doing.—In fighting dogs at dog-pits.—In making dogs draw trucks.—Some account of famous fighting-dogs, and of their value.—Description of persons concerned in dog-fighting.—Mode of treating dogs when wounded and exhausted.—Best fighting-dogs, and mode of training.—Cock-fighting ; patronized by persons of rank.—In fighting the badger.—Hyprophobia propagated by dog-fighting.———And *see* under Head XX., No. 25.

Drunkenness :

7.—Report from the Select Committee of Inquiry into the extent, causes and consequences of the prevailing Vice of Intoxication among the Labouring Classes.   Sess. 1834, (559.) vol. 8, p. 315.

SUBJECTS.—Extent of the evil of drunkenness.—Remote causes.—Immediate causes of its extension.—Its consequences to individual character.—Consequences to national welfare. —Great loss of productive labour in every department of occupation.—Extensive loss of property by sea from shipwrecks, &c.—Comparative inefficiency of the navy and army.— Increase of pauperism.—Spread of crime.—Sum expended in the purchase of intoxicating drinks.—Remedies to be applied.—Separation of houses in which intoxicating drinks are sold into four distinct classes.—Limiting the number thereof.—Closing them at an earlier hour.—Discontinuance of the issues of ardent spirits to the navy and army.—Reduction of the duty on teas, &c.—Encouragement of temperance societies.— National system of education.—Prospective remedies.—Examples of other countries.—National cost of intoxication, and its consequences, are greater in amount than that of the poor-rates.

Fire Prevention, 1774 :

8.—[Report from the Select Committee on Mr. David Heartley's Experiments respecting the Prevention of Fire.   Journals, vol. 34, p. 746.

SUBJECTS.—The plan proposed is to preserve buildings by the application of iron-plates between the ceiling and joists, forming a sheathing.—The plan described.—And the Appendix contains some observations on the peculiarities of buildings which render them combustible.

Hackney Coach-office :

9.—Report from the Select Committee on the Duties and Salaries of the Commissioners for regulating Hackney-coaches, on the present state of Public Carriages, and the Laws affecting the same.   Sess. 1830, (515.) vol. 10, p. 301.

SUBJECTS.—On the manner of managing and licensing hackney-coaches and cabriolets. —The regulation of drivers and watermen.—A police jurisdiction.—Regulation of fares and distances.—Outlay and profit of cabriolets and hackney-coaches.—Mode of letting out on hire.—Establishment of omnibuses running between the Bank and Paddington.—Description of similar vehicles in Paris.———On the management of hawkers' and pedlars' licences by the Hackney-coach office.

Insects, 1781–1784 :

10.—[Reports from the Select Committee on the Petition of Henry Phillips for the Discovery of a Composition for destroying Insects.
   Journals, vol. 38, p. 467 ; vol. 39, p. 1031.

SUBJECTS.—Experiments to show the efficacy of the powder ;—on fruit trees ;—on weevils in granaries ;—on insects on board ships.—Certificates of its effects on board several of His Majesty's ships.

Lotteries, 1792 :

11.—[Report from the Select Committee on the Laws for preventing illegal Insurances, and other Evils attending the Drawing of the State Lotteries.
   Journals, vol. 47, p. 809.

SUBJECTS.—Nature of the evils.—Inefficacy of the laws in the metropolis.—How the illegal practices are carried on.—Insurance bets collected by persons going from house to house, who are paid a commission.—A kind of exchange kept, at which insurances taken by those collectors are transferred.—Tardiness of the magistrates in making convictions.— Books with numerical columns for taking insurances regularly sold.—Evidence of pawn-brokers as to the increase of pawns during the drawing of the lottery.—Representation of the London and Middlesex grand jury, condemning the lottery.—Persons committed as vagrants for making illegal insurances.

1808 :

12.—Reports from the Select Committee on the Laws relating to Lotteries.
   Sess. 1808, (182. 323.) vol. 2, pp. 147. 151. [134.]

SUBJECTS.—The First Report is one merely of Resolutions.—The Second states the laws relating to lotteries ; points out inveterate evils which no law can mend ; and condemns, in very forcible language, the system altogether.

Glasgow Lottery :

13.—First Report from the Select Committee on the origin and present state of a Lottery, purporting to be carried on under the authority of Parliament, intituled " The Glasgow Lottery ;" and of any other Lotteries, of which, since the discontinuance of State Lotteries, Schemes, Tickets, &c. have been circulated. Sess. 1834, (279.) vol. 18, p. 87.

> SUBJECTS.—Legislative interference with the drawing of the Glasgow Lottery announced for the present year not necessary.—Bill to be introduced declaring the continuance of the lottery beyond the present drawing to be illegal.

14.—Second Report from the Select Committee on the same subject.

Sess. 1834, (560.) vol. 18, p. 91.

> SUBJECTS.—Origin of the Glasgow Lottery Bill.—Extent to which the powers of that Bill have been exceeded.—Not a money lottery.—Inadequacy of the present forms of the House with respect to private Bills.—Concealment was intended and practised throughout the whole period of the Bill being before the House.—Promoters of the Bill did not expect any more than a pecuniary relief from the passing of the Bill.—Proposal made to Government, after the passing of the Act, by the Glasgow Improvement Commissioners.—Debts of the Commissioners.—Valuation of the property assigned by them to the lottery contractors, and amount paid by them for the same.—Refusal by Government to lend the wheels formerly used in the old State lotteries.

Stationery-office :

15.—First Report from the Select Committee on the Allegations contained in the Petition of several Stationers and Manufacturers of Paper.

Sess. 1833, (673.) vol. 16, p. 39.

> SUBJECTS.—Management of the Stationery-office in entering into contracts.—Alleged corruptions with which the appointment of Mr. Kingsmill Grove Key has been in some degree connected.—Mode of taking security of contractors.

16.—Second Report from the same Committee. Sess. 1833, (674.) vol. 16, p. 99.

> SUBJECTS.—Contracts entered into with Mr. Jonathan Muckleston Key, who is alleged to be the nominal contractor, while his brother, Sir John Key, is the real contractor, and he at the same time a Member of Parliament.—Appointment of Mr. Kingsmill Grove Key, son of Sir John Key, to be storekeeper at the Stationery-office, a youth of 18 or 19 years of age.—His employment in the capacity of storekeeper to examine the paper supplied by the contractors, his relations.—His appointment cancelled.—Sir John Key vacates his seat in Parliament.

York Buildings' Company, 1733–1735 :

17.—[Three Reports from the Select Committee on the Petition of the Proprietors of the Company for raising the Thames Water in York Buildings.

First Series, vol. I., pp. 581. 655. 687.

> SUBJECTS.—Origin, progress, object, and present state of the Company.—Of the affairs of the Company.—Erection of the waterworks.—Engage in mining.—Become purchasers of Scotch Forfeited Estates.—Abuses and mismanagement.—Misconduct of the governors and assistants.

Additions.

Tithes in London, 1819 : [*Insert at p. 2, after article* 7.
Report from the Select Committee on the Petition of the London Clergy.
Sess. 1819, (105.) vol. 8.

SUBJECTS.—Claims of the clergy to sums in lieu of tithes, as regulated by an Act passed soon after the Fire of London in 1666.—The Appendix contains a list of the parishes, and the amount of tithes, according to the valuation in 1638, compared with their present value as augmented in 1834.

Alterations in a Bill, 1809 : [*Insert at p.* 27, *after article* 48.
Report of the Select Committee appointed to inquire into the circumstances relating to an Alteration which had been improperly made in the ingrossed copy of a Bill; with Minutes of Evidence.
Sess. 1809, (24. 208.) vol. 3, p. 177. 193.

SUBJECTS.—Improper alteration by substituting *Great Britain* for *England* in a Bill respecting duties on spirits distilled from sugar, by which a prohibition was extended to Scotland, contrary to the intention of the Bill.—No imputation of improper intention on the part of the clerk by whose means the alteration was made; but the irregular manner of examining the ingrossments on the third reading pointed out, and a remedy recommended.

Public Funded Debt, 1802 : [*Insert at p.* 72, *after article* 3.
Accounts respecting the Public Funded Debt of Great Britain, and the Reduction thereof, to the 1st of February 1802; together with CALCULATIONS showing the effect of the Sinking Fund, created *before* the War, in the Reduction of the National Debt then existing, at different prices of Stock; and of the periods at which such Debt would be wholly redeemed by the Sinking Fund applicable thereto.—Secondly : Similar Estimates and Calculations, showing the effect of the Sinking Fund, created *since* the commencement of the War, on the Debt which has been incurred within the same period.—Thirdly : showing the effect which the Old and New Sinking Funds would have if *consolidated*, and operating at compound interest, without limitation, upon the whole of the National Debt now existing, or to be created within the present Session of Parliament. Sess. 1801–2, (52. 94*.) vol. 4, p. 190. 205.

Longitude : [*Insert at p.* 113, *after article* 33.
Report of the Select Committee on the Petition of Thomas Earnshaw, Watchmaker.
Sess. 1809, (245.) vol. 3, p. 403.

SUBJECTS.—Claim of Mr. Earnshaw for an addition to the reward assigned to him by the Board of Longitude for making timekeepers.—Merit of timekeepers constructed by Mr. Arnold and others.—Insufficiency of grounds for interfering in the determination of the Board.

Duke of York, 1809 : [*Insert at p.* 180, *after article* 21.
Minutes of Evidence taken before the Committee of the whole House, upon the conduct of His Royal Highness the Commander-in-Chief.
Sess. 1809, (20.) vol. 2, p. 1.

SUBJECT.—Charges of misconduct in disposing of the patronage of the Army, under the corrupt influence of Mrs. Mary Ann Clarke, and others.

Scheldt Expedition, 1810 :
Minutes of Evidence taken before the Committee of the whole House, on the Policy and Conduct of the late Expedition. Sess. 1810, (12.) vol. 8.

For other Papers and Accounts on this subject, *see* the *General Index to Parliamentary Papers.*

ERRATA.

p. 2, *before article 10, insert as a sub-head* Ecclesiastical Revenues, 1834 :

p. 10, *before article 28, insert as a sub-head* Returns in 1820 :

p. 18, *in articles 56, 57, for* regulation *read* rejection.

p. 26, *article 32 should be under the head* Parliament.

p. 29, *article 78, insert* 1802 *in the sub-head.*

p. 48, *article 41, for* Report *read* Reports.

p. 64, *article 73, in the sub-head, for* 1834 *read* 1824.

p. 78, *before article 2 insert* 1810–11 :

p. 79, *article 12, in the sub-head, for* 1696–1797 : *read* 1696–1697 :

p. 83, *article 16, line 13, for* Fanning *read* Tanning.

p. 89, *article 64, for* Pall-mall-street *read* Pall-mall-east.

p. 89, *before article 65, insert as a sub-head,* Woods, Forests and Land Revenues, 1833–1834 :

p. 93, *before article 19, insert as a sub-head,* China-trade, 1812 :

p. 117, *before article 62, insert as a sub-head,* Weights and Measures, 1813–1834 :

p. 131, *article 73, insert a bracket before Report, thus* [Report

p. 152, *article 40 should be under the head* Prisons.

INDEX.

INDEX.

Good-will of Premises, p. 87.
On the difficulty of adjusting claims, *see* report on woods, forests and land revenue, No. 50.

Grady, T. W. p. 24.
In report on bargaining for election influence, No. 10.

Grampound Election, p. 35, Nos. 137–139.

Grand Jury Presentments, Ireland, p. 150.
Reports on the methods of raising money, collecting, and abuses in application, Nos. 26–32.

Grant, Mr. p. 98.
Paper of observations on the state of society among the Asiatic subjects of Great Britain, No. 49.

Great Grimsby Election, p. 35, No. 140.

Greathead, Mr. p. 70.
Report on his life-boat, Nos. 20, 21.

Greenwich Hospital, p. 181.
In report of naval inquiry, No. 37.

Greig, Mr. p. 102.
In papers relating to the South African Commercial Advertiser, No. 18.

Grenada, p. 105.
In report on administration of justice in the West Indies, No. 47.

Greville, p. 110.
Collection of minerals, *see* report on the British Museum, No. 5.

Griffith, Mr. p. 117.
Report of the progress in surveying the southern district of Ireland, No. 58.

Griffith, Richard, p. 142–144.
In report on roads in Ireland, No. 220.
In papers on improvement of Pobble-ô-Keefe's lands, No. 231.
His report respecting the Kilkenny canal, No. 237.

Gum Senega, p. 58.
Report on the importation and use, No. 28.

Gurney, Mr. p. 121.
Report on his improvements on steam-carriages, No. 20.

H.

Habeas Corpus, p. 17.
Report on issuing them during vacation, Nos. 55.

Habeas Corpus suspension, p. 38.
In reports in 1801 on the state of Ireland, and the proceedings of disaffected persons, No. 4.
In report in 1819 on the proceedings of disaffected persons, No. 8.

Hackney-coaches, p. 187.
Report on the manner of managing and licensing, No. 9.

Haileybury College, p. 95.
In reports on East India affairs, No. 24.

Hainault Forest, p. 87.
On disafforesting it, *see* report on woods, forests and land revenue, No. 50.

Hammond, Mr. p. 16.
In report on consolidation of criminal law, No. 41.

Handloom Weavers, p. 58.
Report on the state of their trade, distress, inadequate wages, and remedies, No. 29.

Hansard, Messrs.
In report on establishments of the House, p. 29, No. 77.
In report on library and printed reports, p. 30, Nos. 86, 87. 89, 90. 97.
In report on parliamentary printing, p. 32, No. 96.
In report on public documents, p. 33, No. 100.
In report on public expenditure, p. 73, No. 18.
In preface to catalogue of the library, p. 31, No. 91.

Harbour Dues, p. 68.
In report on foreign trade, Nos. 8. 10.

Harbours, p. 131–145.
Ardglass, No. 232.
Dublin and Kingstown, No. 236.
Dunmore, see report on public works, No. 225.
Holyhead, Nos. 101–104. 128. 131–133. 136. 138, 139. 141.
Howth, Nos. 128. 131–133. 136. 138, 139. 141, 233.
Lyme Regis, Nos. 80–90.
Milford, Nos. 73–77.

Harbours—continued.
Plymouth, Nos. 78, 79.
Portpatrick, No. 91.
Ramsgate, No. 70 ; and *see* reports on foreign trade, p. 68, Nos. 8. 10. 12.
Rye and Dover, Nos. 71, 72.
Papers respecting the western harbours of Ireland, No. 239.
In reports on Highland roads and bridges, No. 154.
In report on post-office communication with Ireland, No. 222.
In report on public works, Ireland, Nos. 224, 225.

Harbours, Ireland, p. 145.
Evidence respecting the advantages of the western harbours, for the sailing of packets to America, No. 239.
On the improvement of, *see* report on state of the poor, p. 163, No. 52.

Harbours, Railroads and Canals, Ireland:
Ardglass harbour, p. 144, No. 232.
Dublin ship-canal, Nos. 235, 236.
Dunmore, see report on public works, No. 225.
Howth harbour, No. 233.
Kilkenny canal, No. 237.
Kingstown harbour and railroad, Nos. 225. 234.
In reports on public works, p. 143, Nos. 224, 225.

Hargrave, F., p. 110.
Report on his collection of books and MSS. No. 6.

Harrison, John, p. 112.
Report on his claims for the construction of a time-keeper for ascertaining the longitude, No. 30.

Harvey, Daniel Whittle, p. 18.
Reports respecting the rejection of his claim to be called to the bar, Nos. 56–58.

Hastings, Warren, p. 23.
Report respecting his impeachment, No. 3.

Hat Manufacture, p. 58.
On the state of the trade in 1752, No. 30.
On the foreign trade in 1764, No. 31.
On disputes between masters and journeymen in 1777, No. 32.

Hawkers' and Pedlars' licences, p. 187.
In report on licensing and managing hackney-coaches, No. 9.

Hawkins, Sir Christopher, p. 37.
In report on Penryn election, No. 164.

Helleston Election, p. 36, Nos. 141, 142.

Hemp, purchases of, p. 181.
In report of naval inquiry, No. 35.

Hemp, see *Flax*.

Herculaneum MSS. p. 111.
Report on Dr. Sickler's experiments in unrolling and decyphering, No. 13.

Herring Fishery, p. 63.
In report on fisheries, Nos. 67. 69.

Hertford Election, p. 36, Nos. 143, 144.

Hibernian Society School, p. 8.
Its management and good effects, *see* report on education, No. 19.

Hides and Skins, p. 59.
On laws relating to flaying, No. 33.
On laws relating to the leather trade, No. 34.

High Sheriff, p. 18.
Report on the expense of the office, No. 59.

Higham, Mr. p. 90.
In report on annuities; his plan for converting deposits of savings banks into life annuities, No. 1.

Highland Roads and Bridges, 1803–1821, p. 133–137.
Reports of commissioners on the progress of works under their direction, Nos. 143, 144. 146–149. 151. 153, 154.
Statement of their origin and extent, No. 150.
Report on the application of the funds of the forfeited estates in Scotland, No. 145.
Report of committee on estimates, No. 152.
Estimates of expenses, No. 155.
In report on survey of the central highlands of Scotland, No. 93.
See *Roads and Bridges*.

Highlands of Scotland, p. 133.
Reports on the survey of the central highlands, Nos. 93, 94.

H H

St. Luke's Asylum, p. 115.
  In report on lunatic asylums, No. 46.

St. Martin's-in-the-fields, p. 153.
  In report in 1715 on poor-rates, as to the management of the poor and parochial funds, and the constitution of the vestry in 1715, No. 1.
  Grant of land for vicarage and school-house, *see* report on woods, forests and land revenue, p. 88, No. 58.

St. Paul's School, p. 6.
  In reports on education in 1816–1818, No. 1.

Sabbath-day, p. 1.
  Report on the practices relating to the observance of, No. 4.

Salaries of Members holding Office, p. 25.
  In report on reduction of, No. 27.

Salaries of Officers of the House, p. 29.
  Report on, No. 77.

Salaries, Reduction of, p. 25.
  Report on, into all offices held by members of parliament under the crown, No. 27.

Sale of Parliamentary Papers, p. 29–33.
  In report on House of Commons offices, No. 77.
  In report on public documents, No. 100.

Saleable Offices, p. 13.
  Report on, in the courts of law, No. 11.

Salmon Fishery, p. 64.
  Reports on the state of, Nos. 73–75.

Salt, p. 86.
  Reports on laws relative to salt duties in 1801, No. 41.
  Report on the use of rock salt in fisheries, No. 42.
  As to its use in agriculture, manufactures, and fisheries, Nos. 42, 43.

Salt Trade, p. 92–94.
  In reports on East India affairs, Nos. 3. 22–24.

Savings Banks, p. 90.
  In report on annuities, No. 1.
  In report on friendly societies, No. 5.
  In reports on poor laws, p. 156, Nos. 16. 21, 22.

Savoy, p. 87.
  As to improvement at, *see* reports on woods, forests and land revenue, No. 48.

Scarcity of Corn and Grain, 1793, p. 45.
  Reports on, and on importation, exportation, and deficiency of crops, Nos. 15, 16.

Scholarships, p. 6.
  In reports on education in 1816–1818, No. 1.

Schoolmasters, p. 6.
  Qualification for national schools, *see* report on education, No. 9.

Schools, Parochial, p. 166.
  Good moral effects of, *see* report on police, No. 10.

Schools, Public, p. 6.
  Their management, funds, statutes, and scholarships, *see* reports on education, Nos. 1–8.

Scotch Church Patronage, p. 2.
  Report on the law and accordance of the system with the constitution of the church of Scotland, No. 14.

Scotch Entails, p. 20.
  Report on bill for altering the law of, Nos. 92–95.

Scotch Ministers, p. 2.
  Report in 1751 on provision for their maintenance, No. 13.

Sea Water, p. 120.
  Report in 1772 on Dr. Irving's method of rendering sea-water fresh, No. 13.

Sealy, Edward, p. 119.
  Report on his substitute of elm for oak bark, No. 5.

Seamen Registration, p. 180.
  In report of 1780 on naval volunteers, No. 23.

Secondary Punishments, p. 165–172.
  In report on increase of criminal commitments, No. 2.
  Report in 1778 on the punishment of convicts by hard labour, No. 52.
  Report in 1779 on punishment by transportation to a proposed new colony at Botany Bay, No. 53.

Secondary Punishments, p. 165–172—*continued*.
  Report in 1784 on punishment in penitentiaries, No. 54; and *see* Penitentiaries.
  Report in 1785 on punishment by transportation to Africa, Nos. 55, 56.
  Report in 1812 on punishment by transportation to New South Wales, No. 57.
  Reports in 1831–32 on the best mode of giving effect to secondary punishments; on the effects of punishments on different individuals; on prison discipline; on the management of transported convicts, &c. Nos. 58, 59.

Secretaries of State, p. 183.
  In report on fees in 1786–1788, No. 1.

Sedgwick, Mr. p. 84.
  In report on board of stamps, Nos. 21, 22.

Seditious Practices, p. 38.
  Reports in 1799 on seditious societies, and on the state of Ireland, No. 3.
  On the state of Ireland in 1801, and proceedings of disaffected persons in both countries, No. 4.
  Report on the disturbed state of several counties in 1812, No. 5.
  Reports on secret societies in 1817, Nos. 6, 7.
  Reports on the proceedings of disaffected in 1818, Nos. 8, 9.
  Papers on state of the country in 1819, No. 10.

Seeds, p. 44.
  Reports on the price, importation and adulteration of, Nos. 7–10.

Select Vestries, p. 149.
  Reports on the laws and usages under which they are constituted, No. 19.
  In report in 1715 on management of the poor of St. Martin's-in-the-Fields, p. 153, No. 1.

Sewers, p. 147.
  Report on the management, appointment of officers, and application of funds, No. 8.
  Returns and accounts respecting, Nos. 9, 10.
  Report on the state of the laws respecting, No. 11.

Seychelles, p. 107.
  In report on slave-trade in the Mauritius, No. 58.

Shanavests, a party name, p. 39.
  In report on state of Ireland in 1816, No. 11.

Shannon, p. 141–143.
  Survey of the canal from Lough Allen, No. 213.
  In report on public works, No. 224.
  Its great importance, and plans for improvement, *see* report on public works in Ireland, No. 225.
  Papers on the improvement of the Shannon navigation, Nos. 227, 228.
  Report of committee on the present state and improvement, No. 229.

Sheep and Cattle.
  Reports on jobbing and forestalling, p. 48, Nos. 41. 46, 47.
  Report on the illicit exportation of, p. 61, No. 50.

Sheil, Mr. p. 25.
  In report of privilege, as to reflections made on him by another member, No. 19.

Sheriff, p. 18.
  Report on the expense of the office of high sheriff, No. 59.

Sheriff Courts, Scotland, p. 19.
  In reports on courts of justice, No. 80.

Sheriffs' Office, Ireland, p. 22.
  In report on courts of justice, Nos. 121–123.

Shetland and Orkneys, p. 48.
  Report on deficiency of crops in 1804, Nos. 44, 45.

SHIPPING, COMMERCE and FOREIGN TRADE, IX. p. 67.
  Report on admeasurement of shipping, p. 70, No. 18.

Shipping, see *Morton's Patent Slip*.

Shipwrecks, p. 70, 71.
  Report on Greathead's life-boat, Nos. 20, 21.
  Report on Manby's plans for saving lives, Nos. 22–25.
  Papers on the same subject, Nos. 26–29.
  Report on Mallison's cork jackets, No. 30.
  Papers on the same subject, No. 31.
  Report on Whitfield's plans for saving lives, No. 32.
  Papers on Trengrouse's plans, Nos. 33, 34.

Wages—continued.
Wages, rates of, p. 54–61.
Of artizans, Nos. 2–4.
Of calico printers, Nos. 6, 7.
Of cloth-workers, No. 48.
Of coal-miners, No. 11.
Of coal-whippers, No. 12.
Of cotton manufacturers, Nos. 14–16.
Of framework knitters, Nos. 22. 24.
Of hand-loom weavers, No. 29.
Of hatmakers, No. 32.
Of manufacturers generally, No. 39.
Of silk-weavers, Nos. 43, 44.
Of ribbon-weavers, No. 42.
Proposed minimum of wages in cotton trade, Nos. 14–16; in hand-loom weavers, No. 29.

Wakefield, Mr. p. 121.
His smoke-consuming apparatus for steam-engine flues, No. 17.

Wales, p. 14.
Reports on the administration of justice in, Nos. 21–22.

Walker, Colonel, p. 99.
In papers respecting the suppression of infanticide in India, No. 57.

Walker, James, p. 131.
Report on the stability of New London-bridge, No. 67.

Waltham Forest, p. 87.
On disafforesting it, *see* report on woods, forests and land revenue, No. 50.

War-office, p. 179.
On the establishment, and regimental accounts, *see* reports on military inquiry, No. 7.
On foreign accounts and chaplain-general, *see ibid*, No. 8.
On miscellaneous accounts, *ibid*, No. 9.

Warburton's Asylum, p. 115.
In report on lunatic asylums, No. 46.

Warehousing System, p. 81–83.
In reports on customs and excise in 1820–1824, Nos. 5. 18.

Warehousing system in the Port of London, p. 67.
In reports on foreign trade, No. 1.

Warwick Election, p. 37, Nos. 171, 172.

Waste Lands, p. 43.
Reports in 1795–1800 on promoting the cultivation of, No. 1.

Watch, Parochial, p. 165, 166.
Its defective state in 1770, *see* report on police, No. 3.
Reports on, in 1812 and 1816, Nos. 4, 5.
State of, in 1828, *see* report on police, No. 10.

Watchmakers, p. 61.
Report of the state of their trade, No. 46.
On the laws relating thereto, No. 47.

Water Supply, p. 148.
Report on the supply of, to the Metropolis, and on the management of the several companies, Nos. 12–17.

Waterford, p. 142.
In report on post-office communication with Ireland, No. 222.

Waterloo-bridge to Covent-garden Street, p. 88.
In report on woods, forests and land revenue, No. 56.

Weights and Measures, p. 117.
Reports in 1758–59 on the laws relating to, No. 61.
Report in 1814 on the original standard, No. 62.
Report in 1821 on ascertaining an original standard, No. 63.
Papers on experiments for ascertaining the length of the pendulum on philosophical principles, No. 64.
Reports of commissioners, and papers on the same subject, Nos. 65–69.
Report on, in 1834, No. 70.
Inspectors of, *see* report on county-rates, p. 146, No. 3.

Wellesley, Sir Arthur, p. 97.
In papers respecting the Marhatta war in 1803, No. 33.

Wellesley, Hon. William Long, p. 25.
In report on privilege as to arrest, No. 22.

West, Mr. p. 148.
Experiments on the quality of water supplied to the Metropolis, No. 17.

West India Colonies, p. 105.
On the supplying the colonies with free labourers by emigration from China, No. 45.
On the commercial state of the colonies in 1807, No. 44; and in 1832, No. 53.
On the state of the revenue, No. 46.
On the administration of civil and criminal justice, Nos. 47–52.
Reports on relief of their distress by allowing distillation and brewing from sugar and molasses, p. 53, Nos. 20–22.
On commissions of inquiry, *see* reports on public expenditure in 1812, p. 73, No. 22.
Army expenditure there, *see* reports on military inquiry, p. 179, No. 10.

West India Docks, p. 68.
Exclusive privileges, *see* reports on foreign trade, No. 9.

Westminster Abbey, p. 124.
Reports on the reparation of, Nos. 7–9.

Westminster-bridge, p. 130.
On the expense and state of, *see* report on London port, No. 63.

Westminster Election, p. 37, No. 173.

Westminster Hall, p. 124.
Report in 1788–89, as to how it may be secured from fire arising from the contiguity of other buildings, Nos. 10, 11.
In report on Westminster improvements, No. 17.

Westminster High Bailiff, p. 26.
Report on the office, duties and emoluments, Nos. 30, 31.

Westminster High Constable, p. 26.
Report on his remuneration for attendance on Parliament, No. 32.

Westminster Improvements, p. 123–125.
In reports on improving the approaches to the House, Nos. 4. 22.
Reports on, as to the access thereto, Nos. 12–15.
Report on the style and taste in the architecture of public buildings, No. 16.
Report for improving the streets near Westminster Hall, Nos. 17–20.
Report on new law courts, Nos. 16. 21.

Westminster Mews:
In reports on woods, forests and land revenue, p. 88, No. 53.
In report on office of works, p. 126, No. 31.

Westminster School, p. 6.
In reports on education in 1816–1818, No. 1.

Wexford Election, p. 37, No. 174.

Weymouth Election, p. 37, No. 175.

Wheat :
Report on the mode of taking and returning the average prices, p. 43, No. 2.
Average price of, from 1748–1829, p. 147, No. 4.

Wheels and Carriages, p. 127.
Reports on the construction of, on mechanical and philosophical principles, as effecting easy draught, and preserving the surface of roads, Nos. 35–38.

Whetstone-road, p. 129.
Report on the state of, in 1828, No. 47.

Whitecross-street Prison, p. 169.
Report on the state of, in 1828, No. 27.

Whitefeet, a party name, p. 42.
In report on state of Ireland in 1832, No. 24.

Whitehall-place, p. 87.
As to improvements in, *see* reports on woods, forests and land revenue, Nos. 48–50.

Whitfield, Mr. p. 71.
Report on his plans for saving shipwrecked persons, No. 32.

Wild, Jonathan, p. 166.
His practice and execution, *see* report on Metropolis police, No. 10.

Wilkins, Dr. p. 93.
Glossary of Indian names and terms, No. 16.